AMERICAN MUSICOLOGICAL SOCIETY • STUDIES AND DOCUMENTS, NO. 7

Johannes Ockeghem

COLLECTED WORKS—THIRD VOLUME

Motets and Chansons

Johannes Ockeghem

Collected Works

edited by

RICHARD WEXLER

with

DRAGAN PLAMENAC

THIRD VOLUME

Motets and Chansons

AMERICAN MUSICOLOGICAL SOCIETY

E.C. SCHIRMER • BOSTON

Sole Selling Agent

Publication of this volume was made possible in part
by a grant from the Gustave Reese Bequest to the
American Musicological Society.

Philadelphia, Pennsylvania
ISBN: 1-878528-02-5
PRINTED IN THE UNITED STATES OF AMERICA

TO THE MEMORY OF

DRAGAN PLAMENAC

(1895 - 1983)

CONTENTS

Preface IX

The Sources XI

Publications Cited by Means of Sigla XXV

Editorial Notes XXXIII

List of Plates CXIII

Plates I–X

MOTETS

	Editorial Notes	Edition
UNDISPUTED		
1. Alma Redemptoris mater	XLI	3
2. Ave Maria	XLII	6
3. Intemerata Dei mater	XLIII	8
4. Salve regina [I]	XLIV	13
5. Ut heremita solus	XLV	18
6. Vivit Dominus	XLIX	25
DOUBTFUL		
7. Caeleste beneficium	L	26
8. Deo gratia (Canon XXXVI vocum)	LI	35
9. Gaude Maria	LIII	43
10. Salve regina [II]	LIV	53

CHANSONS

	Editorial Notes	Edition
UNDISPUTED		
1. Aultre Venus	LIX	59
2. Baisiés moy	LX	60
3. D'un autre amer	LX	61
4. Fors seulement l'actente	LXIV	62

	Editorial Notes	Edition
5. Fors seullement contre	LXVI	64
6. Il ne m'en chault	LXIX	66
7. J'en ay dueil	LXX	67
7a. Je n'ay deul	LXXII	69
8. La despourveue	LXXII	70
9. L'autre d'antan	LXXIV	71
10. Les desléaulx	LXXVII	72
11. Ma bouche rit	LXXVIII	73
12. Ma maistresse	LXXXII	75
13. Mort tu as navré	LXXXIV	77
14. O rosa bella	LXXXVI	79
15. Prenez sur moi (Fuga trium vocum)	LXXXVII	80
16. Presque transi	XCI	81
17. Quant de vous seul	XCII	83
18. Qu'es mi vida	XCIII	84
18a. Qu'es mi vida (Johannes Cornago)	XCV	86
19. S'elle m'amera—Petite camusete	XCV	88
20. Se vostre cuer	XCVIII	90
21. Tant fuz gentement	XCIX	91
22. Ung aultre l'a	C	92
DOUBTFUL		
23. Au travail suis	CII	93
24. Departés vous	CIII	94
25. Malheur me bat	CIV	95
26. Permanent vierge	CVII	96
SUPPLEMENT		
Ergone conticuit ("In Ioannem Okegi Musicorum principem, Naenia") (Johannes Lupi?)	CXI	101

PREFACE

This volume makes available all of Ockeghem's surviving chansons and motets, thus completing the edition. The present volume was, in its initial guise, part of Dragan Plamenac's doctoral dissertation, "Johannes Ockeghem als Motetten- und Chansonkomponist" (University of Vienna, 1924). In the years since Prof. Plamenac submitted his study to the musicology faculty in Vienna, much information has come to light concerning original sources, the lives of Ockeghem and his contemporaries, and the evolution of genre and style. Large gains have also been made in terms of editorial method, in particular with regard to *musica ficta*, text underlay, collation of sources, and the various functions of mensural signs.

It is now possible to propose with much greater certainty that some compositions formerly attributed to Ockeghem are not indisputably his. Two motets, *Gaude Maria* and *Caeleste beneficium*, are included here, but the ascription of them to "Johannes Okegus" in their unique source, which is of 16th-century German origin, is questioned on stylistic grounds. Another work with Latin text, the much discussed 36-voice canon *Deo gratia,* bears no attribution to Ockeghem in any of its three sources, does not quite correspond to contemporary descriptions of a piece for that number of voices by Ockeghem, and is so weak stylistically that it is not likely to be by him. It is printed here solely because it is so frequently cited in the literature. The attribution to Ockeghem of another motet, *Salve regina* [II], is unclear in one source, and a concordant source gives the piece to Basiron. However, because the work has been widely supposed to be by Ockeghem since the last century, the editors have decided to include it as an *opus dubium.* On the other hand, an anonymous motet that Ambros (III, 77) attributed provisionally to Ockeghem, *Miles mirae probitatis*, the text of which refers to St. Martin of Tours, has been omitted from this edition on stylistic grounds and because Ambros's suggestion has never won wide acceptance.

The editors have provided transcriptions of three chansons, *Au travail suis*, *Departés vous*, and *Malheur me bat*, despite attributions to other composers, because the questions of their authorship cannot be resolved definitively at this time. A motet-chanson, *Permanent vierge*, which bears no attribution in its unique source, is printed here only because it has been discussed in the modern literature and is otherwise unavailable in a reliable modern edition. However, the chanson *Ce n'est pas jeu*, attributed to Ockeghem in one source but to Hayne van Ghizeghem in several others, is undoubtedly by Hayne and therefore does not figure in the present edition.[1] Likewise *Quand ce viendra*, attributed in one source to Ockeghem but in others to Busnois, has been omitted.[2]

In view of the fact that only one of the works in this volume, *Mort tu as navré*, can be dated securely, the editors have refrained from any attempt to present the contents in a chronological order. The final work in the volume is a setting of a poetic eulogy for Ockeghem by Erasmus of Rotterdam attributed to Johannes Lupi. This piece, *Ergone conticuit*, is much less well-known than Josquin's *Déploration*, another memorial for the composer.

The support of the Publications Committee of the American Musicological Society is gratefully acknowledged, and in particular the unfailing encouragement of its successive chairmen, Arthur Mendel, Gustave Reese, James Haar, Martin Picker, James Webster, Lewis Lockwood, Edward Roesner, and Richard Kramer. We also owe much thanks to Leeman L. Perkins, who provided valuable data concerning variant readings, and to Mary Beth Winn and Howard Garey, who shared their expert knowledge of 15th-century French. Special thanks are due Martin Picker, who observed every phase of the editorial work, read every draft, and made numerous very helpful suggestions.

It is regrettable that Dragan Plamenac did not live to witness the publication of this final volume, and, with it, the completion of a project to which he devoted so many years of scholarship.

Richard Wexler
University of Maryland, May 1991

[1]Modern editions in *AmbG* V, pp. 14–15; *MarM*, pp. 103–04; and *HayneO*, no. 4. See also *AtlasCG*, no. 91. (See p. XXV for sigla.)

[2]Modern editions in *DrozT*, no. 3; *HanE*, no. 105; and *PerkMC*, no. 16. See also Howard Mayer Brown, *Music in the French Secular Theater, 1400-1550*, Cambridge, MA, 1963, p. 270.

THE SOURCES

I. MANUSCRIPTS

BerGlo

Berlin, (former) Preussische Staatsbibliothek, Mus. Ms. 40098 (formerly Z.98; now in Kraków, Biblioteka Jagiellónska) (Glogauer Liederbuch).

Three partbooks on paper (Discantus, Tenor, Contratenor) in oblong octavo, compiled about 1470–80 in Silesia, with Latin sacred compositions and German and French secular pieces. Some of the works in the collection can be identified as chansons by Barbingant, Basin, Bedingham, Brolo, Busnois, Caron, Dufay, Frye, Hayne van Ghizeghem, Martini, Ockeghem, Tinctoris, Touront, and Vincenet.

See H. Ringmann, ed., *Das Glogauer Liederbuch, Erste Teil* (Das Erbe deutscher Musik, Reichsdenkmale, Band 4), 1936; H.-J. Feurich, *Die deutschen weltlichen Lieder der Glogauer Handschrift (ca. 1470)* (Neue musikgeschichtliche Forschungen, Band 4), 1970; *Glogauer Liederbuch, Kraków, Biblioteca Jagiellónska* [facsimile edition], Introduction, J. A. Owens, Renaissance Music in Facsimile VI, 1986; *Census-Cat.* I, pp. 43–44.

Discantus fol. L vij^{v}; Tenor fol. M iij^{v}; Contratenor fol. M viij^{r}. Anonymous (= Ockeghem): H. (= Ma bouche rit).

BQ 16

Bologna, Civico museo bibliografico musicale, Cod. Q 16 (formerly Cod. 109).

A manuscript on paper, 21 × 14 cm, written in Italy in the late 1480s, containing 131 anonymous French, Italian, Spanish, and Latin compositions, including an anonymous three-voice *Missa L'Homme armé* not found elsewhere. Composers who can be identified from other sources include Agricola, Basin, Brolo, Busnois, Caron, Compère, Dufay, Dux Burgensis, Giliardi, Guglielmo, Hayne van Ghizeghem, Josquin, Colinet de Lannoy, Léon, Martini, Obrecht, Ockeghem, Touront, Vincenet, and Wreede.

See E. Pease, "A Report on Codex Q 16 of the Civico Museo Bibliografico Musicale," *Musica Disciplina* XX, 1966, pp. 57–94; S. Fuller, "Additional Notes on the Fifteenth-Century Chansonnier Bologna Q 16," *Musica Disciplina* XXIII, 1969, pp. 81–103; K. Jeppesen, *La Frottola.* 3 vols, 1968–1970. II, 1969, pp. 10–16 and 110; *Census-Cat.* I, pp. 70–71.

Fol. viii^{v}–viiii^{r} (20^{v}–21^{r}). Anonymous (= Malcort? Martini? Ockeghem?): Dieu damors (= Malheur me bat).

Fol. xxv^{v}–xxvi^{r} (37^{v}–38^{r}). Anonymous (= Ockeghem): De partes vous.

Fol. lxxx^{v}–lxxxi^{r} (93^{v}–94^{r}). Anonymous (= Ockeghem): La trentana (= L'autre d'antan).

BQ 17

Bologna, Civico museo bibliografico musicale, Cod. Q 17 (formerly Cod. 148).

A manuscript on parchment compiled towards the end of the fifteenth century, probably of Florentine origin, consisting of seventy-six folios, 11.5 × 19 cm in size. Except for a few sacred pieces on Latin texts, the volume contains mostly French, but also Flemish, Italian, and Spanish secular compositions. Composers named include A. Agricola, Bactio, Boris, A. Busnois, Brumel, Loyset Compere, Hayne, Josquin, Colinet de lannoy, Jo. ockeghem, Nino petit, Philipon, Pierre de la rue, Pierquin, Jo. Stochem, and Yzac. Works by Jannes Agricola, Caron, Japart, Obrecht, Prioris, and Wreede can also be identified.

See R. Wexler, "Newly Identified Works by Bartolomeo degli Organi in the MS Bologna Q 17," *Journal of the A.M.S.* XXIII, 1970, pp. 107–18; *AtlasCG* I, pp. 236–37; *Census-Cat.* I, pp. 71–72.

Fol. 40^{v}–41^{r}. Jo. ockeghem: Dung aultre amer.

Fol. 72^{v}–73^{r}. Anonymous (= Ockeghem): Je nay deul.

BQ 18

Bologna, Civico museo bibliografico musicale, Cod. Q 18 (formerly Cod. 143).

A manuscript on paper from about 1500, 16.8 × 24 cm. The fact that the Bolognese theorist Giovanni Spataro (c. 1458–1541) copied portions of the volume suggests that it was compiled in Bologna. It contains ninety anonymous pieces on French, Latin, and Italian texts. Composers who can be identified from other sources include Agricola, Antenori, Brumel, Busnois, Cara, Caron, Compère, Congiet, Hayne, Isaac, Josquin, Lurano, Martini (?), Obrecht, Ockeghem (?), Pesenti, Tromboncino, Vincenet, and Wreede.

See K. Jeppesen, *La Frottola* II, 1969, pp. 10 and 108–09; *AtlasCG* I, p. 237; S. F. Weiss, "Bologna Q 18: Some Reflections on Content and Context," *Journal of the A.M.S.* XLI, 1988, pp. 63–101; *Census-Cat.* I, pp. 72–73.

Fol. 73^{v}–74^{r}. Anonymous (= Malcort? Martini? Ockeghem?): Malur me bat.

Br 228

Brussels, Bibliothèque royale Albert Ier, Ms. 228.

A manuscript on parchment of c. 1516–23, approximately 36.5 × 26 cm. The volume, originally from the library of Margaret of Austria, contains seventy-three folios on which are written French chansons and a few pieces with Latin texts. Except for one chanson ascribed to "Josquin des Pres," all pieces are anonymous. Composers who can be ascertained include Agricola, Josquin, de Orto, P. de la Rue, Ockeghem, Obrecht (?), and Prioris.

See M. Picker, ed., *The Chanson Albums of Marguerite of Austria*, 1965; *Album de Marguerite d'Autriche* [facsimile edition], Foreword, M. Picker, 1986; *Census-Cat.* I, pp. 91–92.

Fol. 15^{v}–16^{r}. Anonymous (= Ockeghem): Je nay dueil.

Br 11239

Brussels, Bibliothèque royale Albert Ier, Ms. 11239.

A manuscript of c. 1500 on parchment, 20 × 14.5 cm, that, like the preceding item, belonged to the library of Margaret of Austria, whose coat of arms is found in a colored woodcut on the verso of the front cover. The volume includes three- and four-voice chansons and a few pieces with Latin texts. Composers named are Alexander Agricola, A. Bruhier, Brumel, Compere, de la Rue, and H. Ysac. Works by Hayne van Ghizeghem, Josquin, Nino le petit, Obrecht, and Ockeghem can be identified from concordances.

See Picker, *Chanson Albums*; *Chansonnier of Marguerite of Austria* [facsimile edition], 1984; *Census-Cat.* I, pp. 94–95.

Fol. 20^{v}. Anonymous (= Ockeghem): Petitte camusette (S and T only).

Br IV.90

Brussels, Bibliothèque royale Albert Ier, Ms. IV.90. (See also **Tournai**, Bibliothèque de la ville, Ms. 94.)

The superius partbook of a broken set, of which *Tour 94* is the tenor book. Written on parchment in oblong octavo format (7.8 × 11 cm) and richly embellished with miniatures, it contains French and Flemish pieces, all anonymous. Composers who can be ascertained from other sources include Compère, Ghiselin, Hayne, Josquin, Nino le petit, Pipelare, Obrecht, Ockeghem, and P. de la Rue.

See L. Kessels, "The Brussels/Tournai Partbooks: Structure, Illumination, and Flemish Repertory," *Tijdschrift van de Vereniging voor Nederlandse Muziekgeschiedenis* XXXVII, 1987, pp. 82–110; *Census-Cat.* I, pp. 97–98.

Fol. 26^{r}–27(28)^{r}. Anonymous (= Ockeghem): Je nay deul.

Cam R.2.71

Cambridge, Trinity College Library, Ms. R.2.71.

A manuscript on paper, 13.8 × 18 cm, consisting of four leaves, possibly of French origin and from about 1475. The fragment contains portions of seven pieces, one of which is attributed to Ockeghem. A work by Busnois can also be recognized.

See D. Fallows, "Johannes Ockeghem: The Changing Image, the Songs, and a New Source," *Early Music* XII, 1984, pp. 225–26.

Fol. 4^{v}. Ockeghem: Ma maistresse (the superius, *prima pars* only, and the opening of the tenor).

Cop 291

Copenhagen, Det kongelige Bibliotek, Ms. Thott 291, 8°.

A manuscript on parchment, dating from c. 1475, apparently written by the scribe who copied most of *Dij* and part of *WLab*. The volume, which consists of forty-nine folios measuring 17 × 12 cm, contains thirty-three French chansons, all entered without attributions. Composers who can be identified by consulting concordances include Basiron, Busnois, Convert, Delahaye, Hayne van Ghizeghem, Michelet, Molinet, Morton, Ockeghem, Prioris, and Symonet le Breton.

See K. Jeppesen, ed., *Der Kopenhagener Chansonnier*, 1927; G. Thibault and E. Droz, "Le Chansonnier de la Bibliothèque Royale de Copenhague," *Revue de musicologie* XI, 1927, pp. 12–35; *Census-Cat.* I, pp. 162–63.

Fol. 33^v–34^r (39^v–40^r). Anonymous (= Ockeghem): Dun autre amer.
Fol. 40^v (46^v). Anonymous (= Ockeghem): Prenez sur moi.

Cop 1848

Copenhagen, Det kongelige Bibliotek, Ms. Ny kongelige Samling 1848, 2°.

An extensive but carelessly written manuscript in small folio, approximately 28.5 × 20 cm, on paper, dating from c. 1525 and originating from the vicinity of Lyons. The volume is paginated (1–450) and contains secular and sacred music by several generations of composers. The few names provided include Alexandre (Agricola), Dulot, Haquinet, Isaac, Janequin, Johannes de s(an)cto Martino, Maioris, Maistre Jaques Danvers (= Barbireau), Richaffort, and Verbonet (Ghiselin).

See H. Glahn, "Et fransk Musikhåndskrift fra begyndelsen af det 16. århundrede," *Fund og Forskning* V–VI, 1958–59, pp. 90–109; D. Plamenac, "A Postscript to 'The "Second" Chansonnier of the Biblioteca Riccardiana'," *Annales musicologiques* IV, 1956, pp. 261–65; *Census-Cat.* I, pp. 163–64.

P. 35. Anonymous (= Ockeghem): Baisez moy.
P. 145. Anonymous (= Ockeghem): Dung aultre aymer.
P. 401. Anonymous (= Ockeghem): [Ma bouche rit] (textless, *prima pars* only).
P. 427. Anonymous (= Ockeghem): Fort seulement [contre].

Dij

Dijon, Bibliothèque municipale, Ms. 517 (formerly 295).

A manuscript on parchment from c. 1475 with 204 leaves (17.5 × 12.8 cm), perhaps originating at the court of the dukes of Burgundy or in northern France. The last few pieces were probably copied in France about a decade later. The collection consists of secular music plus some song-motets by Barbingant, Busnois, Caron, Compère, Hayne van Ghizeghem, Ockeghem, Tinctoris, and other, unnamed composers.

See D. Plamenac, ed., *Dijon, Bibliothèque Publique, Manuscrit 517* [facsimile edition] (Publications of Mediæval Music 12); M. Picker (review of the previous item), *Journal of the A.M.S.* XXVI, 1973, pp. 336–40; J. Rifkin, "Scribal Concordances for Some Renaissance Manuscripts in Florentine Libraries," *Journal of the A.M.S.* XXVI, 1973, pp. 319 and 325–26; *Census-Cat.* I, pp. 168–69.

Fol. i^r. Anonymous (= Ockeghem): Prenez sur moy (in index; folio missing from source).
Fol. $iiij^v$–vj^r (9^v–$10bis^r$). Anonymous (= Ockeghem): Ma bouche rit.
Fol. $viiij^v$–x^r (12^v–13^r). Okeghem: Les desleaux.
Fol. $xvij^v$–$xviij^r$ (20^v–21^r). Anonymous (= Ockeghem): Lautre dantan.
Fol. xxv^v–$xxvj^r$ (28^v–29^r). Okeghem: Fors seulement lactente.
Fol. $xxxiij^v$–$xxxiiij^r$ (36^v–37^r). Okeghem: Quant de vous seul.
Fol. $xxxviiij^v$–xl^r (42^v–43^r). Okeghem: Dun autre amer.
Fol. lij^v–$liiij^r$ (55^v–57^r). Okeghem: Presque transi.
Fol. $lviiij^v$–lx^r (62^v–63^r). Barbinguant (= Ockeghem?): Au traueil suis.
Fol. $viij^{xx}j^v$–$viij^{xx}ij^r$ (164^v–165^r). Anonymous (= Ockeghem): Selle mamera—Petite camusecte.
Fol. $viij^{xx}ij^v$–$viij^{xx}iij^r$ (165^v–166^r). Anonymous (= Ockeghem): Permanent vierge—Pulchra es et decora—Sancta dei genitrix.
Fol. $viij^{xx}iij^v$–$viij^{xx}v^r$ (166^v–168^r). Anonymous (= Ockeghem): Mort tu as navre—Miserere.

Esc IV.a.24

El Escorial (Madrid), Real monasterio de San Lorenzo del Escorial, Biblioteca y archivo de música, Ms. IV.a.24.

A manuscript on paper, 21.1 × 14.2 cm, probably compiled in or near Naples c. 1470, containing 122 pieces on mostly French, but also Italian, Flemish, English, and Spanish texts. Composers' names given in the source include Braxatoris, P. de Domarto, Hockenghem, Horlay, Morton, and Jo. puillois. Additional attributions can be made to Basin, Bedingham, Binchois, Cornago, Dufay, Dunstable, Legrant, and Ockeghem.

See M. K. Hanen, ed., *The Chansonnier El Escorial IV.a.24*, 3 vols., 1983; E. Southern, "El Escorial, Monastery Library, Ms. IV.a.24," *Musica Disciplina* XXIII, 1969, pp. 41–79; *Census-Cat.* I, pp. 211–12.

Fol. 121^{v}–122^{r}. Hockenghem (= Busnois): Quant ce vendra.
Fol. 123^{v}–124^{r}. Anonymous (= Ockeghem): [Ma maistresse] (textless, *prima pars* only).

FB 2439 **Florence**, Biblioteca del conservatorio Luigi Cherubini, Cod. Basevi 2439.

A manuscript of Flemish provenance in small oblong quarto (16.8 × 24 cm) from about 1510, containing 101 parchment folios with three- and four-voice compositions set to French, Flemish, Italian, and Latin texts. Composers named are Allexander Agricola, Brumel, Busnois, Colinet de lannoy, Compere, Ghiselin (Jo gisling alias Verbonnet), Hobrecht, Hylaire, Jaspar, Josquin, J. Ockeghem, Nino le petit, De Orto, Pipelare, Prioris, Cornelius Rigo de Bergis, Pierson de la Rue, and Yzaac.

See H. Kellman, "Josquin and the Courts of the Netherlands and France: The Evidence of the Sources," in *Proceedings of the International Josquin Festival Conference . . . 1971*, ed. E. E. Lowinsky, 1976, p. 211; M. Staehelin, "Quellenkundliche Beiträge zum Werk von Johannes Ghiselin-Verbonnet," *Archiv für Musikwissenschaft* XXIV, 1967, pp. 120–32; *Census-Cat.* I, pp. 233–34.

Fol. XXX^{v}–XXXI^{r}. Ockeghem: Jen nay deuil.
Fol. XXXI^{v}–XXXII^{r}. Ockeghem: Petite camusette.
Fol. LII^{v}–LIII^{r}. J. Ockeghem: Fors seullement lactante (= Fors seullement contre).
Fol. LIII^{v}–LIIII^{r}. Ockeghem: Baisies moy.

FBNC 176 **Florence**, Biblioteca nazionale centrale, cod. Magliabechi XIX.176.

A manuscript on paper, 16.8 × 11.8 cm, from c. 1480, and probably of Florentine origin. It contains French, Italian, Spanish, and Flemish secular pieces attributed to Arnolfo, Lepetit basque, Bellingan, Busnois, Caron, P. de Domarto, Duffay, Fede, Michelet, Mortom, G. Mueram, Ochechen, Raulin, Simonet, and Jo. Tinctoris.

See B. Becherini, "Autori minori nel codice fiorentino Magl. XIX, 176," *Revue belge de musicologie* IV, 1950, pp. 19–31; idem, *Catalogo dei manoscritti musicali della Biblioteca Nazionale di Firenze*, 1959, pp. 72–75; Rifkin, "Scribal Concordances," pp. 318 and 321; *Census-Cat.* I, pp. 229–30.

Fol. 32^{v}–34^{r}. Ochechen: Ma bouche rit.
Fol. 83^{v}–85^{r}. Anonymous (= Ockeghem): La despourueue.

FBNC 178 **Florence**, Biblioteca nazionale centrale, cod. Magliabechi XIX.178.

A Florentine manuscript on paper from the end of the fifteenth century, 11.4 × 16.5 cm. The volume contains French and Italian secular pieces attributed to Alexander, Loyset Compere, Dufay, Gaspar, Hayne, Japart, Josquin, Joh. Martin, Jacobus Obret, Pictraquin, Stochem, and Enrigus Yzac, and anonymous compositions.

See *AtlasCG* I, p. 247; Becherini, *Catalogo dei manoscritti*, pp. 75–77; *Census-Cat.* I, p. 230.

Fol. 62^{v}–63^{r}. Anonymous (= Ockeghem): Dunaltre amer.

FBNC 229 **Florence**, Biblioteca nazionale centrale, Cod. Banco rari 229 (formerly Magliabechi XIX.59).

An extensive, beautifully written manuscript containing mostly French chansons and a few Italian and Latin pieces compiled in Florence in the 1490s. The volume opens with five parchment leaves embellished with miniatures followed by 325 paper folios, measuring 24 × 17 cm, which together contain 268 compositions. Most prominent in the source are works attributed to Jannes Martini and Henricus Yzac. Other composers named include Agricola, Jacobus Barle, Busnoys, Caron, Collinet de lannoy, Loyset Compere, P. Congiet, J. Deplanqua, Hemart, J. Japart, Josquin, Muriau, Jacobus Obrech, Pietrequin, J. Regis, F. Rubinet, J. Stochem, and J. Tinctoris.

See H. M. Brown, ed., *A Florentine Chansonnier from the Time of Lorenzo the Magnificent*, 2 vols. (Monuments of Renaissance Music VII–VIII), 1983; *Census-Cat.* I, pp. 219–20.

Fol. 10^{v}–11^{r}. Jannes Martini (= Ockeghem? Malcort?): [textless] (= Malheur me bat).

FR 2356 **Florence**, Biblioteca Riccardiana, Cod. 2356.

A manuscript on parchment, compiled about 1480 in or near Florence, containing one hundred folios, 23 × 17.2 cm. It preserves seventy-two anonymous compositions accompanied by frequently corrupt text incipits in French, Latin, Italian, and Spanish. Composers who can be ascertained from other sources include Agricola, Bedingham, Busnois, Caron, Dufay, Frye, Hayne, Josquin, Molinet, Morton, Ockeghem, Touront, and Wreede.

See D. Plamenac, "The 'Second' Chansonnier of the Biblioteca Riccardiana (Codex 2356)," *Annales musicologiques* II, 1954, pp. 105–87; idem, "A Postscript to 'The "Second" Chansonnier'," *Annales musicologiques* IV, 1956, pp. 261–65; Rifkin, "Scribal Concordances," p. 318; *Census-Cat.* I, pp. 244–45.

Fol. 28^{v}–29^{r} (34^{v}–35^{r}). Anonymous (= Ockeghem): Ma boncherit.
Fol. 73^{v}–74^{r} (79^{v}–80^{r}). Anonymous (= Ockeghem): (D)ung aultre amer.

FR 2794

Florence, Biblioteca Riccardiana, Cod. 2794.

A manuscript on parchment from the late fifteenth century, measuring 24 × 16.6 cm, containing French chansons and a few Latin motets attributed to Agricola, Compere, Dufay, Fresneau, Hayne van Ghizeghem, Josquin, Okeghem, and Pietrequin.

See Rifkin, "Scribal Concordances," pp. 318–19 and 322–26; idem, "Pietrequin Bonnel and Ms. 2794 of the Biblioteca Riccardiana," *Journal of the A.M.S.* XXIX, 1976, pp. 284–96; *Census-Cat.* I, pp. 245–46.

Fol. 11^{v}–13^{r}. De okeghem: Alma redemptoris mater.
Fol. 19^{v}–20^{r}. De okeghem: Dung aultre amer.
Fol. 39^{v}–40^{r}. De okeghem: Aultre venus.
Fol. 64^{v}–65^{r}. De okeghem: Ung aultre la (Rondeau royal).

Heilb

Heilbronn, Stadtarchiv, Musiksammlung, Hss. IV–V/2.

Two manuscript partbooks on paper, 13.4 × 19.1 cm, dating from after 1575. The books, which are bound with a copy of *RISM 1539*^{8}, contain tenor and quintus voice parts attributed to Dressler, Josquin, Lassus, Meiland, and Vaet.

See U. Siegele, *Die Musiksammlung der Stadt Heilbronn*, 1967, pp. 35–39; *Census-Cat.* I, p. 265.

No. 7. Anonymous (= Ockeghem?): Deo gratia (tenor voice only).

LonBL 20.A.xvi

London, British Library, Ms. Royal 20.A.xvi.

A manuscript on parchment of the late fifteenth century, 23.2 × 16.5 cm, having thirty-six folios on which writing appears, with miniatures and illuminated initials. The volume contains French chansons attributed to Bouvel, Crespieres, Heyne, and Josquin, and anonymous works that can be ascribed to Agricola, Compère, Fresneau, and Ockeghem on the basis of concordances.

See *London, British Library, Royal 20.A.XVI* [facsimile edition], Introduction, H. M. Brown, Renaissance Music in Facsimile X, 1987; *Census-Cat.* II, pp. 105–06.

Fol. 23^{v}–24^{r}. Anonymous (= Ockeghem): Je nay dueil.

Mantua

Mantua, Palazzo ducale, Study of Isabella d'Este.

Ockeghem's *Fuga trium vocum* inlaid in wood on the door of a cabinet.

See the photographic reproduction in E. Droz, G. Thibault, and Y. Rokseth, eds., *Trois chansonniers français du XV*^{e} *siècle*, 1927, and in V. Scherliess, *Musikalische Noten auf Kunstwerken der italienischen Renaissance*, 1972, plates 65–66; see also Scherliess, pp. 51–52, 78–82, and 164; G. Reese, "Musical Compositions in Renaissance Intarsia," *Miscelánea en homenaje a Mons. Higinio Anglés* II. Barcelona, 1961, pp. 689–706.

Jo. Okenghem: Canon Prendes sur moy.

MC 871

Montecassino, Biblioteca dell'Abbazia, Cod. 871.

A fifteenth-century manuscript of music on parchment, approximately 27.5 × 20.5 cm, bound together with miscellaneous religious writings. The source, of Neapolitan origin, contains Latin motets, hymns, and Magnificats, as well as French, Italian, and Spanish secular compositions attributed to Bernardus, Loyset Compere, Oquegan, Oriola, and Anthonius piccardus, and anonymous compositions.

See I. Pope and M. Kanazawa, eds., *The Musical Manuscript Montecassino 871: A Neapolitan Repertory of Sacred and Secular Music of the Late Fifteenth Century*, 1978; *Census-Cat.* II, pp. 173–74.

Pp. 256–57 (fol. 5^{v}–6^{r}). Cornago-Oquegan (= Ockeghem): Ques mi vida.
P. 270 (fol. 12^{v}). Dufay (= Ockeghem?): Departes vous.
Pp. 388–89 (fol. 158^{v}–59^{r}). Oquegan (= Ockeghem): Mort tu as naure.
P. 392 (fol. 160^{v}). Anonymous (= Ockeghem): Petite camusete.

Mun 1516

Munich, Bayerische Staatsbibliothek, Musiksammlung, Mus. Ms. 1516.

Four manuscript partbooks on paper from the mid-sixteenth century, in oblong 12° (10.3 × 15.2 cm), containing 161 mostly secular works, almost all anonymous. Composers' names found in the source are Josquin, Mouton, and Jörg Blankenmüller. Further attributions can be made to Claudin de Sermisy, Consilium, Jacotin, Janequin, Nic. Revertz, and Richafort, among others.

See J. J. Maier, *Die musikalischen Handschriften der königlichen Hof- und Staatsbibliothek in München*, 1879, No. 204; M. Göllner, *Bayerische Staatsbibliothek: Katalog der Musikhandschriften. 2: Tabulaturen und Stimmbücher bis zur Mitte des 17. Jahrhunderts*, 1979, pp. 92–101; *Census-Cat.* II, pp. 222–23.

No. 11. Anonymous (= Ockeghem): Petite camusete.

MunSche

Munich, Bayerische Staatsbibliothek, Handschriften-Inkunabelabteilung, Cod. Germanicus monacensis 810 (formerly Mus. Ms. 3232 and Cim. 351a) (Schedelsches Liederbuch).

A manuscript of 1460–70 on paper containing 170 folios approximately 15 × 10.5 cm. The volume, written for the most part by Hartmann Schedel (1440–1514), a noted physician and humanist, includes 128 compositions, among them pieces with German, French, Latin, and Italian texts. Composers named include Berbigant, Busnois, Wal Frey, Wenzel Nodler, Ockegheim, Pillois, W. Ruslein, Walterus de salice, Walterus Seam, and Touront.

See P. Gülke, ed., *Das Liederbuch des Dr. Hartmann Schedel* (Das Erbe deutscher Musik, 1. Reihe LXXIV, LXXV, LXXXIV [facsimile edition]), 1978– ; *Census-Cat.* II, pp. 236–37.

Fol. 62^v–64^r. Ockegheim: [textless] (= Ma bouche rit).

NHMel

New Haven, Yale University, Beinecke Rare Book and Manuscript Library, Ms. 91 (Mellon Chansonnier).

A manuscript on parchment copied in Naples c. 1475, containing two song-motets and fifty-five French, Italian, Spanish, and English secular compositions on eighty-one folios, 19.2 × 13.5 cm. Composers named include Barbingant, A. Basin, Binchoys, Busnoys, Caron, G. Dufay, Walterus Fry, G. Joye, Heyne, G. le Rouge, Morton, Jo. Okeghem, Petit Jan, Regis, Jo. Tinctoris, and Vincenet.

See M. Bukofzer, "An Unknown Chansonnier of the 15th Century," *The Musical Quarterly* XXVIII, 1942, pp. 14–49; L. L. Perkins and H. Garey, eds., *The Mellon Chansonnier*, 2 vols., 1979; *Census-Cat.* II, pp. 248–49.

Fol. 4^v–5^r. J. okeghem: Petitte camusette.
Fol. 25^v–26^r. Jo. okeghem: Laultre dantan.
Fol. 38^v–40^r. Okeghem: Ma bouce rit.

PBN 1596

Paris, Bibliothèque nationale, fonds français, Ms. 1596.

A portion of an uncompleted manuscript on parchment from the end of the fifteenth century, containing ten leaves measuring 25 × 19 cm on which were copied six chansons. Composers who can be identified by means of concordances include Agricola, Compère, Ockeghem, and Prioris. The chansonnier was originally owned by Marguerite d'Orléans (= Marguerite de Navarre).

See R. Wexler, "Music and Poetry in Renaissance Cognac," *Le Moyen Français* V, 1980, pp. 102–14; *Census-Cat.* III, pp. 20–21.

Fol. 7^v–8^r. Anonymous (= Ockeghem): Fors seulement contre.

PBN 1597

Paris, Bibliothèque nationale, fonds français, Ms. 1597.

A carefully written manuscript on parchment in quarto, 28 × 20 cm, that at one time belonged to the dukes of Lorraine and was probably compiled about 1500. The volume contains sixty-seven anonymous three- and four-voice pieces with mostly French, but also some Latin texts. The names of the composers may have been excised in the course of binding. Composers who can be identified from concordances include Agricola, Brumel, Compère, Dufay (Binchois?), Fresneau, Hayne van Ghizeghem, Josquin, Ninot le Petit (Compère?), Obrecht, Ockeghem, Pipelare, and Prioris.

See G. Paris and A. Gevaert, *Chansons du XVe siècle*, 1875, p. xii; J. P. Couchman, "The Lorraine Chansonnier," *Musica Disciplina* XXXIV, 1980, pp. 85–157; *Census-Cat.* III, pp. 21–22.

Fol. xxxvi^v–xxxvii^r. Anonymous (= Ockeghem): Fors seullement lattente.

PBN 2245

Paris, Bibliothèque nationale, fonds français, Ms. 2245.

A manuscript on parchment from the last years of the fifteenth century in octavo size, 18 × 12.3 cm, containing thirty-three leaves foliated by a modern hand. The volume, which is apparently of French origin, includes chansons attributed to Agricola, Compere, Fresneau, Hayne, Josquin, Lafoulerie, Mureau, Okeghem, Prioris, and Verjust.

See L. Finscher, *Loyset Compère (c 1450–1518): Life and Works*, 1964, p. 18; *Census-Cat.* III, pp. 22–23.

Fol. 13^{v}–14^{r}. Okeghem: Dung aultre amer.
Fol. 16^{v}–17^{r}. Okeghem: Fors seullement contre.

PBN 4379

Paris, Bibliothèque nationale, nouvelles acquisitions françaises, Ms. 4379

A manuscript on paper that combines elements of four entirely separate sources, the first part of which consists of forty-two leaves detached from *Sev 5–I–43*; for a description, see below.

PCord

Paris, Bibliothèque nationale, fonds Rothschild, Ms. 2973 (the Chansonnier Cordiforme or Chansonnier de Jean de Montchenu).

A beautifully written, heart-shaped manuscript on parchment, embellished with miniatures, probably compiled in Savoy about 1475, containing thirty French and fourteen Italian compositions. The single scribe entered no attributions, but it can be ascertained from other sources that works by Barbingant, Bedingham, Binchois (?), Busnois, Caron, Dufay, Dunstable (?), Fede, Frye, Hayne van Ghizeghem, Morton, Ockeghem, Regis, and Vincenet are present.

See E. L. Kottick, "The Chansonnier Cordiforme," *Journal of the A.M.S.* XX, 1967, pp. 10–27; *Census-Cat.* III, pp. 35–36.

Fol. 24^{v}–25^{r}. Anonymous (= Ockeghem): Lautredantan.
Fol. 42^{v}–44^{r}. Anonymous (= Ockeghem): Ma bouche rit.

PNiv

Paris, Bibliothèque nationale, Réserve Vmc Ms. 57 (Chansonnier Nivelle de la Chaussée).

A manuscript on parchment, perhaps written in France, 1460–65, containing sixty–six chansons on seventy-seven folios, 18 × 12.5 cm. Composers named include Barbingant, Binchois, Busnois, Delahaye, Dufay, Fede, and Ockeghem.

See P. Higgins, ed., *Chansonnier Nivelle de la Chaussée* [facsimile edition], 1984; *Census-Cat.* III, p. 12.

Fol. vj^{r}. Anonymous (= Ockeghem): Quil nest douleur (= lower voices only, *residuum* of Fors seulement l'actente).
Fol. lij^{v}–liiij^{r}. Okeghem: Ma bouche rit.
Fol. lv^{v}–lvj^{r}. Okeghem: Selle mamera—Petite camusete.
Fol. lvj^{v}–lviij^{r}. Okeghem: Tant fuz gentement.
Fol. lxix^{v}–lxx^{r}. Okeghem (Barbingant?): Au travail suis.

PPix

Paris, Bibliothèque nationale, fonds français, Ms. 15123 (Chansonnier Pixérécourt).

A large and attractive manuscript on parchment from approximately 1480, written in Italy (probably Florence), having two hundred folios 18 × 12 cm. The volume contains 170 compositions on mostly French, but also Latin, Italian, and Spanish texts; the French is frequently highly corrupt. Composers named include Busnoys, Caron, L. Compere, Cornago, Duffay, Morton, J. Ochghen, and B. Ycart. Further names that can be supplied from other sources are Agricola, Barbingant, Bedingham, Binchois, Dunstable, Frye, Joye, Hayne van Ghizeghem, Legrant, Martini, Molinet, Touront, and Vincenet.

See *AtlasCG* I, 1975–76, pp. 254–55; E. J. Pease, ed., *Music from the Pixérécourt MS*, 1960; *Census-Cat.* III, pp. 23–24.

Fol. 30^{v}–32^{r}. Anonymous (= Ockeghem): Ma boucherit.
Fol. 32^{v}–33^{r}. Anonymous (= Ockeghem): Laultre dantan.
Fol. 133^{v}–34^{r}. Ochghen (= Dufay?): Departes uous.
Fol. 155^{v}–56^{r}. J. Ochghen: La despourueue.
Fol. 158^{v}–59^{r}. J. Ochghen: Se uostre cuer.
Fol. 189^{v}–90^{r}. Busnoys (= Ockeghem): Dum aultre amer.

RCas 2856

Rome, Biblioteca Casanatense, Cod. 2856 (formerly O. V. 208).

A manuscript on parchment of the late fifteenth century, 163 folios measuring 27 × 20 cm. The volume, which is of Ferrarese origin and dates from the 1480s, contains three- and four-voice French chansons and a few Flemish pieces bearing attributions to Agricola, Ja. Barbirau, Basin, Bosfrin, Brumel, Busnoys, Caron, Colinet de Lannoy, Loiset Compere, Jo. Dusart, Jo. Ghiselin, Haine, Hobrecht, Jo. Jappart, Josquin des pres, Malcort (?), Jo. Martini, Molinet, Morton, Jo okeghem, Phelippon, Paulus de roda, Souspison, and Jo. Tourant.

See J. M. Llorens, "El Códice Casanatense 2.856 identificado como el Cancionero de Isabella d'Este (Ferrara), esposa de Francesco Gonzaga (Mantua)," *Anuario musical* XX, 1965, pp. 161–78; L. Lockwood, "Music at Ferrara in the Period of Ercole I d'Este," *Studi musicali* I, 1972, pp. 101–31; *Census-Cat.* III, pp. 112–14.

Fol. 16^{v}–17^{r} (13^{v}–14^{r}). Jo okeghem: Dunch aulter amer.
Fol. 17^{v}–18^{r} (14^{v}–15^{r}). Okeghem: Se uostre ceur.
Fol. 48^{v}–49^{r} (40^{v}–41^{r}). Okeghem (= Hayne van Ghizeghem): Se ne pas jeulx.
Fol. 52^{v}–53^{r} (44^{v}–45^{r}). Okeghem: Lauter dantan.
Fol. 57^{v}–59^{r} (48^{v}–50^{r}). Malcort (= Martini? Ockeghem?): Mal heure me bat.
Fol. 61^{v}–63^{r} (51^{v}–53^{r}). Ockeghem: Ma bouce fijt.

RCG XIII.27

Rome (Città del Vaticano), Biblioteca apostolica vaticana, Cappella Giulia, Cod. XIII.27.

A manuscript on paper of the late fifteenth century, 23.2 × 17 cm, having 131 folios. The volume contains French, Italian, Spanish, and Latin secular compositions. Texts are limited to incipits, which are often corrupt. Composers named include Agricola, Ayne, Baccio, J. Basiron, Caron, Colinet, Loyset Compere, Enrique, Felice, Jo. Frasnau, Arnulphus G., Isach, Jo. Japart, Josquin despres, Johannes Martini, Gil Murieu, Jacobus Obrech, Okagem, Petrequin, J. Stochen, Vincenet, and Virgilius. The manuscript was owned by a member of the Medici family, probably Giuliano, duke of Nemours.

See *AtlasCG*; *Census-Cat.* IV, pp. 18–19.

Fol. 17^{v}–18^{r} (10^{v}–11^{r}). Okagem: Dung aultrela.
Fol. 72^{v}–73^{r} (65^{v}–66^{r}). Jo. Martini (= Ockeghem? Malcort?): Malior me bat.
Fol. 76^{v}–77^{r} (69^{v}–70^{r}). Anonymous (= Ockeghem): Ma boche rit.
Fol. 104^{v}–05^{r} (97^{v}–98^{r}). Anonymous (= Ockeghem): Frayres y dexedes me (= Fors seulement l'actente).
Fol. 112^{v}–13^{r} (105^{v}–06^{r}). Anonymous (= Ockeghem): Dum altre amer.

RChigi

Rome (Città del Vaticano), Biblioteca apostolica vaticana, Ms. Chigiana C.VIII.234 (Chigi Codex).

Description in vol. I of this work (2nd edition, 1959), p. xvii. Add to bibliographical references: H. Kellman, "Josquin and the Courts of the Netherlands and France," *Proceedings of the International Josquin Festival Conference . . . 1971*, ed. E. E. Lowinsky, 1976, pp. 195–96 and 210; H. Kellman, ed., *Vatican, Biblioteca Apostolica Vaticana, MS Chigi C VIII 234* [facsimile edition], Renaissance Music in Facsimile XXII, 1988; *Census-Cat.* IV, pp. 12–13.

Fol. 139^{v}–40^{r} ($CXXXI^{v}$–$CXXXII^{r}$). Ockeghem: Ave Maria.
Fol. 276^{v}–79^{r} ($CCLXVIII^{v}$–$CCLXXI^{r}$). J. Ockeghem (index: Okeghem): Intemerata dei mater.

RCS 35

Rome (Città del Vaticano), Biblioteca apostolica vaticana, Cappella Sistina, Cod. 35.

Description in vol. I of this work (2nd edition, 1959), p. xvii. Add to bibliographical references: A. Roth, "Zur Datierung der frühen Chorbücher der päpstlichen Kapelle," *Quellenstudien zur Musik der Renaissance* II (Wolfenbütteler Forschungen XXVI), ed. L. Finscher, 1983, 267–68; *Census-Cat.* IV, pp. 41–42.

Fol. 7^{v}–10^{r}. Anonymous (= Ockeghem): (O) Intemerata dei mater.

RCS 42

Rome (Città del Vaticano), Biblioteca apostolica vaticana, Cappella Sistina, Cod. 42.

A choirbook in large folio (54 × 41 cm) written on paper, 170 leaves, in the early sixteenth century. The volume contains motets attributed to Baziron, Brumel, Busnoys, Carpentras, Loyset Compere, Josquin des pres, R. de Fevin, Foliot, Jo. Mouton, Obrecht, Jo. Ockeghen, Jo. le petit, Prioris, Petrus de la rue, Jo. a la venture, and Jo. Viardot, as well as anonymous compositions.

See F. X. Haberl, *Bibliographischer und thematischer Musikkatalog des päpstlichen Kapellarchivs im Vatikan zu Rom*, 1888 (*Beilage* to the *Monatshefte für Musikgeschichte*), p. 19; J. M. Llorens, *Capellae Sixtinae Codices musicis notis instructi* (Studi e testi 202), 1960, pp. 83–86; *Census-Cat.* IV, pp. 46–47.

Fol. CLXXV^{v}–CXX9[sic]^{r} (CLVa–CLVIIIb). Jo. Ockeghen: Salve regina [I].

RCS 46 **Rome (Città del Vaticano)**, Biblioteca apostolica vaticana, Cappella Sistina, Cod. 46.

A choirbook in large folio (55.5 × 42.5 cm) written on paper, 159 leaves, in the early sixteenth century. The volume contains motets and antiphons attributed to Adrian, Brumel, Brunet, Carpentras, L. Compere, Josquin des pres, Eustachius de monte regali, A. Fevin, Constant. Festa, Ysaac, Jo. Mouton, Ockeghem, Richafort, Jo. Escribano, and A. de Silva, as well as anonymous compositions.

See Haberl, *Bibliographischer und thematischer Musikkatalog*, p. 20; Llorens, *Capellae Sixtinae Codices*, pp. 94–98; E. E. Lowinsky, *The Medici Codex of 1518* I (Monuments of Renaissance Music III), 1968, pp. 232–33; *Vatican, Biblioteca apostolica vaticana, Cappella Sistina MS 46* [facsimile edition], Introduction, J. J. Dean, Renaissance Music in Facsimile XXI, 1986; *Census-Cat.* IV, pp. 49–50.

Fol. CXV^{v}–CXVIII^{r}. Anonymous (name cut off; = Ockeghem): Alma redemptoris mater.

Fol. CXVIII^{v}–CXX^{r}. Anonymous (name cut off; = Basiron [Ockeghem?]): Salue regina [II].

RegB 211–215 **Regensburg**, Bischöfliche Zentralbibliothek, Cod. Butsch 211–215.

Five partbooks on paper, dated 1538, designated Discantus, Altus, Tenor, Quintus, and Bassus. (The designations Tenor and Quintus were erroneously interchanged by a modern hand; the designation Vagans does not occur in the source.) The collection, which is of Germanic origin, contains motets by Claudin, De la Fage, Mathias Eckel, Henricus Finck, Johannes Froschius, Johannes Galliculus, Lupus Hellinck, Heurteur, H. Isaac, Josquin, Stephanus Mahu, Petrus Moulu, J. Mouton, Marcus Muscateller, Johannes Okegus (= Ockeghem?), Gregorius Peschin (Pesthin), Ricafort, Ludovicus Senflius, Thomas Stoltzer, Xistus Theodoricus, Hadrianus Willart, and anonymous compositions. The names Chunradus Rupsch and Gaspar Othmair are also encountered.

See P. Mohr, *Die Handschrift B 211–215 der Proske-Bibliothek zu Regensburg* (Schriften des Landesinstituts für Musikforschung Kiel VII), 1955; *Census-Cat.* III, p. 96.

No. 11. Johannes Okegus (= Ockeghem?): Gaude Maria virgo.

No. 82. kegus [sic, in bassus partbook only] (= Ockeghem?): Caeleste beneficium.

Sev 5–I–43 **Seville**, Biblioteca Colombina, Ms. 5–I–43 (with *PBN 4379*, part 1).

A manuscript on paper of the late fifteenth century measuring 21 × 16 cm and containing 167 compositions in all, mostly French and Italian secular with a few Flemish and German pieces and Latin song-motets. The volume was bought by Ferdinand Columbus at Rome in 1515. Four fragments of the manuscript comprising forty-two leaves were torn out of the binding in 1884 and now constitute part 1 of *PBN 4379*. Composers' names found in either *Sev 5–I–43* or *PBN 4379* include Agricola, Busnois, Dufay, Frye, Gaspar, Georgius Zuny (?), Morton, and Phillipet de pres. Composers who can be ascertained from other sources are Basin, Bedingham, Binchois, Caron, Convert, Cornago, Dunstable, Hayne, Japart, Josquin, Joye, Colinet de Lannoy, Martini, Molinet, Ockeghem, Tinctoris, Touront, and Vincenet.

See D. Plamenac, "A Reconstruction of the French Chansonnier in the Biblioteca Colombina, Seville," *The Musical Quarterly* XXXVII, 1951, pp. 501–42, and XXXVIII, 1952, pp. 85–117 and 245–77; idem, ed., *Facsimile Reproduction of the Manuscripts Sevilla 5.I.43 and Paris n. a. fr. 4379*, 1962; *Census-Cat.* III, pp. 139–40.

No. 30 (Paris), fol. 4^{v}–6^{r} (e5^{v}–e7^{r}). Anonymous (= Ockeghem): Ma bouce rit.

No. 71 (Seville), fol. 51^{v}–52^{r} (j1^{v}–j2^{r}). Anonymous (= Ockeghem): Dung aultre amer.

No. 129 (Paris), fol. 42^{v} (o1^{v})—(Seville), fol. 100^{r}–01^{r} (o2^{r}–o3^{r}). Anonymous (= Ockeghem): Ma maistresse.

Sev 7–I–28 **Seville**, Biblioteca Colombina, Ms. 7–I–28.

A manuscript on paper, probably copied in Spain at the end of the fifteenth century, containing ninety-nine folios, measuring 21.8 × 15 cm. The volume was obtained by Ferdinand Columbus in 1534. It contains Spanish secular and sacred compositions attributed to Belmonte, Cornago, Francisco de la Torre, Gijon, Hurtado de Xeres, Juanes, J. de Leon, Madrid, Triana, and J. Urrede.

See H. Anglés, *La música en la corte de los reyes católicos* I, 1941, pp. 103–06; G. Haberkamp, *Die weltliche Vokalmusik in Spanien um 1500*, 1968; M. Querol, ed., *Cancionero musical de la Colombina*

(Monumentos de la música española XXXIII), 1971; *Census-Cat.* III, pp. 142–43.

Fol. xxiiij^{v}–xxvj^{r} (20^{v}–22^{r}). Anonymous (= Cornago-Ockeghem): Ques mi vida.

Fol. cj^{v}–cij^{r} (92^{v}–93^{r}). Anonymous (= Ockeghem): De la momera—Petit le camiset.

SG 461 **St. Gall**, Stiftsbibliothek, Ms. 461.

A manuscript on parchment containing forty-eight leaves measuring 17.5 × 14.1 cm. The volume carries the inscription "Liber fridolini sichery ... organiste in Scto Gallo 154[5?]." The Germanic spellings of Flemish text incipits suggest that the Swiss organist may have copied the manuscript himself, perhaps from materials collected over an extended period. In addition to Flemish songs, it contains French chansons, including a large group of settings of *Fors seulement*, and some Italian pieces. Composers represented are A. Agricola, J. Agricola, Basiron, Brumel, Busnois, Compère, De la Val, De Orto, Ghiselin, Japart, Josquin, Isaac, Martini (?), Obrecht, Ockeghem, Pipelare, Jacobus Romanus, Pierre de la Rue, and Stockem.

See Brown, *A Florentine Chansonnier* I, p. 193; F. J. Giesbert, ed., *Ein altes Spielbuch: Liber Fridolini Sichery*, 2 vols., 1936; *Census-Cat.* III, pp. 144–45.

Pp. 2–3. Ockenhem: Fors seullement [l'actente].

Pp. 4–5. Ockengem: Fors solament [contre].

Pp. 52–53. Ockenghem (Malcort? Martini?): Malor me bat.

Tour 94 **Tournai**, Bibliothèque de la ville, Ms. 94. (See also **Brussels**, Bibliotèque royale Albert Ier, Ms. IV.90.)

The tenor partbook of a broken set, of which *Br IV.90* is the superius. (See the description above.)

Fol. 25^{r}–26^{r}. Anonymous (= Ockeghem): Je nay deul.

Tr 90 **Trent**, Museo nazionale del Castello del buon Consiglio, Ms. 90.

A choir book, 31 × 21 cm, on paper, copied by Johannes Wiser (fl. 1459–1470s), containing 465 folios on which writing appears, with masses, motets, and scattered secular pieces. Composers named include Christofferus Anthony, Bedingham, Benet, Benigni, Barth. de Bruollis, H. Collis, Constans, Cousin, Duffay, Dunstable, Hert, Joye, Ludwicus Krafft, Jo. Legrant, Leonell Anglicus, Ockeghen, Pyllois, W. de Rouge, W. de Salice. To these may be added Binchois, Brassart, Frye, and Loqueville.

See G. Adler and O. Koller, eds., *Sechs Trienter Codices* (Denkmäler der Tonkunst in Österreich VII/14–15), 1900, pp. 57–67; *Codices Musicales Tridentini* [facsimile edition], 1969–70; G. Spilstedt, "Toward the Genesis of the Trent Codices: New Directions and New Findings" (*Studies in Music from the U. of W. Ontario* I), 1976, pp. 55–70; D. Fallows, "Songs in the Trent Codices: An Optimistic Handlist," *I codici musicali trentini a cento anni dalla loro riscoperta*, ed. N. Pirrotta and D. Curti, 1986, pp. 170–79; S. E. Saunders, "The Dating of Trent 93 and Trent 90," *I codici musicali trentini*, 1986, pp. 60–83; *Census-Cat.* III, pp. 226–28.

Fol. 445^{r}. Ockeghen: Alius discantus super O rosa bella.

Tr 93 **Trent**, Museo diocesano, Biblioteca capitolare, Cod. B. L. (Ms. 93).

A choirbook of c. 1460 on paper, 31 × 21 cm, a large part of which consists of copies of compositions found in *Tr 90*.

See R. Ficker, *Sieben Trienter Codices, V. Auswahl* (Denkmäler der Tonkunst in Österreich XXXI/61), 1924, pp. vi–x; *Codices Musicales Tridentini* [facsimile edition], 1969–70; Spilstedt, "Toward the Genesis of the Trent Codices," pp. 55–70; Fallows, "Songs in the Trent Codices," pp. 170–79; Saunders, "The Dating of Trent 93 and Trent 90," pp. 60–83; *Census-Cat.* III, pp. 233–34.

Fol. 375^{v}–76^{r}. Anonymous (= Ockeghem): [textless] (= Ma maistresse).

WLab **Washington, D.C.**, Library of Congress, Music Division, Ms. M2.1.L25 Case (Laborde Chansonnier).

A large chanson collection on parchment, 12.5 × 8.5 cm, written in part by one of the scribes of *Dij* and *Cop 291*. The manuscript seems to date from around 1475, although the concluding section was likely compiled in about 1490 at or near the French court. Composers named include Baziron, Busnoys,

Caron, Compere, Convert, Dufay, Frye, Hayne, Joye, Ockeghem, and Tinctoris. Further attributions can be made to Barbingant, Basin, Binchois, Delahaye, Michelet, Molinet, Morton, and Prioris.

See H. E. Bush, "The Laborde Chansonnier," *Papers of the A.M.S. for 1940*, 1946, pp. 56–97; Rifkin, "Scribal Concordances," pp. 318–26; M. Gutiérrez-Denhoff, "Untersuchungen zu Gestalt, Entstehung und Repertoire des Chansonniers Laborde," *Archiv für Musikwissenschaft* XLI, 1984, pp. 113–14; James Pruett (complete edition with facsimile, in progress); *Census-Cat.* IV, pp. 125–26.

Fol. viiij^{v}–xj^{r}. Anonymous (= Ockeghem): Ma maistresse.
Fol. xviij^{v}–xviiij^{r}. Anonymous (= Ockeghem): Dung aultre amer.
Fol. xxxij^{v}–xxxiiij^{r}. Anonymous (= Ockeghem): Ma bouche rit.
Fol. lxj^{v}–lxij^{r}. Anonymous (= Ockeghem): La despourueue.
Fol. lxxvj^{v}–lxxvij^{r}. J. Okeghem: Il ne menchault.
Fol. iiii^{xx}j^{v}–iiii^{xx}iij^{r}. Anonymous (= Ockeghem): Presque transi.
Fol. iiii^{xx}xviiij^{v}–c^{r}. Anonymous (= Ockeghem): Fors seulement lactente.
Fol. 105^{v}–06^{r}. Anonymous (= Ockeghem): Les desloyaulx.
Fol. 120^{v}–21^{r}. Anonymous (= Ockeghem): Je nay dueil.

Wol 287 **Wolfenbüttel**, Herzog August Bibliothek, Ms. Guelferbytanus 287 Extravagantium.

A manuscript from about 1475, measuring 14.8 × 10.4 cm and containing fifty-six compositions, fifty-four of which are French chansons. The scribe of the volume apparently also copied the first portion of *WLab*, while the decoration resembles that of *Cop 291*. All pieces are anonymous, but composers who can be identified from other sources are Barbingant, Basiron, Bedingham, Binchois, Busnois, Caron, Convert, Dufay, Dunstable, Frye, Joye, Hayne van Ghizeghem, Michelet, Morton, Ockeghem, Phillipet des pres, and Prioris.

See Perkins and Garey, *The Mellon Chansonnier* II, p. 183; K. Hortschansky, "Notationsgewohnheiten in den burgundischen Chansonniers des 15. Jahrhunderts," *Wolfenbütteler Forschungen* VI, 1981, pp. 9–23; M. Gutiérrez-Denhoff, "Der Wolfenbütteler Chansonnier," *Wolfenbütteler Forschungen* XXIX, 1985; *Census-Cat.* IV, 140–41.

Fol. 27^{v}–29^{r}. Anonymous (= Ockeghem): Ma maistresse.
Fol. 29^{v}–31^{r}. Anonymous (= Ockeghem): Ma bouche rit.
Fol. 33^{v}–34^{r}. Anonymous (= Ockeghem): Dung aultre aymer.
Fol. 43^{v}–45^{r}. Anonymous (= Ockeghem): Fors seullement latente.
Fol. 61^{v}–62^{r}. Anonymous (= Ockeghem): Selle maymera—Petite camusette.
Fol. 62^{v}–63^{r}. Anonymous (= Barbingant? Ockeghem?): Au traueil suis.

II. PRINTS

RISM 1501 **Harmonice musices Odhecaton A.** Venice, Ottaviano Petrucci, May 15, 1501.

See H. Hewitt, ed., *Harmonice musices Odhecaton A*, 1942; *Harmonice musices Odhecaton A* [facsimile edition], 1973; *Répertoire International des Sources Musicales*, F. Lesure, ed., *Recueils imprimés, XVIe–XVIIe siècles*, 1960 (= RISM BI), p. 91.

Fol. 59^{v}–60^{r}. Okenhem: Ma bouche rit.
Fol. 68^{v}–69^{r}. Okenghen (= Malcort? Martini?): Malor me bat.

RISM 1504^{1} **Motetti C.** Venice, Ottaviano Petrucci, September 15, 1504.

See C. Sartori, *Bibliografia delle opere musicali stampate da Ottaviano Petrucci*, 1949, pp. 82–85; RISM BI, p. 92.

No. 15. Anonymous (= Ockeghem): Ut heremita solus.

RISM 1504^{3} **Canti C. N°. cento cinquanta.** Venice, Ottaviano Petrucci, February 10, 1503 (= 1504 n. st.).

See Sartori, *Bibliografia*, pp. 69–74; *Canti C. N°. cento cinquanta* [facsimile edition], 1978; RISM BI, p. 92.

Fol. 93^{v}–94^{r}. Okenghem: Je nay deul.
Fol. 1026^{v} (*recte* 124^{v})–1023^{r} (*recte* 125^{r}). Okenghem: Petite camusete.
Fol. 167^{v}. Okenghem: Prennes sur moy.

RISM 1520[1]

Motetti novi libro secondo. Venice, Andrea Antico, November 30, 1520.

See M. Picker, ed., *The Motet Books of Andrea Antico* (Monuments of Renaissance Music VIII), 1987; RISM BI, p. 99.

No. 8. Basiron (= Ockeghem?): Salve regina [II].

RISM [c. 1535][14]

[Title unknown. Frankfurt am Main, Christian Egenolff, c. 1535], discantus partbook only (= **Paris**, Bibliothèque nationale, Réserve Vm[7] 504).

See N. Bridgman, "Christian Egenolff, imprimeur de musique," *Annales musicologiques* III, 1955, pp. 77–177; M. Staehelin, "Zum Egenolff-Diskantband," *Archiv für Musikwissenschaft* XXIII, 1966, pp. 93–109; RISM BI, p. 114.

Part III, No. LVIII. Anonymous (= Malcort? Martini? Ockeghem?): Malheur me bat.

RISM 1538[9]

Trium vocum carmina. Nuremberg, Hieronymus Formschneider, 1538.

See H. M. Brown, *Instrumental Music Printed before 1600*, 1965, pp. 59–62; RISM BI, p. 120.

No. 47. Anonymous (= Ockeghem): Fors seulement [contre].

No. 86. Anonymous (= Ockeghem): Male bouche rit.

No. 91. Anonymous (= Malcort? Martini? Ockeghem?): Mal heur me bat.

RISM 1542[6]

Tomus tertius psalmorum selectorum. Nuremberg, Johannes Petreius, 1542.

See RISM BI, p. 136.

No. XL. Anonymous (= Ockeghem?): Deo gratia.

RISM 1549[16]

Diphona amoena et florida (ed. Erasmus Rotenbucher). Nuremberg, Johannes Montanus and Ulrich Neuber, 1549.

See RISM BI, p. 169.

No. XXXIII. Ockekem: Vivit dominus.

RISM 1568[7]

Cantiones triginta selectissimae (ed. Clemens Stephani). Nuremberg, Ulrich Neuber, 1568.

See RISM BI, p. 266.

No. XXX. Anonymous (= Ockeghem?): Deo gratia.

RISM 1590[30]

Selectae artificiosae et elegantes fugae (ed. Jacob Paix). Lavingen, Leonhard Reinmichael, 1590.

See H. M. Brown, *Instrumental Music Printed Before 1600*, 1965, pp. 361–62; RISM BI, p. 352.

No. XV. Okenhemius: Fuga trium vocum in epidiatessaron.

III. THEORETICAL TREATISES

Finck

Hermann Finck, **Practica musica.** Wittenberg, Georg Rhau, 1556.

See P. Matzdorf, *Die Practica musica Hermann Fincks*, 1957; *Practica musica* [facsimile edition], 1967; RISM BVI, p. 317.

Fol. Kk 1[v]–Ll 1[r]. Anonymous (= Ockeghem): Canon (= Ut heremita solus, *prima pars* only, in separate voice parts; the tenor in both canonic notation and resolution, apparently after *RISM 1504*[1]).

Heyden

Sebald Heyden, **De arte canendi.** Nuremberg, Johannes Petreius, 1540 (2nd ed. of **Musica, id est, artis canendi**, 1537).

See C. Miller, ed., *De arte canendi* (Musicological Studies and Documents XXVI), 1972; *De arte canendi* [facsimile edition], 1969; RISM BVI, p. 412.

P. 39. Okeghem: Fuga trium vocum, in Epidiatessaron.

Glareanus Henricus Glareanus, ΔΩΔΕΚΑΧΟΡΔΟΝ. Basel, Henricus Petrus, 1547.

See C. Miller, ed., *Dodecachordon* (Musicological Studies and Documents VI), 1965; *Dodecachordon* [facsimile edition], 1969; RISM BI, p. 159; RISM BVI, p. 366.

P. 454. Okenheim: Fuga trium vocum in Epidiatessaron.

Faber Gregorius Faber, **Musices practicae erotematum.** Basel, Henricus Petrus, 1553.

See RISM BVI, p. 301.

Pp. 152–53. Okeghem: Fuga trium partium.

Wilphlingseder Ambrosius Wilphlingseder, **Erotemata musices practicae.** Nuremberg, Christophorus Heussler, 1563.

See RISM BVI, p. 893.

Pp. 57–63. ORenhemius [sic] (index: Okhenhemius): Fugra [sic] trium vocum in Epidiatessaron cum Resolutione.

IV. SOURCES OF TEXTS

BerRoh **Berlin**, Staatliche Museen der Stiftung preussischer Kulturbesitz, Kupferstichkabinett, Ms. 78.B.17 (Hamilton 674) (Rohan Chansonnier).

Fol. 69ʳ. Fors seullement lattente.
Fol. 79ʳ. Les desloyaulx.
Fol. 83ᵛ–84ʳ. Ma bouche rit.
Fol. 100ʳ–100ᵛ. Ma maistresse.
Fol. 118ʳ. Dung autre amer.
Fol. 152ᵛ. Presque transi.
Fol. 185ʳ. Prenez sur moy.
Fol. 185ʳ–185ᵛ. La despourueue.

ErasA **Adagiorum collecteana ... Varia epigrammata**, Desiderius Erasmus. Paris, 1506–07.

No. 44. Ergone conticuit ("Iohanni okego musico summo: Epitaphium").

Fiore **Il Fiore delle elegantissime cancionete del nobile messere Leonardo Justiniano.** Venice, 1482.

Fol. biiᵛ–biiiʳ. O rosa bella.

LonBL 380 **London**, British Library, Ms. Lansdowne 380.

Fol. 242ʳ. Dung autre amer.
Fol. 243ʳ. Prenez sur moy.
Fol. 251ʳ. Fors seulement lattente.

PBN IV.6.25 **Paris**, Bibliothèque nationale, fonds Rothschild, Ms. IV.6.25.

Fol. 29ᵛ. Dun autre amer.

PBN 226 **Paris**, Bibliothèque nationale, fonds espagnol, Ms. 226.

Fol. 35ᵛ. Ques mi vida.

PBN 1035 **Paris**, Bibliothèque nationale, fonds italien, Ms. 1035.

Fol. 34ᵛ. O rosa bella.

PBN 1719 **Paris**, Bibliothèque nationale, fonds français, Ms. 1719.

Fol. 26^{v}–27^{r}. Je nay dueil.
Fol. 34^{r}. Fors seullement lactente.
Fol. 61^{r} and 132^{r}. Ma bouche rit.
Fol. 61^{v} and 132^{r}. Les desloyaulx.
Fol. 87^{r}. Selle maymera.

PBN 1722 **Paris**, Bibliothèque nationale, fonds français, Ms. 1722.

Fol. 72^{v}. Fors seullement lattente.

PBN 7559 **Paris**, Bibliothèque nationale, nouvelles acquisitions françaises, Ms. 7559.

Fol. 66^{v}. Selle maymera.

VerChasse **La Chasse et le départ d'Amours.** Paris, Antoine Vérard, 1509.

Fol. Piiii^{v}. Selle Maymera.
Fol. Qiiii^{r}. Dun autre amer.
Fol. Qiiii^{r}. Jen ay dueil.

VerJard **Le Jardin de plaisance et fleur de Réthoricque.** Paris, Anthoine Vérard, n.d.

Fol. lxi^{r}. Ma bouche rit (as a *rondeau cinquain*).
Fol. lxxi^{r}. Ma maistresse.
Fol. lxxi^{v}. Ma bouche rit.
Fol. lxxxiiii^{r}–lxxxiiii^{v}. Dun autre amer.
Fol. lxxxxi^{r}. Quant de vous seul.
Fol. Cxiiii^{r}–Cxiiii^{v}. Les desloyaulx.
Fol. Cxv^{r}. Fors seulement lattente.

PUBLICATIONS CITED BY MEANS OF SIGLA

AdlerST Adler, Guido, and Oswald Koller, eds. *Sechs Trienter Codices: Geistliche und weltliche Kompositionen des XV. Jhs.* Denkmäler der Tonkunst in Österreich VII/14–15. Vienna, 1900.

AltaR Altamura, Antonio. *Rimatori napoletani del quattrocento.* Collana di studi e testi di letteratura III. Naples, 1962.

_AM_ *Antiphonale monasticum pro diurnis horis.* Tournai, 1934.

AmbG Ambros, August Wilhelm. *Geschichte der Musik*, 3rd ed. Leipzig, 1887–1911.

_AR_ *Antiphonale sacrosanctae romanae ecclesiae pro diurnis horis.* Tournai, 1949.

AtlasCG Atlas, Allan, ed. *The Cappella Giulia Chansonnier*, 2 vols. Musicological Studies XXVII. Brooklyn, N.Y., 1975–76.

Bancel Bancel, E. M., ed. *Cent quarante-cinq rondeaux d'amour publiés d'après un manuscrit autographe de la fin du XV*[e] *siècle.* Paris, 1875.

BarbO Meier, Bernhard, ed. *Jacobi Barbireau: Opera omnia.* Corpus mensurabilis musicae VII. Rome, 1954–57.

BellingB Bellingham, Bruce A. "The *Bicinium* in the Lutheran Latin Schools during the Reformation Period." Unpublished Ph.D. dissertation, University of Toronto, 1971.

BesAM Besseler, Heinrich, ed. *Altniederländische Motetten.* Kassel, 1929.

BesSMM Besseler, Heinrich, and Peter Gülke. *Schriftbild der mehrstimmigen Musik.* Musikgeschichte in Bildern III/5. Leipzig, 1973.

BlackLP Blackburn, Bonnie J. "The Lupus Problem." Unpublished Ph.D. dissertation, University of Chicago, 1970.

BocF Bockholdt, Rudolf. "Französische und niederländische Musik des 14. und 15. Jahrhunderts." *Musikalische Edition im Wandel des historischen Bewusstseins.* Ed. Thrasybulos Georgiades. Kassel, 1971, pp. 149–66.

BohnGD Bohn, Peter, ed. *Glareani Dodecachordon*. Publikationen älterer praktischer und theoretischer Musikwerke XVI/1–3. Leipzig, 1888–90.

BrenV Brenet, Michel. *Musique et musiciens de la vieille France*. Paris, 1911.

BrownFC Brown, Howard Mayer, ed. *A Florentine Chansonnier from the Time of Lorenzo the Magnificent*. Monuments of Renaissance Music VII. Chicago, 1983.

Burney Burney, Charles. *A General History of Music from the Earliest Ages to the Present Period*. 4 vols. London, 1776–89.

Busby Busby, Thomas. *A General History of Music from the Earliest Times to the Present*. 2 vols. London, 1819.

Census-Cat. *Census-Catalogue of Manuscript Sources of Polyphonic Music, 1400–1550*. 5 vols. *Renaissance Manuscript Studies* I. Neuhausen-Stuttgart, 1979–1989.

CouS Coussemaker, Ch. Edmond H. de, ed. *Scriptorum de musica medii aevi*. 4 vols. Paris, 1864–76.

DahlO Dahlhaus, Carl. "Ockeghems 'Fuga trium vocum'." *Die Musikforschung* XIII (1960), pp. 307–10.

DartIM Dart, Thurston, ed. *Invitation to Medieval Music* II. London, 1969.

DèzS Dèzes, Karl. "Das Dufay zugeschriebene Salve Regina: eine deutsche Komposition." *Zeitschrift für Musikwissenschaft* X (1927–28), pp. 327–62.

DiseFP Disertori, Benvenuto, ed. *Le Frottole nell'edizione principe di Ottaviano Petrucci*, vol. I. Istituzione e monumenti dell'arte musicale italiana, nuova serie I. Cremona, 1954.

DiseM Disertori, Benvenuto, ed. *Johannes Martini: Magnificat e messe*. Archivium musices metropolitanum mediolanense XII. Milan, 1964.

DrozJP Droz, Eugénie, and Arthur Piaget, eds. *Antoine Vérard: Le Jardin de plaisance*. 2 vols. Paris, 1910–25.

DrozT Droz, Eugénie, Geneviève Thibault, and Yvonne Rokseth, eds. *Trois Chansonniers français du XVe siècle*. Paris, 1927.

DufayO Van, Guillaume de, and Heinrich Besseler, eds. *Guillaume Dufay: Opera omnia*. Corpus mensurabilis musicae I. Rome, 1948–66.

DunstO Bukofzer, Manfred F., ed. *John Dunstable: Complete Works*, 2nd revised edition. Prepared by Margaret Bent, Ian Bent, and Brian Trowell. Musica Britannica VIII. London, 1970.

EitB Eitner, Robert. *Bibliographie der Musik-Sammelwerke des XVI. und XVII. Jahrhunderts*. Berlin, 1877.

EitM Eitner, Robert. "Mitteilung." *Monatshefte für Musikgeschichte* XIX (1887), p. 59.

EitWL Eitner, Robert. "Das Walter'sche Liederbuch." *Monatshefte für Musikgeschichte* VI (1874), pp. 147–60.

ErasP Reedijk, Cornelius, ed. *The Poems of Desiderius Erasmus, with Introduction and Notes.* Leiden, 1956.

EvansM Evans, Edward G., ed. *Johannes Martini: Secular Pieces.* Recent Researches in the Music of the Middle Ages and Early Renaissance I. Madison, Wis., 1975.

FallJO Fallows, David. "Johannes Ockeghem: The Changing Image, the Songs and a New Source." *Early Music* XII (1984), pp. 218–30.

FerraB Ferrari, Severino, ed. *Biblioteca di letteratura popolare italiana*, 2 vols. Florence, 1882.

FétB Fétis, François-Joseph. *Biographie universelle des musiciens et bibliographie générale de la musique*, 2nd ed. 8 vols. Brussels, 1878–80.

FétE Fétis, François-Joseph. *Esquisse de l'histoire de l'harmonie considerée comme art et comme science systématique.* Paris, 1840.

FinHM Finney, Theodore M. *A History of Music.* New York, 1935.

ForkA Forkel, Johann Nikolaus. *Allgemeine Geschichte der Musik.* 2 vols. Leipzig, 1788–1801.

FoxB Fox, Charles Warren. "Barbireau and Barbingant: A Review." *Journal of the A.M.S.* XII (1960), pp. 79–101.

FranAP Françon, Marcel, ed. *Albums poétiques de Marguerite d'Autriche.* Cambridge, Mass., 1934.

FreyR Frey, Herman-Walther. "Regesten zur päpstlichen Kapelle unter Leo X. und zu seiner Privatkapelle." *Die Musikforschung* VIII (1955), pp. 58–73, 178–99, 412–37, and IX (1956), pp. 46–57, 139–56.

FröB Fröhlich, Joseph. *Beiträge zur Geschichte der Musik der älteren u. neueren Zeit.* 2 vols. Würzburg, 1874.

GiesS Giesbert, Franz J., ed. *Ein altes Spielbuch: Liber Fridolini Sichery.* Mainz, 1936.

GomO Gombosi, Otto. *Jacob Obrecht: Eine stilkritische Studie.* Leipzig, 1925.

Grove VI Sadie, Stanley, ed. *The New Grove Dictionary of Music and Musicians.* 20 vols. London, 1980.

HaarCM Haar, James, ed. *Chanson and Madrigal, 1480–1530.* Cambridge, Mass., 1964.

HabBV Haberl, Franz X. *Bibliographischer und thematischer Musikkatalog des päpstlichen Kapellarchivs im Vatikan zu Rom.* Bausteine für Musikgeschichte II. Leipzig, 1888.

HabR Haberl, Franz X. *Die römische "Schola Cantorum" und die päpstlichen Kapellsänger bis zur Mitte des 16. Jahrhunderts.* Bausteine für Musikgeschichte III. Leipzig, 1888.

HabkWVS Haberkamp, Gertraut. *Die weltliche Vokalmusik in Spanien um 1500.* Tutzing, 1968.

HAM Apel, Willi, and Archibald T. Davison, eds. *Historical Anthology of Music.* 2 vols. Cambridge, Mass., 1946.

HawkH Hawkins, Sir John. *A General History of the Science and Practice of Music.* 5 vols. London, 1776.

HayneO Hudson, Barton, ed. *Hayne van Ghizeghem: Opera omnia.* Corpus mensurabilis musicae LXXIV. Neuhausen-Stuttgart, 1977.

HewFS Hewitt, Helen. "*Fors seulement* and the Cantus Firmus Technique of the Fifteenth Century." *Essays in Musicology in Honor of Dragan Plamenac.* Ed. Gustave Reese and Robert J. Snow. Pittsburgh, 1969, pp. 91–126.

HewO Hewitt, Helen, and Isabel Pope, eds. *Ottaviano Petrucci: Harmonice musices Odhecaton A*. Cambridge, Mass., 1942.

HoffS Hoffmann-Erbrecht, Lothar. "Stolzeriana." *Die Musikforschung* XXVII (1974), pp. 18–36.

Hunt Hunter, George, ed. *Jean de Ockeghem: Salve Regina.* Pro Musica Series XXXIV. New York, 1973.

JepK Jeppesen, Knud, ed. *Der Kopenhagener Chansonnier.* Copenhagen and Leipzig, 1927.

JosqMS Smijers, Albert, ed. *Josquin des Prés: Werken, Missen.* Amsterdam and Leipzig, 1926–56.

JosqWW Smijers, Albert, Myroslaw Antonowycz, and Willem Elders, eds. *Josquin des Prés: Werken, Wereldlijke Werken.* Amsterdam, 1923–68.

KennF Kenney, Sylvia. *Walter Frye and the* Contenance Angloise. New Haven, 1964.

KiesV Kiesewetter, Raphael Georg. *Die Verdienste der Niederländer um die Tonkunst.* Amsterdam, 1829.

LenE Lenaerts, René B. "Erasmus en de Muziek." *Erasmus plechtig herdacht op 30 April 1969.* Ed. Joseph Coppens. Brussels, 1969, pp. 75–78.

LeviO Levitan, Joseph S. "Ockeghem's Clefless Compositions." *The Musical Quarterly* XXIII (1937), pp. 440–64.

LitR Litterick, Louise. "The Revision of Ockeghem's 'Je n'ay dueil'." *Le Moyen Français* V (1979), pp. 29–48.

LlorCS Llorens, Josephus M. *Capellae Sixtinae codices.* Studi e testi CII. Vatican City, 1960.

LöpL Löpelmann, Martin, ed. *Die Liederhandschrift des Cardinals de Rohan*. Göttingen, 1923.

LowMCE Lowinsky, Edward E., ed. *The Medici Codex of 1518*. Monuments of Renaissance Music III-V. Chicago, 1968.

LowO Lowinsky, Edward E. "Ockeghem's Canon for Thirty-Six Voices: An Essay in Musical Iconography." *Essays in Musicology in Honor of Dragan Plamenac*. Ed. Gustave Reese and Robert J. Snow. Pittsburgh, 1969, pp. 155–80.

LU *The Liber Usualis, with Introduction and Rubrics in English*. Tournai, 1963.

MaldP Maldeghem, Robert van, ed. *Trésor musical: Musique profane*. 29 vols. Brussels, 1865–93.

MandaR Mandalari, Mario, ed. *Rimatori napoletani del quattrocento dal codice 1035 della Biblioteca nazionale di Parigi*. Caserta, 1885.

MarM Marix, Jeanne, ed. *Les Musiciens de la cour de Bourgogne au XVe siècle (1420–1467)*. Paris, 1937.

MGG Blume, Friedrich, ed. *Die Musik in Geschichte und Gegenwart: Allgemeine Enzyklopädie der Musik*. 17 vols. Kassel, 1949–79.

MillerE Miller, Clement A. "Erasmus on Music." *The Musical Quarterly* LII (1966), pp. 332–49.

MillerFG Miller, Clement A., ed. *Franchinus Gaffurius: Practica musicae*. Musicological Studies and Documents XX. Rome, 1969.

MillerG Miller, Clement A., ed. *Heinrich Glareanus: Dodecachordon*. 2 vols. Musicological Studies and Documents VI. Rome, 1965.

MillerH Miller, Clement A., ed. *Sebald Heyden: De arte canendi*. Musicological Studies and Documents XXVI. Rome, 1972.

MoD Morelot, Stéphan. "Notice sur un manuscrit de musique ancienne de la Bibliothèque de Dijon." *Mémoires de la Commission des Antiquités du Département de la Côte-d'Or* IV (1856), pp. 133–60.

MorelC Morel-Fatio, Alfred. *Catalogue des manuscrits espagnols et des manuscrits portugais dans la Bibliothèque nationale*. Paris, 1881–92.

ObrO Smijers, Albert, ed. *Jacobus Obrecht: Opera omnia: Missen*. Amsterdam, 1953–57.

ObrW Wolf, Johannes, ed. *Werken van Jacob Obrecht: Missen*. Amsterdam and Leipzig, 1908–21.

OckCW Plamenac, Dragan, and Richard Wexler, eds. *Johannes Ockeghem: Collected Works*. 3 vols. New York and Philadelphia, 1947–1992.

Pal mus *Paléographie musicale*. 19 vols. Tournai, 1889–1958.

ParrishT Parrish, Carl, ed. *Johannes Tinctoris: Terminorum musicae diffinitorium*. London, 1963.

PerkMC Perkins, Leeman L., and Howard Garey, eds. *The Mellon Chansonnier.* 2 vols. New Haven, 1979.

PickA Picker, Martin, ed. *The Motet Books of Andrea Antico.* Monuments of Renaissance Music VIII. Chicago, 1987.

PickCA Picker, Martin, ed. *The Chanson Albums of Marguerite of Austria.* Berkeley and Los Angeles, 1965.

PickFS Picker, Martin, ed. *Fors seulement: Thirty Compositions for Three to Five Voices or Instruments from the Fifteenth and Sixteenth Centuries.* Recent Researches in the Music of the Middle Ages and Early Renaissance XIV. Madison, Wis., 1981.

PirH Pirro, André. *Histoire de la musique de la fin du XIVe siècle à la fin du XVIe.* Paris, 1940.

PlamA Plamenac, Dragan. "Autour d'Ockeghem." *Revue musicale* IX (1928), pp. 26–47.

PlamR Plamenac, Dragan. "On Reading Fifteenth-Century Chanson Texts." *Journal of the A.M.S.* XXX (1977), pp. 320–24.

PopeMC Pope, Isabel, and Masakata Kanazawa, eds. *The Musical Manuscript Montecassino 871.* Oxford, 1978.

PopeME Pope, Isabel. "La Musique espagnole à la cour de Naples dans la seconde moitié du XVe siècle." *Musique et poésie au XVIe siècle.* Paris, 1954, pp. 35–61.

PopeSC Pope, Isabel. "The Secular Compositions of Johannes Cornago." *Misceláneа en homenaje a Mons. Higinio Anglés* II. Barcelona, 1961, pp. 689–706.

RaphQ Raphael, Alfred. "Über einige Quodlibet mit dem Cantus Firmus 'O rosa bella' und über dieses Lied selbst, mit Musikbeilage." *Monatshefte für Musikgeschichte* XXXI (1899), pp. 161–79.

ReMC Reese, Gustave. "Musical Compositions in Renaissance Intarsia," *Misceláneа en homenaje a Mons. Higinio Anglés* II. Barcelona, 1961, pp. 689–706.

ReMR Reese, Gustave. *Music in the Renaissance.* Rev. ed. New York, 1959.

ReOD Reese, Gustave, and Steven Ledbetter, eds. *Ornithoparcus/Dowland: A Compendium of Musical Practice.* New York, 1973.

RestC Restori, Antonio. "Un Codice musicale pavese." *Zeitschrift für romanische Philologie* XVIII (1894), pp. 381–401.

RieH Riemann, Hugo. *Handbuch der Musikgeschichte.* 2 vols. Leipzig, 1904–13.

RifSC Rifkin, Joshua. "Scribal Concordances for Some Renaissance Manuscripts in Florentine Libraries." *Journal of the A.M.S.* XXVI (1973), pp. 305–26.

RingGL Ringmann, Heribert, ed. *Das Glogauer Liederbuch*, vol. I. Das Erbe deutscher Musik. Reichsdenkmale IV. Kassel, 1936.

RittHM Ritter, Frédéric Louis. *History of Music*, 2nd ed. 2 vols. Boston, 1880.

ScherG Schering, Arnold, ed. *Geschichte der Musik in Beispielen*. Leipzig, 1931.

ScherR Schering, Arnold. "Ein Rätseltenor Okeghems." *Festschrift Hermann Kretzschmar zum siebzigsten Geburtstage überreicht von Kollegen, Schülern und Freunden*. Leipzig, 1918, pp. 132–35.

ScherlMN Scherliess, Volker. *Musikalische Noten auf Kunstwerken der italienischen Renaissance. Hamburger Beiträge zur Musikwissenschaft* VIII. Hamburg, 1972.

SmijO Smijers, Albert, ed. *Van Ockeghem tot Sweelinck*. Amsterdam, 1952–56.

Stam Stam, Edward, ed. *Josquin des Prez, Qui habitat 24 vocum; Johannes Ockeghem, Deo gratias 36 vocum*. Exempla musica neerlandica VI. Amsterdam, 1971.

SteB Stephan, Wolfgang. *Die burgundisch-niederländische Motette zur Zeit Ockeghems*. Kassel, 1937.

StevSM Stevenson, Robert. *Spanish Music in the Age of Columbus*. The Hague, 1960.

StrunkSR Strunk, W. Oliver, ed. *Source Readings in Music History*. New York, 1950.

TarusD Taruskin, Richard, ed. *D'ung aultre amer*. Ogni Sorte Editions RS 6. Miami, 1983.

ThoinanD Thoinan, Ernest. *Déploration de Guillaume Crétin sur le trépas de Jean Okeghem, musicien, premier chapelain du roi de France et trésorier de Saint-Martin de Tours*. Paris, 1864.

TrowIMM Trowell, Brian, ed. *Invitation to Medieval Music* III. London, 1976; IV. London, 1978.

VaccJO Vaccaro, Jean-Michel. "Jean de Ockeghem, trésorier de l'église Saint Martin de Tours de 1459(?) à 1497." *Johannes Ockeghem en zijn Tijd*. Dendermonde, 1970, pp. 60–76.

Wallis Wallis, Norbert Hardy, ed. *Anonymous French Verse: An Anthology of Fifteenth-Century Poems Collected from Manuscripts in the British Museum*. London, 1929.

WalS Wallner, Bertha A. "Sebastian Virdung von Amberg: Beiträge zu seiner Lebensgeschichte." *Kirchenmusikalisches Jahrbuch* XXIV (1911), pp. 85–106.

WieseNL Wiese, Berthold. "Neunzehn Lieder Leonardo Giustinianis nach dem alten Drucken." *Bericht des Grossherzoglichen Real-gymnasiums*. Ludwigslust, 1885, pp. 1–13.

WolfS Wolf, Johannes, ed. *Sing- und Spielmusik aus älteren Zeit*. Leipzig, 1926.

WoolP Wooldridge, H. E. *The Polyphonic Period*. 2nd ed., revised by Percy C. Buck. *Oxford History of Music* I and II. London, 1929–32.

YoungG Young, Irwin, ed. *The* Practica musicae *of Franchinus Gafurius*. Madison, Wis., 1969.

EDITORIAL NOTES

The reading of a single main source has supplied, insofar as possible, the basis of the music and text of each transcription in this edition. The choice of a main source was not clear-cut in every instance, but preference was given to one deriving from the composer's milieu or dating from his lifetime. All other things being equal, a source that attributes a given piece to Ockeghem, providing that it is largely free from error, was favored over one that does not.

Relatively minor errors such as still exist in the main source have been rectified, where possible, on the basis of correct readings of the passages in question located in other sources. All changes to the musical text as preserved in the main source are listed among the VARIANT READINGS, along with alternative readings deriving from the other sources, using the following abbreviations:

bl	black	mens sig	mensuration sign
br	breve	mi col	minor color
col	coloration	miss	missing
dot	dotted	perf	perfect
err	erroneously	sbr	semibreve
fu	fusa	sig	signature
imperf	imperfect	sig congr	signum congruentiae
lig	ligature	sm	semiminim
m	minim	temp perf	tempus perfectum

The location of a variant in a particular piece is indicated in the VARIANT READINGS list by means of the number of the measure in the transcription, separated by a slash from the number of the notational symbol (including rests) within that measure. Following the listed variant are the *sigla* (in parentheses) of the sources that contain it. Succeeding variants are separated by semicolons, except when a variant occupies the same location as its predecessor. In that event, a comma is employed and the number of the location is not repeated. It was the aim of the editors to record variants as succinctly but as clearly as possible, and it is hoped that the reader, should he wish to do so, can reconstruct what may be found in any of the sources from the list without recourse to the original.

In the interest of presenting the music in a form convenient to performers, the policy of leaving clefs unchanged and all note values unreduced followed in volumes I and II has been set aside here. Clefs employed consist of modern treble and bass, including treble with an eight suspended to indicate transposition to the lower octave.

Regarding note values, the question of how to interpret the relationships among the mensuration signs O, C, ⦶, and ₵ is one of the most difficult facing any editor of late fifteenth-century music. One cannot determine for certain whether Ockeghem was consistent in his choice of these signs, or, if he was, whether the scribes who wrote the surviving sources of his works reproduced his choices faithfully. It is not securely known today if, when one mensuration sign succeeds another, the relationship between them should be reckoned in terms of the minim, the semibreve, or the breve. There is also no sure way of knowing whether the virgule (the vertical line) in a mensuration sign invariably stands for duple proportion. Is Ф, for example, the exact equivalent of O2 or something less precise than that? Or if a sign is succeeded by a numeral 3 in the signature of all voices, does the 3 stand for *proportio tripla* (3:1) or *proportio sesquialtera* (3:2)? One cannot easily tell whether the theorists of Ockeghem's time interpreting the signs are describing actual practice or seeking to correct what they perceive as improper, but perhaps widespread, usage.[3]

An examination of the music attributed to Ockeghem reveals little in terms of a definitive solution to the problem. At the beginning of the *secunda pars* of *Ut heremita solus* (no. 5 below), the signature of the tenor is O while the other voices have ₵ . The context suggests that the relationship of O to ₵ is O-semibreve = ₵ - breve. But is the equivalency still valid when a passage having ₵ in all voices succeeds a passage with all voices signed O? In *Ut heremita solus* the proportions are exact, but the work is an elaborate canon, a piece belonging to a special category of deliberately erudite compositions in which theoretical precepts are observed perhaps more strictly than usual. In *Gaude Maria* (no. 9 below, a work of doubtful authenticity), the four successive *partes* have the mensuration signs O, ₵ , ₵ , and Ф, respectively. On account of the responsory design of the work, mm. 237–46 in the *quarta pars* are identical to mm. 91–100 in the *prima pars*, although the mensuration of the *prima pars* is O, while that of the *quarta pars* is Ф. It would seem very unlikely that the composer intended the same counterpoint and words to be sung twice as fast at the end of a motet in responsory form as at the beginning.

At one time, the present editors considered transcribing motet *partes* in ₵ or Ф with their note values reduced to one quarter of their original values. But in light of numerous apparent contradictions and inconsistencies such as those mentioned above, it was decided that reducing the values uniformly by a half throughout and showing the original signs above the modern time signatures where appropriate was the more judicious course to follow.[4] Therefore, in performing this music, one must cultivate a knowledge of what might be the possibilities, based on the writings of theorists, and then decide which among the available alternatives serves best.[5]

Final longs remain unreduced at the conclusions of one-section pieces and interior *partes* of longer works in order that they may continue to represent their original meaning of notes having indeterminate value. The transcription of each voice begins with a diplomatic facsimile showing the musical incipit of that voice according to the main source. Square brackets enclose those passages where conjecture has been necessary on account of errors that could not be corrected by means of concordant sources or on account of damage to the sole extant source.

It has seemed advisable to seek a middle ground between those who advocate the abolition of barlines in transcriptions of music from before 1600 and those who would follow the modern conventions of vocal part music notation. Therefore, the present editors have adopted the practice of barring between the staves, which has been employed in many modern editions of medieval and Renaissance music. Assuming that a measure of

---

[3]For an illuminating discussion of what the theorists of Ockeghem's time wrote concerning *tempus*, see Anna Maria Busse Berger, "The Relationship of Perfect and Imperfect Time in Italian Theory of the Renaissance," *Early Music History* V (1985), pp. 1–28.

[4]Our views on this position are similar to those expressed by Arthur Mendel, who wrote:

> In actual music, when there is a change of signature, modern editors are not agreed as to how the relation between the time-values under the two signatures [O and C] is to be indicated. In many instances there is no way of being sure what that relation is, on the basis of our present knowledge. I cannot see that anything is gained by presenting a "solution" to a problem that one has not in fact solved, . . . ("Some Ambiguities of the Mensural System," *Studies in Music History: Essays for Oliver Strunk*, ed. by Harold Powers, Princeton, 1968, p. 154).

[5]Busse Berger, *op. cit.*, provides evidence suggesting that there is a theoretical basis for considering the proportion of O followed by ₵ to be *sesquitertia* (4:3); that is, four semibreves in ₵ should be performed in the time of three semibreves in the previous O. She does not offer a suggestion, however, concerning how one might proceed then from ₵ to Ф . Does the semibreve remain equivalent to the semibreve in ₵, still 4:3 in comparison with O, or does the virgule in the Ф stand for the duple proportion of plain O (6:3, that is, 2:1)? *Sesquitertia* has found favor with many modern performers, who generally have adopted the relationship after much trial and error. See also Eunice Schroeder, "The Stroke Comes Full Circle: Ф and ₵ in Writings on Music, ca. 1450–1540," *Musica Disciplina* XXXVI (1982), pp. 119–66, and Busse Berger, "The Myth of *diminutio per tertiam partem*," *The Journal of Musicology* VIII (1990), pp. 398–426.

For further information concerning the writings of theorists on this subject, see Mendel, *op. cit.*, and J. A. Bank, *Tactus, Tempo and Notation in Mensural Music from the 13th to the 17th Century*, Amsterdam, 1972.

the transcription should correspond to the time of one breve in the original notation, this technique is only feasible if all voices are in the same mensuration. It could not be used, for example, in the edition of *Ut heremita solus*.

In the transcription, all original accidentals are positioned on the staff directly in front of the notes they modify. On occasion, an accidental occurs in an original source well before the note it was meant to affect; here it undoubtedly served to indicate a need for hexachordal mutation. The actual locations of such pre-placed accidentals are given in the VARIANT READINGS lists.

Editorial accidentals have been supplied according to precepts of *musica ficta* and solmization set forth by the theorists of Ockeghem's time, such as Johannes Tinctoris, among others. It should be borne in mind, however, that no theorist provides us with an itemized list of *musica ficta* rules. Principles governing the editorial application of unwritten accidentals must be inferred today from various points raised in theoretical discussions of counterpoint and solmization. In effect, there really are no rules of *musica ficta* but rather exceptions to the normal method of solmization (singing at sight using the standard hexachord names for the tones of the gamut) or else suggestions for proceeding smoothly from one interval to the next in counterpoint. Editors today are in the habit of extrapolating the following "rules" from the writings of the theorists:[6]

I. a. Editorial accidentals should be applied at cadence points, where they will serve to keep simultaneously sounding unisons, fourths, fifths, and octaves perfect. Almost invariably the theorists speak of this in terms of avoiding "mi contra fa," since, for example, an augmented fourth or diminished fifth would result from singing b-mi in one part against f-fa in another.[7]

b. Direct melodic leaps of a fourth or fifth should be perfect in order to avoid singing mi immediately followed by fa or vice versa. (It stands to reason that rules governing melodic motion may well be considerably older than those for part writing.) Certain theorists seem to imply that when melodies outline a fourth or fifth, the interval formed by the outer notes should also be perfect. It is doubtful that such a rule could have had a pervasive effect, for the practical sources appear to contradict it innumerable times .

c. Several theorists allude to the need for solmizing the note above "la" in a given hexachord as "fa" when subsequently remaining within that hexachord. There is reason to think that this rule is related to the avoidance of mi contra fa. It is not a simple matter, however, to apply the rule, since certain details of the solmization system are still not known at present, and one cannot be certain beyond a doubt that a given note would have been solmized as "la."

II. a. The approaches to cadences may also need alteration in order for the imperfect interval preceding the perfect interval at the cadence point to be of the optimum size; that is, a sixth proceeding to an octave should be major, a third to a unison should be minor, or a third to a fifth should be major. It is not necessarily clear in any given situation whether the higher or the lower note of the interval is the one to be altered.

b. Certain theorists suggest that the melodic patterns G-F-G, D-C-D, A-G-A, and sometimes E-D-E

---

[6]Note that these rules are most often expressed in terms of two-voice counterpoint. For extended discussions of *musica ficta*, including citations of the old theoretical writings, see especially Gaston G. Allaire, *The Theory of Hexachords, Solmization and the Modal System*, Musicological Studies and Documents 24, n.p., 1972; Margaret Bent, "Musica Recta and Musica Ficta," *Musica Disciplina* XXVI (1972), pp. 73–100; Karol Berger, *Musica ficta: Theories of Accidental Inflections in Vocal Polyphony from Marchetto da Padova to Gioseffo Zarlino*, Cambridge, 1987; Andrew Hughes, *Manuscript Accidentals: Ficta in Focus*, 1350–1450, Musicological Studies and Documents 27, n.p., 1972; Joseph S. Levitan, "Adrian Willaert's Famous Duo *Quidnam ebrietas*," *Tijdschrift van de Vereniging voor Nederlandse Muziekgeschiedenis* XV (1939), pp. 166–233; and Lewis Lockwood, "A Sample Problem of *Musica Ficta*: Willaert's *Pater noster*," *Studies in Music History: Essays for Oliver Strunk*, ed. Harold S. Powers, Princeton, 1968, pp. 161–82.

[7]Of all the *musica ficta* "rules," the avoidance of singing mi contra fa seems to have been the oldest and most important, but it was by no means inviolate. Evidently tritones or diminished fifths were not prohibited between upper voice parts of three- or four-voice pieces. See Johannes Tinctoris, *Liber de arte contrapuncti*, *CouS* IV, p. 127. Tinctoris also discusses three compositions by Ockeghem's contemporaries Faugues, Busnois, and Caron in which each of these composers deliberately permits a diminished fifth between the lowest voice and one of the upper parts (ibid., p. 164). Although Tinctoris disapproves, calling the passages in question "errores evidentes," he makes it abundantly plain that competent composers did not necessarily observe the principle without fail.

should be solmized "fa-mi-fa," which is to say that the middle note of each should be raised a semitone. This seems to represent a melodic way of stating the rule concerning the appropriate size for an imperfect interval preceding a perfect one at a cadence. In other words, if the cadence is to incorporate, for example, a G octave, then the F (undoubtedly preceded by the customary suspension on G) should be sharped (made a *subsemitonium*) in order to form a major sixth with an A below it.

c. Perhaps also on the principle that the size of imperfect intervals ought to be appropriate to the context, some theorists advocate making a third major, if a final sonority otherwise comprised of perfect intervals contains one. Again, it seems doubtful that this rule can apply in all such circumstances.

A number of theorists speak of *causa necessitatis* and *causa pulchritudinis*, which is to say that there are two reasons for *musica ficta*, one for necessity and the other for the sake of beauty. Editors of early music have widely supposed that the above "rules" of *musica ficta* must be applied, with all due caution, *causa necessitatis*, while other accidentals may be added as desired *causa pulchritudinis*. Edward E. Lowinsky has gone so far as to suggest that the principles stated above as I.a, b, and c regarding perfect intervals are what theorists thought of as for necessity, while those relating to imperfect intervals represented by II.a, b, and c stood for what they advocated adding for beauty.[8]

It seems doubtful, however, that the theorists intended to draw so sharp a distinction between the two reasons for *musica ficta*. The anonymous writer who is among the earliest to mention them says:[9]

> Fuit autem inventa falsa musica propter duas causas, scilicet causa necessitatis, et causa pulchritudinis cantus per se.
> Causa necessitatis, quia non poteramus habere diapente, diatessaron, diapason ...
> Causa pulchritudinis, ut patet in cantinellis coronatis.
>
> [False music (that is, *musica ficta*) was invented moreover for two reasons, namely for reason of necessity and for reason of the beauty of song for its own sake.
> For reason of necessity when we would not have a (perfect) fifth, fourth, octave ...
> For reason of beauty as is evident in cantus coronatus.][10]

There is no essential reason for reading this statement as saying that *musica ficta* accidentals may be applied either by reason of necessity or else by beauty. The word connecting the two reasons is *et*, not *aut*, *seu*, *sive*, or *vel*. Quite likely, the theorist meant that performers added accidentals both because they were needed and also because they enhanced the beauty of the music.

Therefore, both reasons may well be valid with regard to all of the above "rules" of *musica ficta*, and it may be that there are no circumstances beyond what those rules encompass calling for the application of accidentals on account of beauty alone. On the other hand, it did not seem practical to try justifying every single accidental the editors have decided to add here on the basis of one or another of the above rules. Given their apparent vagueness, the ultimate arbiter has to be, and has in fact been, our ears. And because the rules are somewhat ambiguous, frequently dependent on context, and often contradictory, certain editorial accidentals have been supplied in parentheses.

All editorial accidentals have been placed above the notes they modify in the transcription. Contrary to standard modern practice, an accidental, whether original or editorial, applies to one note only.

The presence of a ligature in the main source is signaled by means of a horizontal solid bracket. The presence of coloration of whatever kind is indicated by an open bracket. Differences concerning ligatures and coloration in the concordant sources are cited in the VARIANT READINGS lists. All signs of congruence have

[8]Edward E. Lowinsky, Foreword to H. Colin Slim, ed., *Musica nova*, Monuments of Renaissance Music I, gen. ed. E. E. Lowinsky, Chicago and London, 1964, pp. viii–ix. See also M. Bent, *op. cit.*, p. 78.

[9]Anonymous II, *Tractus de discantu*, *CouS* I, p. 312.

[10]It is not clear what the theorist intends by "cantus coronatus," if that is what is meant by "cantinellis coronatis."

been rendered in transcription by means of the symbol corresponding to the modern fermata. It should be noted, however, that this sign did not then have its current meaning; most commonly it indicated a place where two or more voices in a contrapuntal context arrive at points of repose together. It also had various other meanings and uses, such as serving to mark the point from which the performer should return to the opening of the music in a *rondeau* at the conclusion of the short strophe and short refrain. Either from oversight or uncertainty, scribes frequently omitted signs needed to indicate such repetitions, and the editors have had to supply them in square brackets on a conjectural basis when they are absent.

The title of each composition is the same as the incipit of its text as spelled in the main source. The bibliographical entry for a given work provides the location of the piece in each of its sources, followed by the attribution in its original form and the spelling of the text incipit, if it differs from what appears in the main source. The symbols "t+," "t," "x," and "–" indicate to what extent text is present in a given source, and stand for, respectively, text with *additamenta* for performance of the music with repetitions required by the form of the piece, text more or less sufficient for at least one complete statement of the music with words, text incipit only, and no text whatever. For example, "t+xt–" means that the top voice contains a full text with refrain and all additional strophes, the second voice bears no more than the incipit of the text, the third voice has text for all of the music, but perhaps no more than the refrain of a *rondeau*, and the lowest voice has no text at all.

Insofar as possible, the text of an edition derives from the main source of the piece. The editors have made every effort to provide an accurate reading of the text for each work, as well as a literal translation of it in idiomatic English. All textual variants that occur in the sources, both musical and literary, have been considered, and the texts have been emended, with all due caution, when necessary. The most significant text variants are provided in notes following the translations; minor differences of orthography and the like have not been cited.

With respect to the secular works, the original spellings of the main source are retained, unless otherwise noted. Capitalization, punctuation, and those accents necessary for pronunciation have been supplied editorially. Certain noteworthy modern editions of French chansons have served as a guide to making elisions in the French texts.[11] When a word ending with a vowel is followed in the same line by a word that begins with one, the last syllable of the first word remains together with its preceding syllable. In the Italian and Spanish texts, however, the last syllable of the first word connects to the vowel at the beginning of the next by means of a slur, and they are centered together beneath the note on which they are sung. Except as noted, the spelling, capitalization, and punctuation of the sacred texts have been brought into conformity with what is published in modern liturgical books.

The editors have endeavored to follow principles of text underlay described by theorists of the period, primarily Gioseffo Zarlino and Gaspar Stoquerus.[12] It should be noted, however, that most of the information they provide concerning fitting the text to the music applies to music of a later time, when the relationship between words and music was noticeably closer and perhaps more attention was paid to matters of declamation.

Repetitions of words or phrases when they do not occur in the main source are signaled in the transcriptions by means of italics. Italics also serve to indicate textual matter that is absent in a particular voice part but could be provided editorially, according to what appears in another voice. When a word or phrase is entirely lacking in the main source but could be supplied from a concordant source or, in the absence of any source, could be conjectured with a fair degree of certainty, it has been provided in square brackets. In a few instances, where no certainty obtained, dots of ellipsis were employed to indicate a lack of one or more syllables.

---

[11] See, for example, *DrozT*.

[12] See further *StrunkSR*, pp. 259ff., for Zarlino's teachings on the subject. Stoquerus's amplifications of Zarlino's rules and his especially valuable "Five Obligatory Rules of the Older Composers" and "Five Optional Rules of the Older Composers" (presumably composers of the generation following Ockeghem's) are described in Lowinsky, "A Treatise on Text Underlay by a German Disciple of Francisco de Salinas," *Festschrift Heinrich Besseler zum sechzigsten Geburtstag*, Leipzig, 1961, pp. 231–51. See also Leeman L. Perkins, "Towards a Rational Approach to Text Placement in the Secular Music of Dufay's Time," *Papers Read at the Dufay Quincentenary Conference, Brooklyn College, December 6–7, 1974*, ed. Allan W. Atlas, New York, 1976, pp. 102–14.

The editors have used their judgment, taking into account the testimony of the sources and considerations of style, in deciding the question of which voices should have text underlaid. Generally, the voices that have texts in the main sources of the music are the ones provided with texts in the editions. In any event, only the refrains of the *rondeaux* have been printed in the music, since it is not certain whether the additional strophes should be underlaid identically or in some other way. These *additamenta* are provided, therefore, at the conclusion of each piece, and performers may adopt the placement of the refrain as a guide to fitting them to the music or else follow their own taste. The same policy applies to the *tierces* of the *bergerettes*.

MOTETS

UNDISPUTED WORKS

1. ALMA REDEMPTORIS MATER

MAIN SOURCE:

RCS 46, fol. 116^{v}–19^{r}. *Io.* _______________ (?).

OTHER SOURCE:

FR 2794, fol. 11^{v}–13^{r}. *De Okeghem.*

MUSIC PUBLISHED:

BesAM, no. 1.

CANTUS FIRMUS:

LU, pp. 273–74.

TEXT AND TRANSLATION:

Alma Redemptoris mater,
quae pervia caeli porta manes,[1]
et stella maris, succurre cadenti
surgere[2] qui curat populo.
Tu quae genuisti, natura mirante,
tuum sanctum Genitorum.
Virgo, prius ac posterius,
Gabrielis ab ore sumens illud Ave,
peccatorum miserere.

[1]manens (*RCS 46*, *FR 2794*).
[2]missing (*RCS 46*).

Nourishing mother of the Redeemer,
who keepeth the gate of heaven open,
and star of the sea, help those sinking
who seek to rise up.
Thou who, to the wonder of nature,
hath borne thy holy Creator.
Virgin, before and also after,
hearing from the mouth of Gabriel the "Ave,"
have mercy on sinners.

VARIANT READINGS:

Superius: written on upper right of opening, as though a Ct voice (*FR 2794*); before 1/1 no flat on top line in sig (*FR 2794*); 6/5–7/1 no mi col (*FR 2794*); before 14/1 flat (for f) (*FR 2794*); 19/3 e (*FR 2794*); 20/5–21/1 mi col (*FR 2794*); 21/4 e sbr, d m (*FR 2794*); 21/4–22/1 no lig (*FR 2794*); 22/4 d dot m, c sm (*FR 2794*); 31/3–5 sbr, m (*FR 2794*); 32/1–2 mi col (*FR 2794*); 33/1–3 d dot m, c sm, b sm, a sm (*FR 2794*); 42/6–7 1 a m (*FR 2794*); 51/3–52/1 octave lower (*FR 2794*); 54/1–3 e bl br, c bl sbr (*FR 2794*); 64/1–5 g dot sbr, e m (*FR 2794*); 66/1–2 2m (*FR 2794*); 74/1–2 lig (*FR 2794*); 79/1–2 1 c m (*FR 2794*); 95/1–4 g m, g m, f m (*FR 2794*); 101/2–102/1 lig (*FR 2794*); 102/2–3 1 d m (*FR 2794*); 112/4–113/1 lig (*FR 2794*); 113/1–2 no lig (*FR 2794*); 113/2–3 dot sbr, sbr (*FR 2794*); 117/1–2 lig (*FR 2794*).

Contra: written on upper left of opening, as though a S voice (*FR 2794*); 2/4–3/1 2 m (*FR 2794*); 3/3–4 miss err (*FR 2794*); 6/1–7/2 miss err (*FR 2794*); 8/2 g sm, e sm (*FR 2794*); 9/3–4 mi col (*FR 2794*); 13/1 sig congr (*FR 2794*); 21/5 sbr, m (*FR 2794*); 22/3–4 1 g sbr (*FR 2794*); 24/2–25/1 lig (*FR 2794*); 33/3 e dot m, c sm (*FR 2794*); 35/2–3 1 a m (*FR 2794*); 37/2–3 2 m (*FR 2794*); between 38/2 and 3 c dot sbr a m err (*FR 2794*); 39/2–3 mi col (*FR 2794*); 47/2 c m, d m (*FR 2794*); 47/2–3 no lig (*FR 2794*); 48/4–49/1 lig (*FR 2794*); before 50/1 flat (for e) (*FR 2794*); 51/3 c (*FR 2794*); 53/1–54/3 c br, c bl br, a bl sbr (*FR 2794*); 57/3–58/1 1 sbr (*FR 2794*); 63/1–3 g bl sbr, f bl m (*FR 2794*); 74/2–75/1 no lig (*FR 2794*); 80/2–81/1 no lig (*FR 2794*); 108/3–4 1 a m (*FR 2794*); 112/1–2 no lig (*FR 2794*); 118/2–119/1 lig (*FR 2794*); 119/1 sig congr (*RCS 46*).

"[C]ontra" (*FR 2794*); before 1/1 no mens sig (*FR 2794*); before 1/1 and for remainder of voice, flat in sig (partially erased) (*RCS 46*); 14/5–15/1 lig (*FR 2794*); before 22/5 flat (*FR 2794*); 24/4 miss err (*FR 2794*); 25/4–26/1 lig (*FR 2794*); 31/1 dot sbr, m (*FR 2794*); before 31/2 flat (*FR 2794*); before 32/1 flat in sig (*FR 2794*); 32/1 2 sbr (*FR 2794*); 34/1–4 c dot sbr, d m (*FR 2794*); 36/2–3 e m, f m (*FR 2794*); 40/3 g (*FR 2794*); before 46/1 flat (*FR 2794*); 49/2 a sbr (*FR 2794*); 51/3 g (*FR 2794*); 65/3–66/1 no mi col (*FR 2794*); 69/1–2 1 d m (*FR 2794*); 71/3 sbr, m (*FR 2794*); 71/3–72/1 no lig (*FR 2794*); 74/2–75/1 no lig (*FR 2794*); 78/2–79/1 lig (*FR 2794*); 79/1–80/1 1 c br (*FR 2794*); 84/1–2 lig (*FR 2794*); 84/2–85/1 no lig (*FR 2794*); 87/1–2 lig (*FR 2794*); 89/1–90/1 lig (*FR 2794*); 100/1–102/1 br, longa rest (*FR 2794*); 103/1–2 1 g br (*FR 2794*); 113/1–114/2 no col (*FR 2794*); 113/3 sbr, m rest (*FR 2794*).

Bassus: written on bottom left of opening and labeled "[T]enor" (*FR 2794*); before 1/1 no mens sig (*FR 2794*); 9/2–3 mi col (*FR 2794*); 13/3 sig congr (*FR 2794, RCS 46*); 25/2 octave higher (*FR 2794*); 31/1 dot sbr, m (*FR 2794*); 33/1–2 2 m (*FR 2794*); 33/3–4 no lig (*FR 2794*); 47/4–48/1 no lig (*FR 2794*); 49/3 m err (*FR 2794*); 50/4–5 mi col (*FR 2794*); 53/1 labeled "[C]ontra" (*FR 2794*); 62/2–63/1 lig (*FR 2794*); 73/2–74/1 lig (*FR 2794*); 74/2–75/1 no lig (*FR 2794*); 77/2–78/2 lig (*FR 2794*); 80/1–82/1 lig (*FR 2794*); 86/1–2 no lig (*FR 2794*); 87/1 b (*FR 2794*); 89/1–2 no lig (*FR 2794*); 90/3 a sm, b sm (*FR 2794*); 92/1–93/1 no lig (*FR 2794*); 94/1–95/1 lig (*FR 2794*); 95/1–96/1 no lig (*FR 2794*); 96/1–2 no mi col (*FR 2794*); 97/1–98/1 no lig (*FR 2794*); before 99/1 flat (to b) (*FR 2794*); 104/1–105/1 lig (*FR 2794*); 106/1–107/1 no lig (*FR 2794*); before 117/3 flat (*FR 2794*); 119/1 a err (*FR 2794*).

COMMENTARY:

The plainsong cantus firmus of this motet, the Marian antiphon *Alma Redemptoris mater*, has been transposed up a fifth from its traditional position and paraphrased in the contratenor altus. Perhaps as a result of this, the concomitant voices lie in unusually elevated ranges for Ockeghem, and the tessitura is generally higher than in his other motets.

Despite the high tessitura, the piece is undoubtedly authentic. *Alma Redemptoris mater* bears the attribution "De Okeghem" in *FR 2794*, a manuscript that was probably compiled at the French royal court when the composer was active there.[13] *CS 46*, however, serves as the main source of the present edition on account of the unusually large number of errors found in the reading of the piece as *FR 2794* transmits it. The highness of the tessitura fosters an illusion of translucence, but in fact the texture is typically dense, especially in the approaches to the final cadences of each of the two *partes*. In these passages, Ockeghem introduces smaller note values and employs relatively fewer lengthy rests in the individual voice parts, thereby creating his characteristic drive to the cadence. Other representative style traits include flowing melodic lines, asymmetrical rhythms, equality of voices, sparing use of imitation, and elided cadence points.

2. AVE MARIA

SOURCE:

RChigi, CXXXI^{v}–CXXXII^{r} (139^{v}–40^{r}). *Okeghem.*

TEXT AND TRANSLATION:

Ave Maria, gratia plena, Dominus tecum;	Hail Mary, full of grace, the Lord is with thee;
benedicta tu in mulieribus,	blessed art thou among women,
et benedictus fructus	and blessed is the fruit
ventris tui, Jesus Christus.	of thy womb, Jesus Christ.
Amen.	Amen.

ERRORS IN SOURCE:

Superius: between 10/5 and 11/1 sbr rest err.
Altus: 23/3 g err.
Tenor: (none).
Bassus: 19/4 a err.

COMMENTARY:

One of Ockeghem's shorter motets, *Ave Maria* is a setting of the well-known salutation to the Virgin (Luke 1:28). No recognizable cantus firmus is present, and all voices have approximately the same note values.

The harmonic plan of this motet is somewhat unusual. Some of the notes *b* are signed with a flat, while others not so altered clearly must remain natural: for example, those in the superius, altus, and tenor in m. 5. Although there are two authentic cadences on *a* in the course of the work, in mm. 11 and 33, the penultimate note of the bassus appears to require the application of a *musica ficta*

[13] *Census-Cat.* I, p. 246.

flat, which renders the final cadence on *a* Phrygian.

RChigi, the unique source of *Ave Maria*, reports no text for the bassus other than the opening word, "Ave." Given the melodic, highly vocal character of this voice, which corresponds in every way to the character of the upper three voices, the remainder of the text has been supplied by the editor.

RChigi, the preeminent source of Ockeghem's sacred music, contains all but one of his extant mass cycles and another of his motets, *Intemerata Dei mater* (no. 3 below). All of these works were copied into *RChigi* around 1500 by the main scribe, a Burgundian, but *Ave Maria* was added subsequently on a blank opening in a different hand. The script of the text of this motet corresponds to that of the table of contents of the manuscript, which is written, in part, in Spanish. The same scribe also added Mouton's *Quis dabit oculis*, a lament for Anne of Brittany, who died in 1514. Therefore, it may be supposed that *Ave Maria* was added to *RChigi* some fifteen years after the mass cycles and *Intemerata Dei mater*. Although these circumstances might seem to raise some doubts concerning the motet's authenticity, *Ave Maria* surely has a great many stylistic traits in common with Ockeghem's indisputably genuine motets, *Alma Redemptoris mater*, *Intemerata Dei mater*, and *Salve regina* [I].

3. INTEMERATA DEI MATER

MAIN SOURCE:

RChigi, fol. CCLXVIII^{v}–CCLXXI^{r} (276^{v}–79^{r}). *J. Ockeghem*.

OTHER SOURCE:

RCS 35, fol. 7^{v}–10^{r}. Anonymous: O intemerata dei mater.

MUSIC PUBLISHED:

SmijO I, no. 2.

TEXT AND TRANSLATION:

Intemerata Dei mater, generosa puella
milia carminibus quam stipant
agmina divum,
respice nos tantum si quid
jubilando meremur.
Tu scis, virgo decens, quanti discrimine[1] agatur
exsulibus passimque quibus jactemur arenis.

Nec sine te manet ulla quies, spes
nulla laboris,
nulla salus patriae, domus aut
potiunda parentis
cui regina praees, dispensans
omnia; laeto
suscipis[2] ore pios, dulci quos
nectare potas,
et facis assiduos epulis
accumbere sacris.

Aspiciat facito miseros
pietatis ocello
Filius, ipsa potes; fessos hinc arripe sursum,
diva virgo manu, tutos et in
arce locato.
Amen.[3]

Undefiled mother of God, noble maiden,
whom the divine hosts attend
with a thousand songs,
provide well for us, if in
exultation we are deserving.
Thou knowest, comely virgin, how we are divided
as exiles and through what deserts we are scattered.

Without thee there is no peace nor hope
in our travail,
nor salvation for our country, nor the regaining
of our ancestral home
over which thou dost preside
as queen, dispensing all.
Thou dost raise up the pious with a joyful face,
giving sweet nectar to drink,
and dost cause the constant
to recline at sacred feasts.

Cause thy Son to behold the
miserable with a pitying eye,
as thou art able; henceforth lift up the weary,
O virgin, by your divine hand, and place them
safely in the citadel.
Amen.

[1]discrimen (*RChigi*).
[2]suscipe (*RCS 35*).
[3]missing (*RChigi*).

VARIANT READINGS:

Superius: 7/1–2 mi col (*RCS 35*); 7/3–4 mi col (*RCS 35*); 7/5–6 mi col (*RCS 35*); 17/3 f (*RCS 35*); 29/4–30/1 no lig (*RCS 35*); 36/4–5mi col (*RCS 35*); 38/1–2 mi col (*RCS 35*); 38/2–3 1 c bl m (*RCS 35*); 87/2 c (fifth lower) (*RCS 35*); 92/2–3 mi col (*RCS 35*); 98/1 no sig congr (*RCS 35*); 99/1 2 sbr (*RCS 35*); 101/2–3 no lig (*RCS 35*); 103/3 2 sbr (*RCS 35*); 106/2–4 sbr, m, m (*RCS 35*); 110/2–3 no lig (*RCS 35*); 119/2 2 sbr (*RCS 35*).

Contra: 6/2–3 1 a sm (*RCS 35*); 7/1–2 mi col (*RCS 35*); 7/3–4 mi col (*RCS 35*); 8/3–4 mi col (*RCS 35*); 8/4 b bl m (*RCS 35*); 21/2–3 no mi col (*RCS 35*); 26/1–2 mi col (*RCS 35*); 31/1–2 no lig (*RCS 35*); 34/4–6 no mi col (*RCS 35*); 35/5–6 1 a sbr (*RCS 35*); 38/2 white err (*RCS 35*); 58/3 b dot m, a sm (*RCS 35*); 79/1–2 no lig (*RCS 35*); 87/2–88/1 m, sbr (*RCS 35*); 98/1 sig congr (*RCS 35*); 108/2–3 lig (*RCS 35*); 108/3–109/1 no lig (*RCS 35*); 111/2–3 1 br (*RCS 35*); 125/1–2 mi col (*RCS 35*); 127/2–3 no mi col (*RCS 35*); 133/5–134/1 no lig (*RCS 35*); 136/1 br–longa lig (*RCS 35*).

Tenor: 8/2 e (*RCS 35*); 18/2–3 mi col (*RCS 35*); 20/2–3 no mi col (*RCS 35*); 20/4–5 no mi col (*RCS 35*); 25/1 2 sm (*RCS 35*); 26/1–2 no mi col (*RCS 35*); 37/2–3 no mi col (*RCS 35*); 90/2–3 no mi col (*RCS 35*); 90/3 f (*RCS 35*); 93/2–94/1 no lig (*RCS 35*); 96/1–2 mi col (*RCS 35*); 103/3 2 sbr (*RCS 35*); 113/3–4 c dot m, b sm, b sm, a sm (*RCS 35*).

Vagans: 4/1–2 lig (*RCS 35*); 4/2–3 no lig (*RCS 35*); 21/3–4 mi col (*RCS 35*); 31/1–2 no lig (*RCS 35*); 35/4–5 no lig (*RCS 35*); 38/3–4 no mi col (*RCS 35*); 38/5–6 no mi col (*RCS 35*); before 42/1 labeled "[B]assus" (*RCS 35*); 72/2–4 m, sm, sm (no mi col) (*RCS 35*); 73/1–2 no lig (*RCS 35*); 78/2–3 mi col (*RCS 35*); 86/1–2 1 br (*RCS 35*); 88/2–89/1 1 dot sbr (*RCS 35*); 90/1–2 no lig (*RCS 35*); 93/2–3 mi col (*RCS 35*); 98/1 no sig congr (*RCS 35*); 124/1–2 no mi col (*RCS 35*); 124/3–4 1 dot sbr (*RCS 35*); 125/2–3 no mi col (*RCS 35*).

Bassus: 5/1 bl (*RCS 35*); 21/5 b (*RCS 35*); 34/1–2 mi col (*RCS 35*); 35/5–36/1 no lig (*RCS 35*); before 38/5 flat (for b) (*RCS 35*); 83/1 2 sbr (*RCS 35*); 84/1–85/1 lig (*RCS 35*); 98/1 no sig congr (*RCS 35*); 130/5–6 mi col (*RCS 35*); 133/5–6 mi col (*RCS 35*); 135/4–136/1 longa (*RCS 35*).

COMMENTARY:

The extremely dense part writing for low alto (i.e., countertenor), tenor, two basses, and contrabass helps to make *Intemerata Dei mater* a particularly striking example of Ockeghem's art. The lowest voice frequently descends to *E* and *D*, twice to great *C*, and never rises higher than *e*. Ockeghem explores this low range elsewhere mainly in his masses. The somberness of the tessitura is occasionally somewhat relieved by recourse to alternating passages for three higher and three lower voices, as at the beginning of the *secunda pars*, mm. 42–79. Also remarkable are the frequent use of dotted rhythms, as for example in mm. 7–8, and the sudden, dramatic shifts in texture, as in the largely homorhythmic settings of the words "dulci quos nectare," mm. 80–84, and "miseros pietatis ocello filius, ipsa potes," mm. 103–11.

The text, which as far as can be determined does not occur in the liturgy, may well refer to events in fifteenth-century politics. No discernible cantus firmus is present, and it may be supposed that the counterpoint is altogether free. On the other hand, Ockeghem seems to quote melodic material from two of his other works: The basic motif of his *Missa Mi-mi* is sung by the vagans voice at the outset of *Intemerata Dei mater*, and simultaneously the melodic line of the motet's contratenor somewhat resembles the continuation of the bassus of the mass, mm. 2–4. Also the contratenor begins the *secunda pars* ("Nec sine te," mm. 42–45) with an apparent quotation from one of Ockeghem's best-known chansons, *Fors seulement l'actente*. It is conceivable, however, that the quotations were not intended, but represent nothing more than two of Ockeghem's stock melodic ideas. One of the most distinctive features of the "Fors seulement" motif is the descending fourth comprised of a dotted semibreve followed by two semiminims and a semibreve, a rhythmic figure that already was heard in measure 6 of the contratenor voice in the *prima pars* and that recurs throughout the work. This suggests that Ockeghem, who is sometimes celebrated for the elusive quality of his melodic material, was nevertheless capable of drawing upon a personal melodic vocabulary.

4. SALVE REGINA [I]

SOURCE:

RCS 42, fol. 144^{v}–48^{r}. *Jo. Okeghem.*

MUSIC PUBLISHED:

Hunt.

CANTUS FIRMUS:

LU, p. 276.

TEXT AND TRANSLATION:

Salve regina, mater misericordiae;	Hail queen, mother of mercy;
vita, dulcedo, et spes nostra, salve.	our life, sweetness, and hope, hail.

Ad te clamamus, exules filii Evae,
ad te suspiramus, gementes et flentes
in hac lacrimarum valle.

Eia ergo, advocata nostra, illos tuos
misericordes oculos ad nos converte.
Et Jesum, benedictum fructum ventris tui,
nobis post hoc exsilium ostende.
O clemens, O pia, O dulcis virgo semper Maria.

To thee we cry, exiled children of Eve,
to thee we sigh, lamenting and
weeping in this vale of tears.

Therefore, our advocate, turn thy
pitying eyes toward us.
And after this exile, show us Jesus,
the blessed fruit of thy womb.
O mild, O kind, O sweet Mary, ever virgin.

ERRORS IN SOURCE:

Superius: occupies the position of the contra until m. 72.
Contra: occupies the position of the superius until m. 72.
Tenor: 173/2 c err.
Bassus: (none).

COMMENTARY:

The manuscript *RCS 42*, which bears the date 1507 in two places,[14] is the only surviving source of Ockeghem's indisputably authentic setting of *Salve regina*. This motet contains many of the typical characteristics of the master's style: flowing melodic lines, asymmetrical rhythms, equality of voice parts, sparing use of imitation, elided cadence points that create a sense of continuous motion, and a gradual shortening of note durations in the approach to the final close—the often cited drive to the cadence.

The motet commences with a duo for the two highest voices, in which the superius paraphrases the opening of the celebrated Marian antiphon. Upon its entry in m. 9, the bassus begins to present the cantus firmus in longer notes, transposed to the lower fourth. A measure later, the tenor enters with the antiphon melody at original pitch and also in longer note values. However, it becomes apparent by approximately m. 16 that the bassus voice is to contain the cantus firmus, a somewhat unusual, but not unprecedented circumstance.[15] By this point, the durations of notes in the bassus more nearly resemble those of the other voices, and the cantus firmus treatment has become paraphrase.

Although precise details are obscured to some extent by the paraphrases, one can discern that the melodic content of the cantus firmus is the same in this setting of the antiphon as in *Salve regina* [II] (no. 10 below), a work of questionable authenticity. In several respects, this version differs from what is printed in the *LU*, p. 276, and, with some minor variants, in the *AM*, pp. 176–77. Most notably, the four opening notes of the antiphon return at the words "O dulcis virgo semper" in the cantus firmi of both motets, but they do not in the modern liturgical books. This discrepancy, among others, does not imply, however, that the same composer was necessarily responsible for both settings, but only that a different version of the famous melody was current in the late fifteenth century. Confirmation of this is manifest in another setting of *Salve regina* in Trento, Castello del buon Consiglio, Cod. 89, fol. 349^{v}–52^{r},[16] which provides an unusually clear contemporaneous reading of the antiphon melody, lightly paraphrased in the superius. This version corresponds closely to what one finds in the two settings under consideration here.

5. UT HEREMITA SOLUS

MAIN SOURCE:

RISM 1504^{1}, no. 15. Anonymous.

OTHER SOURCE:

Finck 1556, fol. Kk 1^{v}–Ll 1^{r}. Anonymous: Canon (*prima pars* only).

---

[14]See *LlorCS*, p. 83.

[15]See Ockeghem's *Missa Caput*, vol. II, no. 11, of the present edition, in which the cantus firmus resides in the lowest voice throughout.

[16]This setting is attributed to "Wilhelmus Duffay" in Munich, Bayerische Staatsbibliothek, Mus. Ms. 3154, fol. 86^{v}–88^{r}, although the ascription has been questioned on stylistic grounds; see *DèzS*. The work also appears anonymously in Milan, Fabbrica del Duomo, Cod. 2269, fol. 184^{v}–87^{r}. Mod. ed. after Trento in *AdlerST*, pp. 178–83.

MUSIC PUBLISHED:

ScherG, no. 52.

TEXT AND TRANSLATION:

(See COMMENTARY below.)

VARIANT READINGS:

Superius: labeled "Discantus" (*Finck 1556*); 62/4 m, sm (*Finck 1556*); 86/5 e err (*Finck 1556*); 91/5–96/1 mi col (*Finck 1556*); before 96/2 no flat (*Finck 1556*); 96/2 m, sm (*Finck 1556*); 97/7–98/1 mi col (*Finck 1556*); 102/2 c err (*Finck 1556*).

Altus: 6/3–7/1 br, m (*Finck 1556*); 8/1–3 mi col (*Finck 1556*); 16/1–2 1 br (*Finck 1556*); 58/6 dot miss err (*RISM 1504*[1], *Finck 1556*); 61/4 sm, fu (*Finck 1556*); 66/3–67/1 br rest miss err (*RISM 1504*[1]); 73/2 sbr, m (*Finck 1556*); 80/1 e err (*Finck 1556*); 98/5 d err (*Finck 1556*).

Tenor: 109/1 d err (*Finck 1556*).

Bassus: 28/1–2 1 dot br (*Finck 1556*); 34/2 miss (longa not imperfected) (*Finck 1556*); 42/2–3 br, m (*Finck 1556*); 43/1 m, sm (*Finck 1556*); 68/1–3 m, 2 sm (*Finck 1556*); 93/2 br rest err (*RISM 1504*[1]); 100/4–5 2 sm (*Finck 1556*).

COMMENTARY:

Ottaviano Petrucci printed this work in *RISM 1504*[1] (*Motetti C*) without attribution. Guillaume Crétin, in his *Déploration sur le trespas de feu Okergan*, portrays an imaginary concert in honor of Ockeghem's arrival in the afterworld, at which the composer's fellow deceased musicians performed his masses *Mi-mi*, *Au travail suis*, *Cuiusvis toni*, and *Pro defunctis*, after which

> Hame [= Haine?; i.e., Hayne van Ghizeghem] en la fin dict avecques son lucz
> Ce motet, ut heremita solus,
> Que chascun tint une chose excellente.

There is no known connection between a text beginning "Ut heremita solus" and the liturgy of the church, and no other motet with a similar incipit survives. The juxtaposition of a piece having this title with four authentic masses by Ockeghem makes it reasonably certain that Crétin knew it as the composer's work. It is difficult to envisage, however, precisely how Hayne could have performed a composition as intricate as the one printed in *RISM 1504*[1] with just voice and lute accompaniment or, as Crétin may have intended, on lute alone. Possibly Crétin must be granted a modicum of poetic license.

In the aforementioned unique printed source of *Ut heremita solus*, several unusually elaborate verbal canons govern the tenor. That voice assumes the appearance shown here in diplomatic facsimile:[17]

Example 1

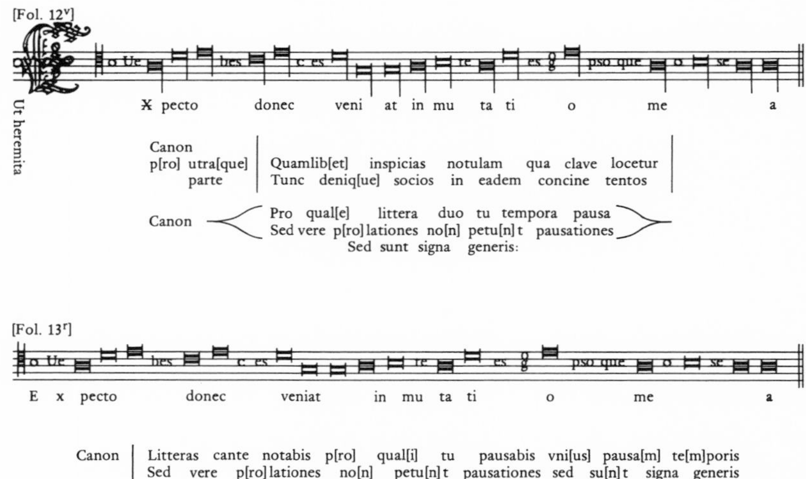

Here one sees a staff upon which is printed a mysterious amalgam of mensuration signs, cryptic syllables, and longs, under which appears an enigmatic sentence of "text." Below that, one finds two lengthy canons. Then there is a second staff containing the same material as the first but in diminution, with breves in place of the longs. That, too, is followed by the same enigmatic text and another lengthy canon. Taken altogether, this is a remarkably complex puzzle, perhaps the *ne plus ultra* of its kind. Undoubtedly it was with

[17] A photographic facsimile of the original is published in *MGG* IX, cols. 1831–34.

works of this type in mind that Johannes Tinctoris, in his *Terminorum musicae diffinitorium*, defined "canon" as "regula voluntatem compositoris sub obscuritate quadam ostendens."[18]

As frequently was his custom, Petrucci provided a fully worked-out "Resolutio," which takes the following form:

Example 2

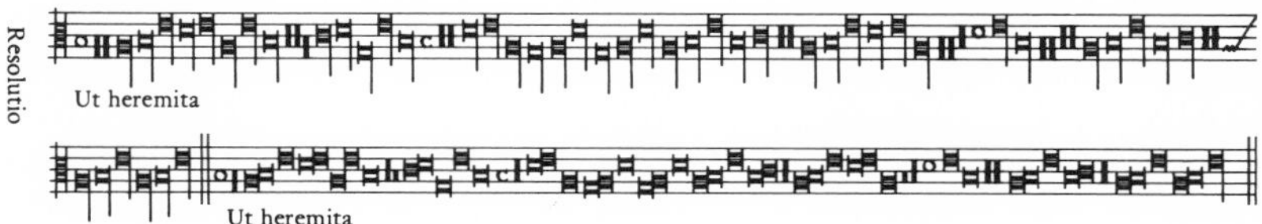

It is this solution that provides the reading of the tenor voice in the present edition, and one wonders how a performer of Ockeghem's day might have arrived at a workable decipherment without the aid of Petrucci. In 1918, Arnold Schering published a brief article (*ScherR*) that shed a great deal of light on this question.

In viewing the "Resolutio," Schering observed that, throughout, one or two notes were added between the longs and breves in the original presentation of the voice. He concluded correctly that a rationale for these additions should be sought in the hexachord system. As he pointed out, the title of the work provides a clue, inasmuch as the majority of its syllables correspond to hexachord degrees. According to Schering, the title yields the scheme "ut (he) re mi la (in place of ta) sol (us)." Since the first note is *a*, which does not function as ut in any hexachord, Schering maintains it must be the re of the scheme suggested by the title, the ut being precluded by the syllable "ue" that stands on the staff before the first note. Therefore, because *a* is re in the hard hexachord, the next two notes to be added would be *b* and *e*, mi and la in the hard hexachord, in keeping with the two following syllables of Schering's scheme. The "Resolutio" confirms that the first three notes are indeed *a*, *b*, and *e*. From this Schering deduced that, in every instance, the first additional note should lie a second above each original note, while the second additional note should be placed again a fourth higher, which is true for the most part.

It may well be that the composer meant for the title to hint at a hexachordal solution, but in fact one of the verbal canons provides the same finding in much more certain terms. The interpretation of this rule, the one preceded by the rubric "Canon p(ro) utraq(ue) parte" (Rule for both parts), hinges on the understanding, which may have eluded Schering, of two technical terms of medieval music theory: *clavis*, meaning hexachord syllable, and *socius*, meaning companion, here referring to *socialis*, a pitch designated with the same syllable in another hexachord; for example, *c* ut in the natural hexachord, which has the *sociales f* and *g* in the soft and hard hexachords, respectively.

Schering translates the rule, "Siehe zu … auf welchem Tone [*clavis*] die Note steht, alsdann singe die auf sie bezüglichen Genossen hinzu" ("Look … on which pitch the note stands, thereupon sing it with reference to its companions besides"), but a more useful translation might read, "May you examine on what hexachord syllable a given note is located, then finally sing it together with its acquired companions on the same [syllable]." In other words, the opening note in the canonic voice is *a*, that is, mi in the soft hexachord, to which must be added *b* and *e*, also mi in the hard and natural hexachords. Subsequently, each note in the canonic voice must be read in the soft hexachord (barring certain exceptions to be discussed below), followed by notes on the same syllable in the hard and natural hexachords.

This interpretation of the canon gives the same result as deduced by Schering from the title of the work: Two additional notes follow each original note, the first of these a second above and the next yet a fourth higher. But this does not account for two further aspects, with respect to pitch, of the "Resolutio." 1) Now and again, only one note follows the original note, instead of two, and 2) the second added note is sometimes a fifth lower, rather than a fourth higher, than the first.

In order to explain these circumstances, Schering turned to the enigmatic phrase that is positioned, in the manner of text, below the original voice, "Expecto donec veniat inmutatio mea." Apparently he did not realize that the source of this phrase is the Old Testament (Job 14:14), where it has the meaning "I wait until my change should come." Joining the title of the work with the phrase from the Book of Job—where, incidentally, they do not occur together—Schering interpreted them, "Ich, der Tenor, warte wie ein Einsiedler (nämlich gegenüber den beweglichen übrigen Stimmen) jedesmal auf meinen langen Noten, bis der Fall der Mutation eintritt, die ich, da ans Hexachord gebunden, mit entsprechender Modifikation vornehme" ("I, the tenor, wait like a recluse [namely, opposite the moving remaining voices] each time on my long notes, until the event of mutation occurs, which I, bound in a hexachord, undertake with corresponding modification").

Undoubtedly, Schering was on the right track, for the word *inmutatio*, which means essentially the same as *mutatio* in biblical Latin, surely must refer, in this context, to the theoretical concept of hexachordal mutation. As Schering understood the phrase, it points to the fact that all the original notes of the canon belong exclusively to and occupy the range of a single hard hexachord. He suggested, therefore, that whenever the original note is *b*, one "companion," *c*, may be added, but the second, *f*, would give rise to a proscribed "mi contra fa" (the tritone) and must be omitted. By the same token, whenever the original note is *e*, the first companion, *f*, is omitted, because otherwise it would form "fa contra mi" with the second, *b*. Alternatively, a more simple interpretation might be that *f* has no place whatever in the solution, because there is no *f* in the hard hexachord.

---

[18] *ParrishT*, p. 12.

As far as original notes *b* are concerned, however, the situation is complicated somewhat by the fact that *b*-natural belongs only to the hard hexachord and therefore does not really have any *sociales*. But in the hexachord system *b*-natural is paired with *b*-flat as *b* mi-*b* fa. Assuming that Schering is right that everything should remain "bound" in the hard hexachord, then *b*-flat has no place in the solution, and the fa of that hexachord, *c*, must substitute for it.

Regarding the descents of a fifth in the "Resolutio," Schering proposed they substitute for ascents of a fourth that would take the melodic line beyond the compass of a single hard hexachord. This explanation seems entirely plausible.

One might well ask how the performer of the tenor voice should know that, on one hand, he must employ the hexachord theory of mutation to supply the companions, while on the other, he must remain within the bounds of the hard hexachord. Assuming Ockeghem to be the composer, it may be that, because he was addressing Franco-Netherlandish musicians, he deliberately selected the phrase from the Book of Job for the ambiguity of "inmutatio-mutatio." To be sure, these words share the same meaning in biblical Latin, but no doubt a native French speaker would have been well aware of the opposite meanings of the adjectival cognates *immuable* and *muable*.

Having ascertained the pitch material of the solution by means of the "canon pro utraque parte" in conjunction with the biblical quotation, one must still determine rhythmic values. This can be accomplished quite readily with the two remaining canons. The first, which governs the staff containing the longs, reads, "Rule: For whatever is a letter, pause for two breves; however the true prolations do not stand for rests, but are signs of their own type." This canon thus explains the purpose of the mensuration signs and the cryptic syllables in the staff. As the canon implies, the mensuration signs function conventionally; the longs comprise ternary breves at the outset, then duple breves following the C, and finally ternary breves again once the O has been reinstated. The canon also explains how to determine the rests that appear in the "Resolutio." Each letter of the syllables in the staff is to be replaced with a two-breve (i.e., longa) rest.[19]

All that now remains to solve the puzzle is the second staff and its accompanying canon. As stated above, it consists of a repetition in diminution of the material on the preceding staff. Accordingly, the canon paraphrases the previous instruction concerning the syllables, rests, and mensuration signs, with such modification as is needed to accommodate the diminished rhythmic values: "Rule: You will note the letters in the song, for which you shall pause one breve rest; however, the true prolations do not stand for rests, but are signs of their own type."

With the pitches established, the rests properly distributed, the mensuration signs correctly applied, and the repeat in diminution taken into consideration, the solution—one corresponding to Petrucci's "Resolutio"—is complete.[20] But still, one can hardly imagine how the performer of the voice could have discovered it unaided. Perhaps after much thought and protracted experimentation, he could have turned, as a last resort, to the composer for assistance.

It stands to reason, as Schering recognized, that the letters in the staff for which rests become substituted should have some further significance. In order to reveal their meaning, Schering first assigned the appropriate solmization syllable in the hard hexachord to each note in the original canon. He then combined these hexachord degrees with the syllables and the mensuration signs, yielding the following:

> O vere sol labes fa[l]aces solut[i] ut remit[t]ere soles (?) pro [g für p?] lapsoque reo miserere.

As Schering pointed out, the sense of this expression is obscure. His rendering of it requires a slight emendation, the substitution of "ergo" for "pro," inasmuch as the abbreviation "go" has the former meaning. A translation might read:

> O true sun, free from false stain, as you are accustomed to forgive, therefore have mercy on one guilty of falling.

Most probably, this apostrophe to God is a quotation, but, for the present, its source is unknown. It may derive from the writings of one of the many notable hermits in church history, such as St. Jerome or St. Anthony Abbot.[21] Suffice it to say that the expression, wherever it was obtained, very likely represents the starting point of the composition. First the composer assigned notes to the syllables corresponding to hexachord degrees and added the companion notes. Next he adopted the opening "O" as a mensuration sign and borrowed a subsequent "c" and another "o" for the same purpose. Then he converted all of the letters in the remaining syllables to rests and formulated the various canons. Finally, he had the tenor voice before him, which needed only to be repeated in diminution, and he proceeded to compose the other voices in counterpoint.

It is doubtful that any of the verbal material associated with the work, as Petrucci transmitted it, constitutes a text to be sung. Perhaps, as implied by Crétin, *Ut heremita solus* was conceived with instrumental performance in mind.

---

[19]It should be noted that Petrucci spelled out the abbreviation "q3" (= que) erroneously in the first staff, but rendered it correctly in the second. In both instances, it stands for a single longa rest.

[20]Subsequent to the formulation of the solution suggested here, another explanation using hexachord theory, differing from the present one in only relatively minor respects, was published by Andrea Lindmayr as "Ein Rätseltenor Ockeghems: Des Rätsels Lösung," *Acta musicologica* LX (1988), pp. 31–42.

[21]It has been proposed that there may be a connection between *Ut heremita solus* and Busnois's *In hydraulis*, since, in the latter, music similar to the head motive of the former occurs at the words "Hec Ockeghem." If one supposes that Ockeghem composed *Ut heremita solus* in answer to the compliment Busnois paid him in *In hydraulis* (although we have no way of knowing which of these two works was written first), then "heremita" could refer to Busnois's first name, Antoine, as in St. Anthony. See further Paula Higgins, "*In hydraulis* Revisited: New Light on the Career of Antoine Busnois," *Journal of the A.M.S.* XXXIX (1986), pp. 76–78 and especially n. 137.

6. VIVIT DOMINUS

SOURCE:

RISM 1549[16], no. 33. *Ockekem.*

TEXT AND TRANSLATION:

Vivit Dominus, et benedictus Deus meus,	The Lord liveth, and blessed be my God,
et exaltetur Deus salutis meae.	And let the God of my salvation be exalted.

(II Samuel 22:47, and Psalm 18:47)

ERRORS IN SOURCE:

Superior vox: 14/2 e.
Inferior vox: (none).

COMMENTARY:

At least eleven of the ninety-nine duos in *Diphona amoena* (*RISM 1549[16]*) are *contrafacta* of two-voice sections drawn from polyphonic settings of the mass ordinary. (For details, see *BellingB*.) With one exception, the composer attributions of the *contrafacta* in *Diphona amoena* agree with those found in the sources of the complete masses. Therefore, Montanus and Neuber's ascription of this work to Ockeghem may well be correct. It must be pointed out, however, that the style of the duo, with its frequent cadences, regular imitations, and relatively syllabic text setting, strongly suggests the manner of a rather later composer.

In any event, *Vivit Dominus* is not part of a known mass by Ockeghem, but it could represent a duo from one of several of his masses now lost.[22] Therefore, this *bicinium* is most likely a *contrafactum* rather than a motet in the true sense. The present text, which is biblical (II Samuel 22:47, and Psalm 18:47), continues, "Et benedictus Deus meus," perhaps suggesting that the original text was the Benedictus portion of the Sanctus. Alternatively, *Vivit Dominus* could have served as any of several parts of the ordinary that were frequently set polyphonically in two-voice texture, such as "Christe," "Domine Deus," "Pleni sunt caeli," or "Agnus II."

The melody of an antiphon having almost the same words bears no resemblance to the melodic material of this duo.[23]

[22]See further vol. II of this edition, pp. xli–xliii.
[23]See *AM*, p. 24.

DOUBTFUL WORKS

7. CAELESTE BENEFICIUM

SOURCE:

RegB 211–215, no. 82. *kegus.*

TEXT AND TRANSLATION:

Caeleste beneficium introivit in orbem verbum Dei quod fulget nobis per Germaniam.	A heavenly gift hath entered the world, the word of God, which shineth unto us throughout Germany.
Caeleste beneficium accipe Germania grata, quia tibi resonuit vox tandem aeterni numinis salutem adesse nuncians. Ambulate dum lucem habetis.	Accept, O grateful Germany, the heavenly gift, for at last the voice of the eternal God hath resounded unto thee, announcing salvation to be near. Go forth while ye yet have light.

ERRORS IN SOURCE:

Discantus: before 150/2 flat (for b).
Altus: 30/3 d err (corrected to b-flat); 115/1–119/1, 131/4–133/1, 197/1–199/1 all miss (torn page).
Tenor: (none).
Vagans: (none).
Bassus: (none).

COMMENTARY:

Caeleste beneficium survives only in *RegB 211–215*, a manuscript compiled in Germany or Austria in 1538. The motet is ascribed there, in the bassus partbook alone, to "kegus." This attribution presumably refers to the "Johannes Okegus" to whom *Gaude Maria* (no. 9 below) was attributed in all five partbooks of the same set.

Even if Okegus and Ockeghem are one and the same, then at least the text of the composition, as the partbooks transmit it, is probably not authentic. This text exhorts Germany to accept the word of God in terms suggesting that the work was addressed to German listeners. There are no extant biographical data connecting Ockeghem to Germany and no references to Germany in the texts of any of his other known works.

The words of a plainchant responsory formerly belonging to the liturgy of the feast of the Nativity of the Virgin greatly resemble those of the motet under consideration here. In the respond of the chant,[24] they are, "Celeste beneficium introivit in Annam, per quam nobis nata est Maria virgo." This text, which might be the original one, represents, of course, the kind of Marian text to which Ockeghem was attracted repeatedly. But this counts for little in terms of the work's authenticity, since every major composer of the period set Marian texts again and again.

Although the text of the plainchant responsory may be the original, its melody bears no resemblance whatever to the tenor of the motet, which sometimes seems to paraphrase an unidentified preexistent melody and sometimes presents it in long notes. It is

---

[24] *Pal mus* XII, p. 366.

probable, however, that this unknown melody was also a responsory, since the formal design of the motet corresponds to what is commonly found in polyphonic settings of chants of that type. The final approximately twenty measures of the *prima pars* are very similar to the concluding six measures of the *secunda pars*. However, no repetition of text occurs, as would happen in a typical setting of a responsory, but the probable presence of a *contrafactum* may account for the lack of textual correspondence.

The stylistic traits mentioned below in connection with *Gaude Maria* (q.v.), which make the authenticity of that work questionable, are likewise present in *Caeleste beneficium*.

8. DEO GRATIA

MAIN SOURCE:

RISM 1542^{6}, no. 40. Anonymous.

OTHER SOURCES:

Heilb, no. 7 (T only). Anonymous.
RISM 1568^{7}, no. 30. Anonymous.

MUSIC PUBLISHED:

RieH II^{1} (1907), pp. 237–47.
Stam, pp. 21–28.

TEXT AND TRANSLATION:

Deo gratia. — Thanks be to God.

VARIANT READINGS:

Canon: "Novem sunt Musae. / Omnia cum tempore." (*RISM 1542*^{6}), "Musis ter trinis datur hic cum Tempore finis." (*RISM 1568*^{7}).
Superius (1): 7/6–7 2 sm err (*RISM 1568*^{7}); 8/5 br (*RISM 1542*^{6}, *RISM 1568*^{7}); 10/1 longa (*RISM 1542*^{6}, *RISM 1568*^{7}).
Altus (1): 10/7 sm err (*RISM 1568*^{7}); 13/6–17/8 a third too high err (*RISM 1542*^{6}, *RISM 1568*^{7}); 18/1 longa (*RISM 1542*^{6}, *RISM 1568*^{7}).
Tenor (1): 20/2 d (*Heilb*, *RISM 1568*^{7}); 26/2–3 1 sbr (*RISM 1542*^{6}); 30/3–4 1 sbr (*RISM 1542*^{6}).
Bassus (1): 34/2 2 m (*RISM 1568*^{7}); 36/5 2 m (*RISM 1568*^{7}).

COMMENTARY:

There can be little doubt that Ockeghem composed a motet for thirty-six voices, since ample testimony to that effect exists. Concerning his authorship of such a work, Guillaume Crétin wrote, "C'est luy qui bien sceut … trente-six voix noter, escripre, et paindre en ung motet. …"[25]

At the Puy de la Conception de Notre-Dame at Rouen in 1523, the contestants were presented with an "argument" in verse and required to respond with a "chant royal." The argument, which is anonymous but perhaps was devised by Crétin (d. 1523),[26] begins, "Ung facteur fut Okghem nommé, … qui feist en des pars trente six ung motet. …" The response by Nicole Le Vestu praises Ockeghem's learnedness, describes the composition as being in "partz trente six," and further calls it "motet exquis, chef d'oeuvre de nature."

In the first chapter of book IV of his *Musice active micrologus* (1517), Andreas Ornithoparcus writes, "Nam Joannem Okeken mutetum 36. vocum composuisse constat."[27] Henricus Glareanus, perhaps following Ornithoparcus, states, "Quippe quem constat triginta sex vocibus garritum quendam instituisse," but he admits that he has no personal knowledge of the work. ("Eum nos non uidimus.")[28]

The earliest known indication that Ockeghem's thirty-six-voice motet was canonic occurs in a letter from the theorist Sebastian Virdung to Count Palatine Ludwig of Bavaria dated 1504.[29] Virdung wrote that "Johannes ockeghem … hatt ein mütett mit sex stymmen gemacht. Der stymmen itlich ist ein füg mit sex stymmen, vnd alzüsamen xxxvj stymm. …" With reference to the thirty-six-voice motet and Ockeghem's *Missa prolationum*, he adds, "Dye zwey Ding haben wir hye aussen bey uns, … aber aller Ding vngerecht geschreiben. …"

---

[25] *ThoinanD*, p. 29.
[26] See further *PlamA*, p. 36f.
[27] See *ReOD*, p. 92.
[28] *Dodecachordon*, 1547, p. 454.
[29] See *WalS*, pp. 97–98.

In his *Bibliographie der Musik-Sammelwerke*,[30] Robert Eitner suggested that the anonymous thirty-six-voice *Deo gratia* in Petreius's *Tomus tertius psalmorum selectorum* (*RISM 1542*[6]) might possibly be the lost motet by Ockeghem.[31] Eitner was familiar with the mentions of such a piece by Ornithoparcus and Glareanus, but he apparently had no knowledge of Virdung's letter of 1504. *Deo gratia* is notated in four parts, each of which, according to the puzzle rubric "Novem sunt Musae," is a canon for nine voices. As described by Virdung, Ockeghem's thirty-six-voice motet was made up of six six-part canons. This discrepancy makes it at least doubtful that *Deo gratia* is Ockeghem's renowned work.[32]

The earliest known source of *Deo gratia*, *RISM 1542*[6], is quite clear concerning how the canon should begin. Each following voice must enter after the time of one breve ("Omnia cum tempore"). A glance at the solution provided in the present edition reveals that *Deo gratia* is hardly a true thirty-six-voice canon, but rather a series of successive overlapping nine-voice canons for superius, altus, tenor, and bassus voices in turn. The *dux* of the tenor, for example, first enters in m. 17 just as the last superius *comes* is arriving at its conclusion. Except at this point, superius and tenor do not sing together at all. In effect, *Deo gratia* begins as a "duet" for nine canonic superius voices and nine canonic altus voices, becomes a "duet" for nine altus and nine tenor voices, and concludes as a "duet" for nine tenor and nine bassus voices. It should be noted, however, that a full complement of eighteen simultaneously active voices is present only from m. 33 to the end of the composition.

While the correct solution for the opening of the canon is fairly obvious, it is rather more difficult to determine how *Deo gratia* was intended to end. There are no indications in the notation, such as *signa congruentiae*, that might have suggested where the voices should conclude. Ordinarily, the final notated longa represents a rhythmic value of indeterminate length, and if one voice part arrives at its last note somewhat before the others do, then presumably it holds until the remaining voices close. Scrupulous adherence to this principle as applied to *Deo gratia* suggests sustaining the final longa of each voice until all thirty-six voices have ended, ultimately, that is, when the ninth tenor and ninth bassus have arrived at their last notes in what, in transcription, would be m. 45.[33] This procedure creates problems. The first superius completes its part in m. 10 on the pitch *c*'', or, in modern parlance, on the "dominant."[34] Would the singer(s) then be called upon to sustain the *c*'' as a pedal point for another thirty-five measures? By m. 18, all nine superius voices would be holding the *c*''. Is a pedal point balanced and effective if carried by so many voice parts? The latter portion of the altus voice is defective in both extant original sources, in that as many as two dozen consecutive pitches are printed a third too high. However, the final note, *f*', appears to be correct. Does a "tonic" pedal point join the "dominant" one (in m. 18, when the first altus arrives at its last note) and remain until the end of the canon? Should the work end with nine superius and nine altus voices sounding a dominant-tonic pedal point? Should the tenors, which conclude on *a*, and the bassus voices, which end on *F*, be permitted to make the pedal point a full triad beginning as early as m. 37, eight measures before tenor 9 and bassus 9 reach their final cadences? Would it be possible to hear two low voices approach a cadence in the presence of a thirty-four-voice triadic pedal point?

All things considered, it has seemed advisable to abandon the standard principle of sustaining the final note in each voice until the end. The harmonic plan of the work, in which the first two thirds of each transcribed measure provides a "tonic" sonority, while the last third sounds a "dominant," would seem to disallow by itself the employment of a lengthy tonic pedal point. For this reason, it was decided that the concluding notes *f*' of the altus voice should sound for only two thirds of a measure (see mm. 18ff.). By extension, the final notes *c*'' of the superius voices have been transcribed in a single measure, although if one insists on rendering a final longa as equal to two breves, no harmonic clash would result if one were to sustain the *c*'' for an additional measure at the end of each superius voice.

On the other hand, repeated harmonic clashes would occur if tenor and bassus voices were to hold their respective final notes, *a* and *F*, for more than two thirds of a measure. (It is not likely that any composer of the period would have considered the third of the final chord suitable for use as a pedal point, even in the presence of the root and fifth.) As it happens, the tenor and bassus parts are precisely the same length. To take advantage of this circumstance and in order to avoid the subsequent clashes of tonic triads against dominant triads, it was thought best to end the present edition as the first tenor and the first bassus arrive simultaneously at their cadence points.

Doubts concerning Ockeghem's authorship of *Deo gratia* arise not only from a close examination of the historical record, but also from a consideration of the canon's style. In particular, the disjunct melodic writing, with its frequent leaps of a fifth or more, differs markedly from that found in Ockeghem's indisputably authentic motets.[35] In the modern literature, the work is frequently characterized as monotonous on account of its rigid harmonic plan. It is compared unfavorably with Josquin's ***Qui habitat in adjutorio***, a canon for twenty-four voices in which at times all of the parts actually sing together.[36] In defense of Ockeghem's authorship, some suggest that the overall clumsiness of the work may have resulted from the daunting problems of creating a quadruple canon for so

---

[30]P. 311.

[31]In the modern literature, it has become customary to add an "s," often in square brackets, to "gratia," as though the text were to be taken as representing the second portion of either the liturgical formula "Ite, missa est" or "Benedicamus Domino." The surviving sources of the canon, however, all clearly specify "gratia" without an "s," and there is little reason to suppose that anything else was intended.

[32]For a contrasting view concerning the authenticity of *Deo gratia*, see *LowO*.

[33]See *Stam*.

[34]The fact that one can employ such modern terms as "dominant" and "tonic" at all in the discussion that follows says something about how far removed *Deo gratia* is from the authentic corpus of Ockeghem's works.

[35]See, for example, superius 1, mm. 5–7; altus 1, passim; tenor 1, mm. 18–20; bassus 1, mm. 25–26; and elsewhere.

[36]See *ReMR*, pp. 124 and 250.

many voices. But can one argue persuasively that the rigors of composing a thirty-six-voice canon might account for so great a distortion of Ockeghem's normal style? In his *Missa prolationum*, the composition of which, given its intricate mensural and canonic plan, must have presented the master with formidable difficulties, no such impairment is evident.

9. GAUDE MARIA

SOURCE:

RegB 211–215, no. 11. *Johannes Okegus.*

CANTUS FIRMUS:

AM, p. 1195.

TEXT AND TRANSLATION:

Gaude Maria, virgo, cunctas
haereses sola interemisti,
quae Gabrielis archangeli
dictis credidisti:
Dum virgo Deum et hominem genuisti,
et post partum virgo,
inviolata permansisti.

Gabrielem archangelum
credimus[1] divinitus te
esse affatum:
uterum tuum de Spiritu Sancto
credimus impregnatum:

Erubescat Judaeus infelix, qui dicit
Christum de[2] Joseph semine esse natum.
Dum virgo Deum et hominem genuisti,
et post partum virgo,
inviolata permansisti.

[1]scimus (*AM*).
[2]ex (*AM*).

Rejoice Maria, virgin, thou
alone hast refuted all heresies
and hast believed what the
archangel Gabriel said;
Yet a virgin, thou hast borne God and man,
and after the birth, thou
hast remained a virgin inviolate.

We believe the words of the
archangel Gabriel to thee
to have been divinely inspired,
we believe thy womb to have been
impregnated by the Holy Spirit.

Let the unhappy Jew blush, who sayeth Christ
was born of the seed of Joseph;
Yet a virgin, thou hast borne God and man,
and after the birth, thou
hast remained a virgin inviolate.

ERRORS IN SOURCE:

Discantus: 47/3 sig congr (above an "8"); 213/1 sig congr.
Altus: 16/1 sig congr; 47/4 2 sig congr (one directly under the note and another an octave below); 80/4 sig congr.
Tenor: 213/3 sig congr.
Vagans: 80/4 sig congr; 213/4 sig congr.
Bassus: 16/1 sig congr; 31/1 sig congr; 47/5 sig congr; 71/3 sig congr; 77/1 sig congr; 80/5 sig congr; 213/2 sig congr.

COMMENTARY:

If *Gaude Maria* truly is by Ockeghem, then he is the sole representative of his generation in the manuscript *RegB 211–215*. No other source but this set of partbooks, which bears the date 1538 and was compiled, therefore, more than forty years after Ockeghem's death, transmits the piece. Although the provenance of *RegB 211–215* is unknown, it has been pointed out that the prevailing character of its repertory is Catholic and that the presence of works by composers such as Heinrich Finck and Stephanus Mahu perhaps indicates an association with the Austrian court of Emperor Ferdinand I.[37]

In all the partbooks, *Gaude Maria* is attributed to "Johannes Okegus," this being the form of the composer's name employed

[37]See *HoffS*, p. 28.

by Erasmus of Rotterdam in his memorial tribute beginning "Ergone conticuit," which is entitled, "Joanni Okego Musico summo Epitaphium."[38] Given the late date and probable remote provenance of *RegB 211–215*, there is good reason to doubt the authenticity of this work. It may well be that the unknown scribe of the partbooks was mistaken in assigning the work to Ockeghem, but it is also possible that Okegus was a different composer entirely, Erasmus notwithstanding.

An analysis of the formal design of *Gaude Maria* tends to confirm the uncertainty raised by the documentary evidence. Because the cantus firmus is a responsory for the feast of the Annunciation,[39] the basic structure of the motet is aBcB, this being the form polyphonic settings of responsories usually took in the sixteenth century. If Ockeghem composed *Gaude Maria*, then he must have been among the earliest, if not the first, to employ the aBcB responsory design. Credit for being first in that regard has often been given to Walter Frye, whose *Ave regina caelorum, mater Regis* of around 1450 appears to take this form. However, the text of Frye's motet is that of an antiphon, not a responsory. Sylvia Kenney suggested instead that Frye's piece is a contrafact of a *ballade* setting with a musical rhyme;[40] that is, a composition in which the second section ends like the first, creating what may be perceived as abcb, even though it is not a setting of a responsory.

It would seem, then, that Frye is not the inventor of the design for polyphonic responsories, nor did Obrecht intend to employ the responsory form as such when he modeled his own setting of *Ave regina caelorum, mater Regis* on Frye's. Aside from these two apparently spurious examples of fifteenth-century polyphonic responsory design, we have no works in the form until the followers of Josquin des Prez begin to compose them. Thus there are no firm precedents for a responsory motet by Ockeghem. Although *Gaude Maria* is divided into four *partes*, the beginnings of the *partes* do not correspond to the structure of the responsory cantus firmus. But inasmuch as mm. 237–46 consist of a repetition of both the words and the counterpoint of mm. 91–100, the result is a standard aBcB responsory design.

In terms of the style of Ockeghem's unquestionably authentic motets, *Gaude Maria* exhibits still further incongruities. Almost every phrase begins with a point of imitation in which all the participating voices engage. Therefore, the cantus firmus, which is freely paraphrased in the tenor in note values somewhat longer than those of the other four voices, permeates the entire texture. This kind of paraphrase cantus firmus treatment with continuous imitation is not characteristic of Ockeghem. The opening of *Gaude Maria* consists of an imitative duo for superius and altus, followed by the same music repeated an octave lower in the vagans and bassus voices. Literal repetition of this variety does not occur in Ockeghem's indisputably authentic motets.

One might argue that *Gaude Maria* bears little resemblance to authentic motets by Ockeghem, such as *Intemerata Dei mater*, because it was composed in a late style not represented elsewhere on account of the low survival rate of his works in the genre. This hypothetical late style is nowhere to be found, however, among Ockeghem's masses preserved in *RChigi*. Since *RChigi* presumably was compiled after the composer's death, it stands to reason that at least some of the music by him it contains would be in his latest style. Taking everything into consideration, it seems unlikely that Ockeghem could have composed a work in a form and style that were not to be current for two generations. Although *Gaude Maria* is a sometimes striking work by a skilled composer, it appears doubtful that the composer was Ockeghem.

10. SALVE REGINA [II]

MAIN SOURCE:

RCS 46, fol. 119^{v}–21^{r}. *Io.*(?) ________________ (?).

OTHER SOURCE:

RISM 1520^{1}, no. 8. *Basiron*.

MUSIC PUBLISHED:

PickA, no. 9.

CANTUS FIRMUS:

LU, p. 276.

TEXT AND TRANSLATION:

(See no. 4 above.)

---

[38]See below for the musical setting by Jo. Lupi, which has the title "In Ioannem Okegi Musicorum principem, Naenia," an obvious paraphrase of the earlier title.

[39]*AM*, p. 1195, and elsewhere.

[40]*KennF*, pp. 67ff.

VARIANT READINGS:

Superius: labeled "Supranus" (*RISM 1520[1]*); 12/2–3 no mi col (*RISM 1520[1]*); 24/2–3 no lig (*RISM 1520[1]*); 40/1–42/1 lig (*RISM 1520[1]*); 42/1 longa err (*RISM 1520[1]*); 72/1–2 1 c br (*RISM 1520[1]*).

Contra: labeled "Altus" (*RISM 1520[1]*); 20/4 m, sm (*RISM 1520[1]*); 36/2–3 mi col (*RISM 1520[1]*); 38/7–39/2 a sbr, a longa (*RISM 1520[1]*); 67/3–68/1 no mi col (*RISM 1520[1]*); 99/1–2 1 g sbr (no mi col) (*RISM 1520[1]*); 106/3–107/1 no mi col (*RISM 1520[1]*).

Tenor: before 15/1 no flat (*RISM 1520[1]*); before 36/1 no flat (*RISM 1520[1]*); 40/1–45/1 no lig (*RISM 1520[1]*); 77/1–78/1 lig (*RISM 1520[1]*); before 90/1 no flat (*RISM 1520[1]*).

Bassus: before 1/1 flat in sig (*RCS 46*, *RISM 1520[1]*); after 23/3 no flat in sig for remainder of voice (*RCS 46*, *RISM 1520[1]*); 33/2 no col (*RISM 1520[1]*); 39/1–3 1 longa (*RISM 1520[1]*).

COMMENTARY:

When the manuscript *RCS 46* underwent restoration in 1724,[41] the bindery trimmed the top margin and cut off numerous composer attributions. As a result, only "Io." and a few ambiguous descenders of subsequent letters are still legible above the superius of *Alma Redemptoris mater* (no. 1 above) on fol. 116[v]. That Ockeghem is in fact the composer of the motet just named is confirmed by the attribution of it to him in *FR 2794*, which was compiled at the French court while he was serving there.[42] What could be construed as "Io." and some perhaps similar-looking descenders are also still visible above the superius of the following piece, the present setting of *Salve regina*, and both Haberl and Llorens concluded that the abbreviation must refer likewise to Ockeghem.[43]

But Haberl and Llorens were not aware that Andrea Antico published this setting of the well-known Marian antiphon in Venice in 1520 ascribed to "Basiron."[44] No doubt "Basiron" refers to a contemporary of Ockeghem, whose first name is known to have been Philippe or Philippon.[45] However, a handwritten catalogue of music in the Sistine Chapel manuscripts, prepared by Rafaele Panuzzi, who was *magister capellae* in 1687—that is, well before the rebinding and excision of composers' names — attributes the *Salve regina* on fol. 119[v]–21[r] of *RCS 46* to "Bausseron."[46] This very probably refers to Johannes Bonnevin, called "Beausseron," who was a member of the papal chapel after 1514[47] and served there until his death in 1542.[48]

In the absence of comprehensive knowledge of Beausseron's motets, it is not possible to judge with any certainty whether he could have been the composer of the *Salve regina* in *RCS 46*; but, in any event, the style of the composition suggests that it was written in the late fifteenth century, that is, probably before Beausseron's period of activity. Perhaps the exemplar employed by the scribe of *RCS 46*, who is thought to have compiled the source c. 1518–20, was the same as—or at least closely related to—the exemplar used by Antico, who pursued his publishing career in Rome with papal permission until 1518, since the two readings are very similar. This hypothetical exemplar may have contained an ascription to Basiron (d. 1491), and the scribe of *RCS 46*, lacking familiarity with Basiron, attributed the piece to Beausseron, who may have been someone with whom he was acquainted personally.[49] On the other hand, it could have been Panuzzi who confused Basiron with Beausseron.

Considering the divergent musical characters of motets attributed to Ockeghem, such as *Alma Redemptoris mater*, *Ave Maria*, and *Intemerata Dei mater*, one cannot dismiss out of hand on stylistic grounds the possibility of his authorship of the *Salve regina* in *RCS 46*. The piece is in any event highly unusual. The treatment of the plainchant antiphon as a cantus firmus follows a relatively common plan. It is paraphrased mainly in the superius, with occasional brief migrations to the contratenor or the tenor. However, the tenor behaves, for all intents and purposes, like a long-note cantus firmus, despite the apparent absence of any preexistent melody. Should a source for the melody of the tenor, which displays some of the earmarks of a secular tune, someday come to light, a motet having both a paraphrased cantus firmus and a long-note cantus firmus would be something of a curiosity.

All considerations of style aside, the admittedly complicated documentary evidence makes it very doubtful that Ockeghem composed the setting of *Salve regina* in *RCS 46*. Such evidence as exists rather favors Basiron.

---

[41]See *LlorCS*, p. 98.

[42]*Census-Cat.* I, p. 246.

[43]See *HabBV*, pp. 20 and 156, and *LlorCS*, p. 97.

[44]The editors are grateful to Prof. Martin Picker for bringing the concordance to their attention. His edition of the piece, based on Antico's *Motetti novi libro secondo*, appears in *PickA*, pp. 160–68. See also *PickA*, pp. 32–35.

[45]See M. Picker, *Grove VI* 2, p. 240.

[46]The catalogue survives as Capella Sistina MS 630. Panuzzi designates the source no. 27, which is demonstrably the same as *RCS 46*; cf. MS 630, fol. 18[v]. Professor Picker has credited Eric Fiedler with supplying the information to him concerning Panuzzi's list.

[47]See *FreyR*, pp. 71 and 179.

[48]See *HabR*, p. 81.

[49]In a paper read at the 1986 annual meeting of the American Musicological Society in Cleveland, Dr. Jeffery Dean demonstrated that it is possible to see the remnant descenders as belonging to the attribution "P. Basiron."

CHANSONS

UNDISPUTED WORKS

1. AULTRE VENUS

SOURCE:

FR 2794, fol. 39^{v}–40^{r}. *De okeghem*, t+xx.

TEXT AND TRANSLATION:

Aultre Venus estes sans faille
Plus que nulle aultre creature;
De corps, de beaulté, de figure
La semblez et de mesmes taille.

Celuy qui les amours detaille
Peult de vous dire par droicture:

Aultre Venus …

Qui contredit, j'offre bataille
A oultrance et a desmesure,
Maintenant qu'il vous fait injure,
Se le tiltre tel ne vous baille.

Aultre Venus …

You are another Venus, without doubt,
More than any other being;
In body, in beauty, in face
You resemble her and are of the same stature.

He who gives an account of love
Can rightly say of you:

You are another Venus, …

To whoever contradicts, I offer battle
To the death and without limit,
Maintaining that he insults you,
If he does not grant you such a claim.

You are another Venus, …

ERRORS IN SOURCE:

Superius: 13/2–3 2 sm err; 22/1 dot sbr err.
Tenor: (none).
Contra: 13/2–3 2 sm err; 33/1 dot miss err; 34/1 dot miss err.

COMMENTARY:

FR 2794, the unique source of this *rondeau quatrain* setting, was probably compiled in the 1480s at the French royal court during Ockeghem's tenure as *maître de chapelle*.

There is a flat in the signature of the tenor only, but it is evident that virtually all the notes *b* in the superius and contra must be taken as *b*-flat on account of one or another rule of *musica ficta*. Some of the *b*-flats, including some in the tenor as well as some added to the superius for reasons of *musica ficta*, combine with *e*-naturals to produce the supposedly proscribed interval of a tritone between the lowest sounding voice and one of the upper voices (mm. 9, 13, and 15). Perhaps Ockeghem sanctions this usage in m. 4, where *a* in the contra sounds against an *e* requiring an editorial flat for melodic reasons in the superius.

Certain aspects of the style of *Aultre Venus* suggest that it is a relatively early work. The tenor and contra occupy approximately the same range and cross frequently. The approach to the medial cadence (mm. 15–16), with its parallel voice leading, is distinctly reminiscent of *fauxbourdon*. Also, the formulation of the final cadence, which includes a double suspension and may well call for a double leading tone, strikes one as somewhat archaic. On the other hand, there are brief moments of imitation, albeit "hidden." Measures 7–10 of the tenor are heard again in mm. 10–12 of the superius, for example, and mm. 24–26 of the tenor echo mm. 23–25 of the contra.

2. BAISIÉS MOY

MAIN SOURCE:

FB 2439, fol. LIII^{v}–LIIII^{r}. *Ockeghem*, txx.

OTHER SOURCE:

Cop 1848, p. 35. Anonymous: Baisez moy, txx.

TEXT AND TRANSLATION:

Baisiés moy dont fort, ma maistresse,	Kiss me ardently, my lady,
Acollés moy, mon vray[1] refuge,	Embrace me, my true refuge,
Puis que je vous fais mon seul juge	Since I appoint you my sole judge
Pour[2] pugnir mon ceur si vous blesse.[3]	To chastise my heart, if I offend you.

[1]ferray (*FB 2439*).
[2]Sus (*Cop 1848*).
[3]laisse (*FB 2439*).

VARIANT READINGS:

Superius: 17/1–2 lig (*Cop 1848*); 19/1–2 lig (*Cop 1848*); 21/4–5 1 sm d (*Cop 1848*); 23/3–4 1 sbr b (*Cop 1848*); before 28/1 no sharp (*Cop 1848*); 32/1 2 sbr (*FB 2439*);35/2 flat in sig for remainder of voice (*FB 2439*); 36/1 b–flat (*Cop 1848*); 36/2 d (*Cop 1848*); 39/2–3 no lig (*Cop 1848*); 42/1 2 sbr (*Cop 1848*); 43/2 2 m, the second crossed out err (*Cop 1848*); 44/1 sbr err (*Cop 1848*); 50/4–51/1 mi col (*Cop 1848*); 56/3–4 mi col (*Cop 1848*); 57/1 no sig congr (*Cop 1848*).
Tenor: 3/2–4/1 lig (*Cop 1848*); 15/2–16/1 lig (*Cop 1848*); 18/1–2 no mi col (*Cop 1848*); 18/3 1 m e (*Cop 1848*); 22/3–23/1 1 br (*Cop 1848*); 24/1–2 mi col (*Cop 1848*); before 27/2 no flat (*Cop 1848*); 28/1–2 no mi col (*Cop 1848*); 28/2 b-flat (*Cop 1848*); before 36/2 flat (*Cop 1848*, *FB 2439*); 38/1–2 no lig (*Cop 1848*); 54/3–55/2 no lig (*Cop 1848*); 57/2 no sig congr (*Cop 1848*).
Bassus: 3/1–4/1 no lig (*Cop 1848*); 7/1–8/1 no lig (*Cop 1848*); 14/1 br rest err (*Cop 1848*); 22/1 miss err (*Cop 1848*); before 22/3 no flat in sig for remainder of voice (*Cop 1848*); 24/1–25/1 mi col (*Cop 1848*); 26/2–3 no lig (*Cop 1848*); 28/1 sig congr (*Cop 1848*); 30/1–2 mi col (*Cop 1848*); 33/1–2 1 br (*Cop 1848*); before 34/1 no flat (*Cop 1848*); 39/3–40/1 1 br (*Cop 1848*); 41/2–3 1 sbr g (*Cop 1848*); 45/1–2 lig (*Cop 1848*); before 47/2 flat (*FB 2439*); 51/1–2 no lig (*Cop 1848*); 54/1–55/1 no lig (*Cop 1848*); 55/1–2 no mi col (*Cop 1848*).

COMMENTARY:

Neither source of the piece preserves the complete text, but it is evident, from the structure of the surviving lines and the music, that *Baisiés moy* was originally a *rondeau quatrain*.

In *FB 2439*, there is a sharp before the *f* of the medial cadence, superius mm. 28–29, which conflicts with the melodic material of the bassus and in particular with that of the tenor. Most probably the sharp should be applied to the *f* in the final cadences of the short strophe and the short refrain only. For the opening and closing refrains and the full strophe, the *f* should be natural in order to avoid the dissonances.

The style of this chanson marks it as a mature work. Each voice occupies its own distinct range, with the bottom part descending to *d* below the bass staff. Except momentarily in m. 36, the voices never cross. Imitation is present between the superius and the tenor in the first two phrases, although it plays no major structural role in the composition as a whole. The opening consists of a series of duos between tenor and bassus, superius and bassus, and superius and tenor, and full three-voice texture does not manifest itself until m. 16.

The overall texture consists of a superius-tenor duo supported by the bassus, as opposed to the treble-dominated texture of the apparently early works, such as *Ma maistresse* (no. 12 below). However, neither of the sources provides more than a text incipit for the tenor, which fact accounts for the absence of text in that voice in the present edition. The final cadence is unusual in that it bears little resemblance to any of the standard cadence formulas of the period. That the composition is perhaps a late work is not precluded by the dates of *FB 2439* (1506–14, probably c. 1508) and *Cop 1848* (c. 1525).

3. D'UN AUTRE AMER

MAIN SOURCE:

Dij, fol. xxxviiij^{v}–xl^{r} (42^{v}–43^{r}). *Okeghem*, t+xx.

OTHER SOURCES:

BQ 17, fol. 40^v–41^r. *Jo. ockeghem*: Dung aultre amer, xxx.
Cop 291, fol. 33^v–34^r (39^v–40^r). Anonymous, t+xx.
Cop 1848, p. 145. Anonymous: Dung aultre aymer, t+–x.
FBNC 178, fol. 62^v–63^r. Anonymous: Dunaltre amer, x––.
FR 2356, fol. 73^v–74^r (79^v–80^r). Anonymous: (D)ung aultre amer, x–x.
FR 2794, fol. 19^v–20^r. *De okeghem*: Dung aultre amer, t+xx.
PBN 2245, fol. 13^v–14^r. *Okeghem*: Dung aultre amer, t+tx.
PNiv, fol. LXVI^v–LXVII^r. *Okeghem*: Dung autre amer, t+xx.
PPix, fol. 189^v–90^r. *Busnoys*: Dum aultre amer, txx.
RCas 2856, fol. 16^v–17^r (13^v–14^r). *Jo okeghem*: Dunch aulter amer, xxx.
RCG XIII.27, fol. 112^v–13^r (105^v–06^r). Anonymous: Dum altre amer, x––.
Sev 5–I–43, fol. 51^v–52^r (j1^v–j2^r). Anonymous: Dung aultre amer, xxx(x).
WLab, fol. xviij^v–xviiij^r. Anonymous: Dung aultre amer, t+xx.
Wol 287, fol. 33^v–34^r. Anonymous: Dung aultre aymer, t+xx.

TEXT ALONE:

BerRoh, fol. 118^r.
LonBL 380, fol. 242^r.
PBN IV.6.25, fol. 29^v.
VerChasse, fol. Qiiii^r.
VerJard, fol. lxxxiiii^r–lxxxiiii^v.

MUSIC PUBLISHED:

DrozT, no. 36.
JepK, no. 28.
JosqMS XI, p. 140.
SmijO I, no. 3.
TarusD, no. 1.

TEXT PUBLISHED:

DrozJP, no. 243.
LöpL, no. 293.

TEXT[a] AND TRANSLATION:

D'un autre amer mon cueur s'abesseroit; Il ne fault ja[1] penser[2] que je l'estrange Ne que pour rien de ce[3] propos me[4] change, Car mon honneur en[5] appetisseroit.[6]	By loving another, my heart would demean itself; One need never think that I might spurn her Nor that for anything I might change from this purpose, For my honor would thus diminish.
Je l'aime tant que jamais[7] ne seroit Possible a moi de[8] consentir l'eschange[9]	I love her so much that never would it be Possible for me to consent to exchange her.
D'un autre amer …	By loving another, …
La mort, par Dieu, avant[10] me desferoit Qu'en mon vivant j'acoinctasse ung estrange.	Death, by God, would undo me, Before in my lifetime I should accept an estrangment.

Ne cuide nul qu'a cela[11] je me range;
Ma[12] leauté trop fort se mesferoit.[13]

D'un autre amer …

Let no one think that I should allow that;
My strong loyalty would prevent it.

By loving another …

[a]The reading of the text transmitted by *PPix* is notably corrupt.

[1]pas (*BerRoh*, *Cop 1848*, *FR 2794*, *LonBL 380*, *Wol 287*).
[2]missing (*LonBL 380*).
[3]missing (*LonBL 380*).
[4]ung (*Cop 1848*).
[5]sen (*WLab*, *Wol 287*).
[6]abesseroit (*Cop 1848*).
[7]pas il (*PPix*, *Wol 287*).
[8]den (*Cop 1848*, *FR 2794*, *Wol 287*).
[9]le change (*BerRoh*, *FR 2794*, *LonBL 380*, *PNiv*, *Wol 287*).
[10]avant par dieu (*Cop 1848*); avant plus tost (*LonBL 380*).
[11]Celle (*Wol 287*).
[12]Car (*Cop 1848*); car ma (*LonBL 380*).
[13]en amainderoit (*PNiv*).

VARIANT READINGS:

Superius: before 1/1 flat in sig (for b below middle c) (*RCas 2856*), no flat in sig (*PNiv*, *RCG XIII.27*); 3/1–3 no mi col (*BQ 17*, *Cop 1848*, *FBNC 178*, *FR 2794*, *PBN 2245*, *RCas 2856*, *RCG XIII.27*, *Sev 5–I–43*); 4/1–2 1 br (*RCas 2856*, *Sev 5–I–43*); 5/2 2 sbr (*Cop 1848*); 7/1–2 1 dot sbr (*BQ 17*, *FR 2794*, *PBN 2245*, *RCas 2856*); before 8/1 flat (for b) (*FR 2356*); 10/1–2 lig (*RCas 2856*); before 10/2 no flat in sig for remainder of voice (*FR 2356*); 11/1 2 sbr (*Cop 1848*); 13/1 e m, d m (*BQ 17*, *FBNC 178*, *FR 2794*, *PBN 2245*, *PNiv*, *PPix*, *RCas 2856*, *RCG XIII.27*), e dot m, d sm (*FR 2356*); 13/2–14/1 1 dot br (*BQ 17*); before 15/2 flat (*FR 2356*, *WLab*); 17/1–2 f dot m, e sm (*RCas 2856*), 1 f sbr (*FBNC 178*, *FR 2794*, *PBN 2245*); 17/3 2 sbr (*Cop 1848*), d dot sbr, b m (*FR 2794*, *PBN 2245*); 18/1–2 1 c sbr (*BQ 17*, *Cop 1848*, *FBNC 178*, *FR 2356*, *FR 2794*, *PBN 2245*, *PNiv*, *PPix*, *RCas 2856*, *RCG XIII.27*, *Sev 5–I–43*, *WLab*, *Wol 287*); 19/1 no sig congr (*BQ 17*, *Cop 291*, *Cop 1848*, *FBNC 178*, *FR 2356*, *FR 2794*, *PPix*, *RCG XIII.27*, *Sev 5–I–43*), 2 br (*Cop 1848*); before 21/1 flat (for b) (*FR 2356*, *FR 2794*); before 22/1 flat (*Dij*); 24/1–25/1 1 dot br (*BQ 17*); 25/1 c err (*Cop 1848*); 26/1–2 1 dot sbr (*RCas 2856*); 26/3 b-flat sm, a sm (*FBNC 178*, *FR 2356*, *FR 2794*, *PBN 2245*, *RCas 2856*, *RCG XIII.27*, *Sev 5–I–43*); before 27/1 flat (for b) (*Sev 5–I–43*); 27/1–2 lig (*FR 2356*, *PNiv*, *PPix*, *WLab*); 27/2 dot miss err (*Cop 1848*); 28/1 e sm, d sm (*FR 2794*, *PBN 2245*, *RCas 2856*, *Sev 5–I–43*), e (*BQ 17*, *Cop 1848*, *FBNC 178*, *FR 2356*, *PPix*, *RCG XIII.27*, *Wol 287*); before 28/2 flat (for b) (*FR 2794*); 28/2–29/1 no lig (*BQ 17*, *Cop 1848*, *FBNC 178*, *PPix*, *RCas 2856*, *RCG XIII.27*); before 29/1 flat (for b) (*PPix*); 29/1–2 1 d br (*RCas 2856*); before 29/2 flat (*Wol 287*); 29/2 c sm, b-flat sm (*FBNC 178*); 30/1–2 no lig (*BQ 17*, *Cop 1848*, *FR 2794*, *PBN 2245*, *PPix*, *RCG XIII.27*, *Wol 287*); 30/2–31/1 lig (*Wol 287*); before 31/2 flat (*FR 2356*, *WLab*); 31/2–32/1 no lig (*BQ 17*, *FBNC 178*, *FR 2356*, *FR 2794*, *PBN 2245*, *RCas 2856*, *RCG XIII.27*, *WLab*), 1 b-flat br (*BQ 17*, *FBNC 178*, *FR 2794*, *RCas 2856*, *RCG XIII.27*), b-flat dot sbr, a sm, g sm (*WLab*), dot sbr, m (*FR 2356*); 39/1–2 lig (*FR 2356*, *FR 2794*, *PBN 2245*, *RCas 2856*, *Sev 5–I–43*); 39/2–40/1 lig (*PPix*); 42/1 m err (*Cop 1848*); 42/3–43/1 mi col (*BQ 17*, *RCG XIII.27*); 44/2–3 g dot m, f sm, f sm, e sm (*Sev 5–I–43*).

Tenor: before 1/1 no flat in sig (*Sev 5–I–43*), no mens sig (*Cop 291*, *Wol 287*); 1/1–2 1 g br (*RCas 2856*), no mi col (*FR 2794*); 2/1–2 no lig (*WLab*); 2/1–5/1 no lig (*FBNC 178*, *FR 2794*, *PBN 2245*, *Sev 5–I–43*); 2/2–3/1 no lig (*PPix*); 2/2–5/1 no lig (*BQ 17*, *RCas 2856*, *RCG XIII.27*); 3/1–5/1 no lig (*Cop 1848*, *PNiv*); 4/1–5/1 no lig (*WLab*); 5/1–2 no mi col (*BQ 17*, *FR 2794*, *PNiv*, *RCas 2856*, *RCG XIII.27*, *WLab*); 6/1–2 no lig (*Sev 5–I–43*); 6/1–8/1 no lig (*BQ 17*, *FBNC 178*, *FR 2794*, *PBN 2245*, *RCG XIII.27*); 6/2–8/1 no lig (*Cop 1848*, *RCas 2856*); 7/1 g dot sbr, f sm, e sm (*FR 2794*, *PBN 2245*, *RCas 2856*); 9/1–2 no lig (*BQ 17*, *FBNC 178*, *RCG XIII.27*, *Sev 5–I–43*); 9/2–10/1 lig (*Sev 5–I–43*); 10/1–2 no lig (*BQ 17*, *FBNC 178*, *RCG XIII.27*, *Sev 5–I–43*); 11/3–4 1 e m (*BQ 17*, *FBNC 178*, *FR 2794*, *PBN 2245*, *Sev 5–I–43*); 14/3–4 1 e m (*BQ 17*, *PBN 2245*, *RCas 2856*, *Sev 5–I–43*); before 15/1 no flat in sig for remainder of voice (*RCG XIII.27*); 15/2 e (*WLab*), e sm, d sm (*PNiv*); 16/1 g bl br, f bl m, e bl m (*PBN 2245*), 2 sbr (*FBNC 178*, *RCG XIII.27*); 17/1–19/1 no lig (*FBNC 178*, *RCG XIII.27*); 17/2–19/1 no lig (*BQ 17*, *Cop 1848*, *RCas 2856*); 18/1–19/1 no lig (*FR 2794*, *PBN 2245*, *PPix*, *WLab*); 19/1 sig congr (*FR 2356*, *PNiv*, *RCas 2856*, *WLab*); before 20/1 flat (*FR 2356*, *WLab*); 21/1–2 1 br (*FBNC 178*); before 22/1 flat in sig for remainder of voice (*Sev 5–I–43*); 22/1 2 sbr (*Cop 1848*); 22/1–23/1 no lig (*BQ 17*, *Cop 1848*, *FBNC 178*, *FR 2794*, *PPix*, *RCG XIII.27*); 23/1 2 sbr (*RCG XIII.27*); 26/1 2 sbr (*RCG XIII.27*); 26/1–27/1 no lig (*Cop 1848*, *FBNC 178*, *FR 2356*, *FR 2794*, *RCG XIII.27*); 28/1–2 no lig (*BQ 17*, *Cop 1848*, *FBNC 178*, *FR 2794*, *PBN 2245*, *PPix*, *RCas 2856*, *RCG XIII.27*, *Sev 5–I–43*, *WLab*); 31/1–32/1 no lig (*PPix*, *WLab*); 31/1–33/1 no lig (*BQ 17*, *Cop 1848*, *FBNC 178*, *FR 2794*, *PBN 2245*, *RCas 2856*, *RCG XIII.27*, *Sev 5–I–43*); 31/2–32/1 lig (*Cop 1848*); 32/1 2 sbr (*Cop 1848*); 32/1–33/1 no lig (*PNiv*, *Wol 287*); 33/1–2 no mi col (*Cop 1848*, *FBNC 178*, *FR 2794*, *PBN 2245*, *RCas 2856*, *RCG XIII.27*, *Sev 5–I–43*); 34/1–2 no lig (*BQ 17*, *Cop 1848*, *FBNC 178*, *FR 2794*, *PBN 2245*, *RCas 2856*, *RCG XIII.27*, *Sev 5–I–43*, *WLab*); 34/2–35/1 lig (*FR 2356*, *PNiv*, *PPix*); 35/1 g dot sbr, f m (*FR 2794*, *PBN 2245*); 35/1–36/1 no lig (*BQ 17*, *RCas

2856); 35/1–39/1 no lig (*Cop 1848*, *FBNC 178*, *FR 2794*, *PBN 2245*); 36/1–37/1 no lig (*PPix*, *Sev 5–I–43*); 37/1 2 sbr (*Cop 1848*); 37/1–39/1 no lig (*RCas 2856*); 38/1–39/1 no lig (*Cop 291*); 39/1 2 sbr (*Cop 1848*); 40/1–41/1 no lig (*BQ 17*, *Cop 1848*, *FBNC 178*, *FR 2794*); 40/2–41/1 no lig (*PBN 2245*); 42/2–3 dot m, sm (*FR 2356*); 43/1–2 d m, c sm, b-flat sm (*FBNC 178*); 43/1–2 mi col (*BQ 17*).

Conctratenor:[a] labeled "Bassus" (*RCG XIII.27*); before 1/1 ₵ in sig (*BQ 17*, *Cop 1848*, *FBNC 178*, *FR 2356*, *PBN 2245*, *PNiv*, *PPix*, *RCas 2856*, *RCG XIII.27*, *Sev 5–I–43*, *WLab*, *Wol 287*); 1/1–3 no mi col (*FR 2794*, *RCas 2856*); 1/2–3 1 a m (*RCas 2856*); 2/1–3/1 no lig (*FBNC 178*, *Sev 5–I–43*); 2/2–3/1 no lig (*BQ 17*, *Cop 1848*, *RCas 2856*, *RCG XIII.27*); 3/1 2 sbr (*Cop 1848*); 3/1–5/1 lig (*Sev 5–I–43*); 4/1–5/1 lig (*PBN 2245*, *PPix*); 5/1 2 sbr (*Cop 1848*); 6/1–2 no lig (*BQ 17*, *FBNC 178*, *FR 2794*, *PBN 2245*, *RCG XIII.27*, *Sev 5–I–43*); 7/1–2 1 b-flat sbr (*FR 2794*, *PBN 2245*, *RCas 2856*); 7/1–3 lig (*RCas 2856*); 8/1–2 1 c m (*RCas 2856*); 9/1–2 no lig (*BQ 17*, *Cop 1848*, *FBNC 178*, *RCG XIII.27*, *Sev 5–I–43*); 9/2–10/1 lig (*Sev 5–I–43*); 11/1–2 mi col (*WLab*); 12/2 sbr err (*Cop 1848*); 14/2–4 sbr, m (*BQ 17*, *FR 2794*, *PBN 2245*, *PPix*, *RCas 2856*, *WLab*); 15/2 m err (*FBNC 178*); 16/1 miss err (*FBNC 178*); 16/1–2 1 dot sbr (*BQ 17*, *RCG XIII.27*); 16/3 a (*PPix*, *RCas 2856*); 19/1 sig congr (*PNiv*, *RCas 2856*); 19/1–2 no lig (*BQ 17*, *Cop 1848*, *FBNC 178*, *RCG XIII.27*, *Sev 5–I–43*); 20/3 c sm, b-flat sm (*BQ 17*, *FBNC 178*, *FR 2794*, *PBN 2245*, *PPix*, *RCas 2856*, *RCG XIII.27*, *Sev 5–I–43*); 21/1–2 1 br (*Cop 1848*, *PPix*); 21/1–22/1 lig (*PPix*); 22/1 2 sbr (*Cop 1848*); 24/1–3 mi col (*FR 2356*); 25/1–2 no lig (*BQ 17*, *Cop 1848*, *FBNC 178*, *FR 2356*, *RCG XIII.27*); 26/1–2 lig (*FR 2356*, *FR 2794*, *PBN 2245*, *PPix*, *RCas 2856*, *WLab*); before 27/1 flat (for b) (*BQ 17*, *PPix*, *Sev 5–I–43*); 27/1–2 no lig (*BQ 17*, *Cop 1848*, *FBNC 178*, *RCG XIII.27*); 27/2 c err (*WLab*); before 28/1 flat (*Cop 1848*, *Dij*, *FBNC 178*, *FR 2794*); 28/1 no lig (*RCG XIII.27*); 28/1–29/1 no lig (*FBNC 178*); 28/2–29/1 no lig (*Cop 1848*, *FR 2794*, *RCas 2856*); 29/1 b-flat dot sbr, c m (*RCG XIII.27*); 30/1–2 no lig (*BQ 17*, *Cop 1848*, *FBNC 178*, *PPix*, *RCG XIII.27*); 30/1–32/2 b-flat sbr-a sbr lig, f sbr-g sbr lig, f br (all err?) (*RCas 2856*); before 32/1 flat (*FR 2794*, *PPix*, *Sev 5–I–43*); 32/1–33/1 lig (*Sev 5–I–43*, *WLab*); 33/1–2 no mi col (*BQ 17*, *Cop 1848*, *FR 2794*, *PBN 2245*, *RCas 2856*); 34/1–2 no lig (*BQ 17*, *Cop 1848*, *FBNC 178*, *FR 2794*, *PBN 2245*, *RCas 2856*, *RCG XIII.27*); 35/1–2 1 e br (*RCas 2856*); 35/1–36/1 lig (*RCas 2856*); 36/1–38/1 no lig (*BQ 17*, *Cop 1848*, *FBNC 178*, *PNiv*, *RCas 2856*, *RCG XIII.27*); 37/1 2 sbr (*Cop 1848*); 37/1–38/1 no lig (*PBN 2245*, *Sev 5–I–43*); 39/1–2 lig (*PPix*); 39/2–3 2 m (*FR 2794*, *PBN 2245*, *RCas 2856*), 1 b-flat sbr (*BQ 17*), mi col (*PPix*); 39/2–40/2 sbr, m, sbr, m err (*FBNC 178*, *RCG XIII.27*); 40/3–41/2 lig (*PPix*), g m, a dot sbr err (*FBNC 178*, *RCG XIII.27*); 41/1 miss err (*PPix*); 42/1–3 d m, g sbr (*BQ 17*); 42/4–43/1 mi col (*BQ 17*, *FBNC 178*, *RCG XIII.27*); 42/4–43/2 sbr, 2 m (*FR 2794*); 43/2–3 lig (*PPix*, *RCas 2856*, *Sev 5–I–43*, *WLab*); 44/1 a sm, g sm (*FBNC 178*); 45/1 g (*Cop 1848*).

[a] "Conctratenor" is the spelling of the voice designation in the main source.

Sev 5–I–43 "Bassus ab[s]q(ue) alio"

COMMENTARY:

Sev 5–I–43 transmits a fourth voice in bass clef that is labeled "Bassus ab[s]q(ue) alio" (bass without the other). As its designation suggests, the voice part is intended to substitute for the original contratenor. The scribe of *Sev 5–I–43* does not name the composer of this unique alternative third voice, and he may well have been someone other than Ockeghem. But inasmuch as the "Bassus absque alio" survives in conjunction with all three authentic voices of *D'un autre amer*, it is provided above in full.

The attribution of this piece to Busnois in the peripheral Italian source *PPix* is surely erroneous. It is contradicted by the many ascriptions of the work to Ockeghem in manuscripts (*Dij*, *FR 2794*, *PBN 2245*, *PNiv*) from France and Burgundy. Josquin des Prez quoted *D'un autre amer* in two different motets, *Victimae paschali laudes* and *Tu solus qui facis mirabilia*,[50] and also used it as the basis of his *Missa D'ung aultre amer*.[51]

[50] Mod. eds. in *JosqMT* V, no. 26, and *JosqMT* II, no. 14, respectively.

[51] Printed in *JosqMS* II, no. 11; see further *BrownMFST*, p. 209f., for information concerning settings by other composers.

4. FORS SEULEMENT L'ACTENTE

MAIN SOURCE:

Dij, fol. xxv^{v}–xxvj^{r} (28^{v}–29^{r}). *Okeghem*, t+x–.

OTHER SOURCES:

PBN 1597, fol. xxxvi^{v}–xxxvii^{r}. Anonymous: Fors seullement lattente, tt+x.
PNiv, fol. vj^{r}. Anonymous: (lower voices of second half only, "Quil nest douleur …"), xx.
RCG XIII.27, fol. 104^{v}–05^{r} (97^{v}–98^{r}). Anonymous: Frayres y dexedes me, –x–.
SG 461, pp. 2–3. *Ockenhem*: Fors seullement, –x–.
WLab, fol. iiii^{xx}xviiij^{v}–c^{r}. Anonymous, t+xx.
Wol 287, fol. 43^{v}–45^{r}. Anonymous: Fors seullement latente, t+xx.

TEXT ALONE:

BerRoh, fol. 69^{r}.
LonBL 380, fol. 251^{r}.
PBN 1719, fol. 34^{r}.
PBN 1722, fol. 72^{v}.
VerJard, fol. Cxv^{r}.

MUSIC PUBLISHED:

DrozT, no. 25.
GiesS, pp. 2–3.
GomO, Notenanhang, no. 9.
PickFS, Nos. 1a and 1b.

TEXT PUBLISHED:

DrozJP, no. 496.
EitM, p. 59.
FranAP, no. CXIX (refrain only).
LöpL, no. 77.

TEXT AND TRANSLATION:

Fors seulement l'actente que je meure,
En[1] mon las cueur nul espoir ne demeure,
Car mon maleur si tresfort[2] me tourmente
Qu'il[3] n'est douleur que par[4] vous je
ne sente,
Pource que suis de vous perdre bien seure.

Vostre rigueur[5] tellement[6] m'y[7] queurt[8] seure[9]
Qu'en ce[10] parti il fault que[11] je m'asseure,[12]
Dont je n'ay bien[13] qui en riens me contente[14]

Fors seulement …

Save only the expectation that I shall die,
No hope dwells in my weary heart,
For my misery torments me so severely
That there is no sorrow I do not feel
because of you,
Since I am very sure of losing you.

Your severity pursues me to such a degree
That I must in this regard assure myself
I have nothing at all with which to be content

Save only …

Mon desconfort toute seule je pleure,	All alone I bemoan my distress,
En maudisant sur ma foy a toute heure	Cursing, by my oath, at all times
Ma leauté qui tant m'a[15] fait dolente.	My faithfulness which has made me so unhappy.
Las, que je suis de vivre mal contente[16]	Alas, I am sorry to be alive,
Quant de par vous n'ay[17] riens qui me demeure[18]	Since because of you I have nothing left to me
Fors seulement ...	Save only ...

[1]a (*VerJard*).
[2]fort (*LonBL 380*).
[3]Qui (*PBN 1597*, *WLab*, *Wol 287*).
[4]pour (*WLab*).
[5]beaulte (*PBN 1719*).
[6]si tresfort (*BerRoh*, *PBN 1597*, *PBN 1719*, *PBN 1722*, *VerJard*).
[7]me (*BerRoh*, *LonBL 380*, *PBN 1597*, *VerJard*, *Wol 287*).
[8]court (*BerRoh*, *PBN 1597*, *PBN 1719*, *PBN 1722*, *VerJard*, *Wol 287*).
[9]lines 9–11 exchanged with lines 6–8 (*PBN 1719*).
[10]se (*VerJard*).
[11]nay chose (*BerRoh*); na chose que (*VerJard*).
[12]Quil fault quainsi comble de dueil ie meure (*Wol 287*); dont que je meure (*PBN 1719*).
[13]Ne bien aucun (*BerRoh*, *VerJard*).
[14]ne me sustente (*PBN 1719*).
[15]me (*BerRoh*, *PBN 1597*, *VerJard*, *Wol 287*).
[16]missing (*VerJard*).
[17]nest (*LonBL 380*, *PBN 1597*, *Wol 287*).
[18]sequeure (*BerRoh*, *LonBL 380*, *PBN 1597*, *PBN 1719*, *PBN 1722*, *VerJard*, *Wol 287*).

VARIANT READINGS:

Superius: This voice is positioned as the tenor in *PBN 1597*, *RCG XIII.27*, and *SG 461*; before 1/1 no mens sig (*RCG XIII.27*); 3/1–3 sbr, 2 m (*Dij*, *WLab*), mi col (*SG 461*); 6/2 e sm, d sm (*PBN 1597*, *RCG XIII.27*, *SG 461*, *Wol 287*); 8/2 d dot sbr, c sm, b sm (*RCG XIII.27*); 12/1–3 no mi col (*PBN 1597*, *RCG XIII.27*, *SG 461*); 13/1–2 no mi col (*PBN 1597*, *RCG XIII.27*, *SG 461*, *Wol 287*); 14/1–3 no mi col (*PBN 1597*, *RCG XIII.27*, *SG 461*, *Wol 287*); 14/2–3 1 c m (*PBN 1597*, *RCG XIII.27*, *SG 461*); 15/1–2 lig (*PBN 1597*); 20/1–2 lig (*PBN 1597*); 21/1–2 lig (*PBN 1597*); 22/1–2 lig (*PBN 1597*); 23/2–24/1 1 br (*PBN 1597*); before 26/1 no flat (*PBN 1597*, *RCG XIII.27*); 27/1–3 sbr, 2 m (*Dij*, *WLab*); 28/1–2 dot m, sm (*PBN 1597*); 29/1 g sm, f sm (*RCG XIII.27*); 30/1–2 lig (*PBN 1597*, *RCG XIII.27*); 31/1–2 lig (*PBN 1597*, *RCG XIII.27*); 32/2–33/2 sbr, 2 m (*Dij*, *WLab*); 33/3–34/1 1 br (*RCG XIII.27*); 33/3–34/2 1 dot br (*PBN 1597*); 35/1–3 sbr, 2 m (*Dij*, *WLab*); 41/1–2 dot m, sm (*SG 461*); 41/2 e sm, d sm (*PBN 1597*, *RCG XIII.27*); 41/3 e sbr-c sbr lig (*PBN 1597*), no sig congr (*RCG XIII.27*); 43/1–2 no lig (*PBN 1597*, *RCG XIII.27*, *SG 461*); 44/1–2 bl sbr, bl m (*RCG XIII.27*), dot m, sm (*PBN 1597*, *SG 461*, *Wol 287*); 44/3–4 dot m, sm (*SG 461*); 44/4–45/1 bl sbr, bl m (*RCG XIII.27*); 46/5–6 bl sbr, bl m (*RCG XIII.27*); dot m, sm (*PBN 1597*, *SG 461*, *Wol 287*); 52/1–2 1 br (*RCG XIII.27*); 54/1 b sm, a sm (*PBN 1597*, *RCG XIII.27*, *SG 461*, *Wol 287*); 55/1–56/1 1 longa (*PBN 1597*, *SG 461*); 57/1–2 1 br (*RCG XIII.27*, *SG 461*); 59/1–2 lig (*RCG XIII.27*); 60/1 e sm, d sm (*RCG XIII.27*); 62/1–63/1 no lig (*PBN 1597*, *RCG XIII.27*, *SG 461*); 67/2–3 lig (*PBN 1597*, *SG 461*, *Wol 287*); 69/1–2 1 d sbr (*RCG XIII.27*, *SG 461*).

Tenor: This voice is positioned as the superius in *PBN 1597*, *RCG XIII.27*, and *SG 461*; before 1/1 flat in sig until before 24/2 (err?) (*WLab*); between 11/2 and 12/1 1 a sbr err (*Wol 287*);); 12/1–3 sbr, 2 m (*Dij*, *WLab*); 15/1–2 dot sbr, m (*PBN 1597*); 19/1–20/1 no lig (*RCG XIII.27*, *Wol 287*); 21/1–2 lig (*RCG XIII.27*); 24/1–2 1 br (*SG 461*); 24/1–25/1 1 dot br (*PBN 1597*); 26/1–3 sbr, 2 m (*Dij*, *WLab*); 32/1–3 sbr, 2 m (*Dij*, *WLab*); 33/1–34/2 1 longa (*Wol 287*); 37/1–38/1 no lig (*RCG XIII.27*, *Wol 287*); 38/1–39/1 lig (*RCG XIII.27*, *SG 461*); 39/1 sig congr (*PBN 1597*, *SG 461*, *Wol 287*), dot miss (*SG 461*); 49/1–50/2 lig (*RCG XIII.27*); 50/1–2 1 br (*RCG XIII.27*); 51/1–52/2 lig (*SG 461*); 52/1–2 1 br (*PBN 1597*, *PNiv*, *RCG XIII.27*, *SG 461*, *Wol 287*); 53/1–3 sbr, 2 m (*Dij*, *WLab*); 57/1 2 sbr (*RCG XIII.27*); 63/2–64/1 dot sbr, m (*PBN 1597*, *RCG XIII.27*, *Wol 287*).

Conctratenor: labeled "Bassus" (*RCG XIII.27*); before 1/1 flat in sig until before 29/2 (err?) (*WLab*); ¢ in sig (*PBN 1597*, *SG 461*, *Wol 287*); 3/1 2 br (*RCG XIII.27*); before 5/1 no flat (*PBN 1597*, *RCG XIII.27*, *SG 461*, *Wol 287*); 5/1–2 1 br (*RCG XIII.27*); 6/1–3 mi col (*RCG XIII.27*), sbr, 2 m (*Dij*, *WLab*); 8/1–2 1 f br (*RCG XIII.27*); 8/1–9/1 no lig (*PBN 1597*, *RCG XIII.27*, *SG 461*); 9/1–10/1 lig (*Wol 287*); 10/1–3 no mi col (*PBN 1597*); 11/1–12/1 1 longa (*RCG XIII.27*); 23/1–24/1 lig (*PBN 1597*); 26/1–27/1 lig (*PBN 1597*, *RCG XIII.27*, *SG 461*, *Wol 287*); 28/1–2 dot m, sm (*PBN 1597*, *SG 461*, *Wol 287*);

28/1–2 dot m, sm (*PBN 1597*, *SG 461*, *Wol 287*), bl sbr, bl m (*RCG XIII.27*); 28/4–29/1 dot m, sm (*PBN 1597*, *SG 461*, *Wol 287*); 28/4–29/4 f sbr, e sm, d sm, c sbr (*RCG XIII.27*); 29/3–4 dot m, sm (*PBN 1597*, *SG 461*, *Wol 287*); 30/2–31/2 sbr, 2 m (*Dij*, *WLab*); 31/3–32/1 no lig (*PBN 1597*, *RCG XIII.27*, *Wol 287*); 32/1–3 1 d br (*PBN 1597*, *RCG XIII.27*), sbr, 2 m (*Dij*, *WLab*); 34/2–36/1 no lig (*PBN 1597*); 35/1–36/1 no lig (*RCG XIII.27*, *SG 461*, *Wol 287*); 39/1–2 no lig (*RCG XIII.27*); 40/2 d (*SG 461*); 41/1–2 dot m, sm (*PBN 1597*); 41/3 sig congr (*SG 461*, *Wol 287*); after 41/3 sbr rest, sig congr (*PBN 1597*); 43/1–2 lig (*PNiv*, *Wol 287*); 43/2 br err (*RCG XIII.27*); 44/1 sbr, m (*PBN 1597*); 44/1–2 lig (*PNiv*, *SG 461*, *Wol 287*); 44/2 sbr, m (*PBN 1597*); 45/1–46/1 no lig (*SG 461*); 46/1–47/1 lig (*SG 461*); before 48/1 no flat (*PBN 1597*, *RCG XIII.27*); 48/1–2 1 br (*PBN 1597*); 49/1–2 lig (*PBN 1597*); 52/1–2 lig (*PNiv*); 52/1–53/1 lig (*PBN 1597*, *RCG XIII.27*, *SG 461*, *Wol 287*); 60/1–61/1 no lig (*PNiv*, *Wol 287*); 64/2–65/1 no lig (*SG 461*, *Wol 287*).

COMMENTARY:

One of the best-known and most widely circulated of Ockeghem's works, this *rondeau cinquain* setting served as the basis of a large number of subsequent related compositions.[52] Among them are Ockeghem's *Missa Fors seulement*, published in vol. II of the present edition, no. 13, and no. 5 below.

According to convention, the superius of a three-voice chanson appears on the left of an opening, while the tenor and contra are positioned on the right. The present edition follows *Dij* with respect to the positions of the superius and the tenor. Helen Hewitt pointed out, however,[53] that the superius of *Dij*, with its 2-1 final cadence, behaves more like a typical tenor, while the tenor of *Dij*, with its 7-1 conclusion, more resembles the usual superius. Furthermore, as she indicated, three of the concordant sources reverse their positions. (See the list of VARIANT READINGS above.) It is the part printed here as the middle voice that later composers most often employed as a cantus firmus.

While *Dij* and the other sources that transmit the top voice of the present edition as the superius provide it with a full refrain text, the tenor of each one lacks all but an incipit. Another source, *PBN 1597*, a manuscript in which the voice parts are frequently more fully texted than usual, provides a complete refrain text for both upper voices. In view of this, and because the two upper voices share much melodic material, it was decided to underlay both with the full text of the refrain.

The manuscript *RCG XIII.27*, the only Italian source of the composition, transmits it not with the *Fors seulement l'actente* poem, but with a Spanish incipit, "Frayres y dexedes me." Nothing more of this poem is known, and it seems entirely unrelated to the French text.

Perhaps it should be mentioned here that the version found in the main source, *Dij*, and also in *WLab*, evidently in the same scribal hand, differs from that provided by the other sources in one small but telling detail. *Dij* and *WLab* are alone in transmitting the superius m. 3, the tenor m. 12, and other similar passages as a semibreve and two minims rather than as a dotted semibreve and two semiminims (see the list of VARIANT READINGS). Assuming that the scribe of the Chigi Codex properly represented Ockeghem's intentions, the composer himself adopted the dotted rhythm throughout his *Missa Fors seulement*. The composers of the later settings studied by Hewitt and transcribed by Picker also seem to have favored the dotted semibreve followed by two semiminims. This more prevalent reading of the figure has been incorporated into the present edition.

The style of *Fors seulement l'actente* suggests that Ockeghem composed it not very long before the compilation of its earliest sources. For the most part, each voice occupies its own discrete range, although the superius and the tenor cross once in mm. 49–54. Otherwise the tenor lies consistently higher than the superius. As in *Baisiés moy* (no. 2), this composition starts with a series of duos, and all three voices do not sound together until after the second phrase of the text has begun. Imitation is present to a limited extent, but it is sometimes concealed, as in the superius, m. 20, imitated by the tenor, m. 21, and then the contra, m. 22.

5. FORS SEULLEMENT CONTRE

MAIN SOURCE:

PBN 2245, fol. 16^{v}–17^{r}. *Okeghem*, t+tt.

OTHER SOURCES:

Cop 1848, p. 427 (no. 245). Anonymous: Fort seulement, x– –.
FB 2439, fol. LII^{v}–LIII^{r}. *J. Ockeghem*: Fors seullement lactante, txx.
PBN 1596, fol. 7^{v}–8^{r}. Anonymous: Fors seulement contre, t+tt.
SG 461, pp. 4–5. *Ockengem*: Fors solament, – – x.
RISM 1538^{9}, no. 47. Anonymous: Fors seulement, –xx.

---

[52]See *HewFS* and *PickFS*.
[53]*HewFS*, p. 94f.

MUSIC PUBLISHED:

GiesS, pp. 4–5.
GomO, Notenanhang, no. 10.
PickFS, no. 2.

TEXT[a] AND TRANSLATION:

Fors seullement contre ce qu'ay promys,
Et en[1] tous lieux seray fort[2] entremis
Et acquerray[3] une belle aliance.
J'en ay desir[4] voire dez[5] mon enfance,
Point ne vouldroye avoir nulz enemys.

Mon vouloir j'ay tout en cela soubmis
Et hors de la ja ne serai[6] transmis;[7]
Garder ny[8] veul ordre, sens
ne[9] prudence.

Fors seullement …

Je cuide avoir en terre des amys
Et que en eulx ay ma fiance remys;[10]
On doibt sçavoir que n'ay nulle doubtance,
Ou aultrement querroye ma desfiance,[11]
Car je sçeray de tout honneur desmys.[12]

Fors seullement …

Save only what I have promised,
I will be thoroughly engaged everywhere
And I shall obtain a good alliance.
Indeed, I have desired it from my childhood,
Nor do I wish to have any enemies.

To that end have I submitted my will entirely,
And from that shall I not be deflected;
Nor do I want to preserve order, sense,
or prudence.

Save only …

I believe that I have some friends in the land
And that in them I have placed my trust;
One ought to know that I have no doubt,
Or otherwise I should pursue my misgivings,
For I should be deprived of all honor.

Save only …

[a]The text in *FB 2439* is the refrain of *Fors seulement l'actente*. All variant readings are from *PBN 1596*, unless otherwise noted.

[1]Entre
[2]fors
[3]acquerre
[4]dessus
[5]de
[6]sera
[7]soubmys
[8]je
[9]et
[10]mys (*PBN 2245*).
[11]This line missing in *PBN 2245*; supplied from *PBN 1596*.
[12]remis (*PBN 2245*).

VARIANT READINGS:

Superius: 1/1 longa (*SG 461*); 5/2–6/1 lig (*FB 2439*); 6/1–2 lig (*RISM 1538⁹*); 6/2–7/1 lig (*FB 2439*); 7/1 sbr, m rest (*Cop 1848*, *FB 2439*, *SG 461*, *RISM 1538⁹*); 8/2–3 mi col (*Cop 1848*); 11/1–2 1 br (*RISM 1538⁹*); 13/1–2 lig (*FB 2439*, *RISM 1538⁹*); 13/2–14/1 no lig (*FB 2439*, *PBN 1596*, *RISM 1538⁹*); 14/2–3 no mi col (*Cop 1848*, *FB 2439*, *SG 461*, *RISM 1538⁹*);15/2 e err (*PBN 1596*); 17/1–3 b-flat, a, g (*SG 461*); 19/1–2 lig (*RISM 1538⁹*); 19/2 a (*PBN 1596*); 20/3–21/4 g m, f m, b-flat dot m, a fu, b-flat fu, a m, c sbr (*SG 461*); 20/5–21/1 mi col (*Cop 1848*); 22/1 sbr err (*PBN 2245*); 22/2–23/1 lig (*Cop 1848*); 23/1–3 no mi col (*Cop 1848*, *FB 2439*, *PBN 1596*, *SG 461*, *RISM 1538⁹*); 24/1 sig congr (*Cop 1848*, *SG 461*); 28/1–2 lig (*RISM 1538⁹*); 29/4 bl sbr err (*FB 2439*); 30/3–31/1 mi col (*Cop 1848*, *PBN 1596*); 33/1–2 2 m (*Cop 1848*); 34/2–3 lig (*Cop 1848*); 35/2–36/1 no lig (*FB 2439*, *PBN 1596*, *SG 461*, *RISM 1538⁹*); 36/3–37/1 no mi col (*FB 2439*, *SG 461*, *RISM 1538⁹*); 40/1–2 lig (*RISM 1538⁹*); 41/1–2 1 br (*RISM 1538⁹*); 42/1–2 lig (*RISM 1538⁹*); 43/1–2 1 br (*RISM 1538⁹*); 48/1–2 lig (*Cop 1848*, *FB 2439*, *RISM 1538⁹*); 49/1–3 mi col (*FB 2439*); 50/3–51/1 mi col (*Cop 1848*, *PBN 1596*); 53/2–3 mi col (*Cop 1848*, *PBN 1596*); 54/1–2 e, d (*SG 461*), lig (*RISM 1538⁹*); 55/4–56/1 mi col (*Cop 1848*, *FB 2439*, *PBN 1596*); 60/2–6 m, 4 sm (*RISM 1538⁹*); 60/3–4 1 f sm (*PBN 1596*); 60/5–6 2 sm (*FB 2439*); 62/1 a (*Cop 1848*, *FB 2439*, *PBN 1596*, *SG 461*, *RISM 1538⁹*).

Tenor: 1/1 sbr, 2 m (*FB 2439*); br, sbr, sbr (*SG 461*); 2/1–3 mi col (*Cop 1848*, *SG 461*); 3/1–2 no lig (*SG 461*); before 5/1 flat (*FB 2439*); 5/1–2 no lig (*FB 2439*, *PBN 1596*, *SG 461*, *RISM 1538⁹*); 5/2 d dot m, c sm (*FB 2439*); 8/3–9/1 mi col (*Cop 1848*,

PBN 1596); 9/2 a sm, g sm (*RISM 1538*^{9}); 15/2–3 lig (*Cop 1848*); 18/1–2 lig (*Cop 1848*, *PBN 1596*); 19/2 c sm, b-flat sm (*RISM 1538*^{9}); 20/1–2 mi col (*PBN 1596*); 21/2–22/3 e m, f dot m, e sm, d sbr-c sbr lig (*SG 461*); before 22/2 flat (*FB 2439*, *RISM 1538*^{9}); 23/1–2 mi col (*Cop 1848*, *PBN 1596*); 24/1 sig congr (*Cop 1848*, *SG 461*); 25/1–2 no mi col (*FB 2439*, *SG 461*, *RISM 1538*^{9}); 25/2 e (*Cop 1848*, *FB 2439*, *PBN 1596*, *SG 461*, *RISM 1538*^{9}); 25/4–26/1 mi col (*Cop 1848*, *PBN 1596*); 26/3–27/1 lig (*Cop 1848*); 29/1 c sm, b-flat sm (*RISM 1538*^{9}); 29/2–3 mi col (*Cop 1848*, *PBN 1596*); 30/1–2 no mi col (*Cop 1848*, *FB 2439*, *PBN 1596*, *SG 461*, *RISM 1538*^{9}); 30/3 m, sbr (*Cop 1848*, *FB 2439*, *SG 461*); 31/2–3 no mi col (*FB 2439*, *RISM 1538*^{9}); 34/3–4 mi col (*Cop 1848*, *PBN 1596*); 39/1–2 lig (*RISM 1538*^{9}); 39/2–40/1 lig (*Cop 1848*, *PBN 2245*); 40/1–2 lig (*RISM 1538*^{9}); 41/2–3 no mi col (*FB 2439*, *SG 461*, *RISM 1538*^{9}); 42/1–2 1 dot sbr (*RISM 1538*^{9}); 42/1–43/3 miss err (*Cop 1848*); 42/2 miss err (*PBN 1596*); 42/3–43/1 mi col (*PBN 1596*); 43/4–45/1 a third high err (*Cop 1848*); 44/1–2 mi col (*PBN 1596*); 44/2 a (*FB 2439*, *SG 461*, *RISM 1538*^{9}); 45/1–2 lig (*RISM 1538*^{9}); 49/2 b-flat sm, a sm (*Cop 1848*, *FB 2439*, *PBN 1596*, *SG 461*, *RISM 1538*^{9}); 50/1–2 lig (*RISM 1538*^{9}); 50/2–51/1 lig (*Cop 1848*, *FB 2439*, *PBN 1596*); 51/1–2 lig (*SG 461*, *RISM 1538*^{9}); 53/2–3 mi col (*FB 2439*, *PBN 1596*); 54/1–2 lig (*RISM 1538*^{9}); 54/1–55/1 g, f, g (*SG 461*); 54/2–55/1 no lig (*FB 2439*, *SG 461*, *RISM 1538*^{9}); 55/1–2 lig (*RISM 1538*^{9}); before 58/1 flat (*RISM 1538*^{9}); 58/2–3 no mi col (*FB 2439*, *SG 461*, *RISM 1538*^{9}); 59/2–3 g sbr (*PBN 1596*); 62/1–3 sbr, 2 sm (*RISM 1538*^{9}).

Contra: labeled "Bassus" (*FB 2439*), labeled "Basis" (*PBN 1596*); written in F4 clef at pitch (*Cop 1848*, *FB 2439*, *PBN 1596*, *SG 461*, *RISM 1538*^{9}); 1/1 longa (*SG 461*); 1/1–2/2 1 longa (*RISM 1538*^{9}); 3/1–3 mi col (*FB 2439*); 4/1–2 1 br (*RISM 1538*^{9}); 5/1–2 lig (*RISM 1538*^{9}); 6/1–2 lig (*RISM 1538*^{9}); 10/1–11/1 no lig (*Cop 1848*, *FB 2439*, *PBN 1596*); 10/2–11/1 no lig (*RISM 1538*^{9}); 12/1–2 lig (*FB 2439*, *RISM 1538*^{9}); before 13/1 flat (for b) (*FB 2439*); 13/1–2 lig (*FB 2439*, *RISM 1538*^{9}); 14/1–2 lig (*RISM 1538*^{9}); 14/1–16/1 lig (*FB 2439*; 15/1–2 1 br (*Cop 1848*); 15/1–16/1 1 dot br (*FB 2439*, *PBN 1596*, *SG 461*, *RISM 1538*^{9}); 17/1–3 mi col (*FB 2439*, *SG 461*); 17/1–3 1 g br (*RISM 1538*^{9}); 17/2–3 1 e m (*PBN 1596*); before 21/1 e-flat in signature (until 51/1) (*RISM 1538*^{9}); before 21/2 flat (for b) (*FB 2439*); 22/1–2 lig (*RISM 1538*^{9}); 22/1–23/1 lig (*FB 2439*); 23/1–3 mi col (*FB 2439*, *SG 461*); 24/1–25/2 1 longa (*Cop 1848*, *FB 2439*, *SG 461*, *RISM 1538*^{9}); 26/1–27/1 lig (*FB 2439*, *SG 461*, *RISM 1538*^{9}); 28/1–2 no lig (*Cop 1848*, *FB 2439*, *PBN 1596*, *SG 461*); 29/1–30/1 no lig (*Cop 1848*, *FB 2439*, *SG 461*, *RISM 1538*^{9}); 30/1 sig congr (*Cop 1848*); 38/1–39/1 lig (*RISM 1538*^{9}); 39/1–2 1 br (*RISM 1538*^{9}); 40/1–2 lig (*RISM 1538*^{9}); 40/1–41/2 lig (*FB 2439*, *SG 461*); before 41/1 no flat (*Cop 1848*, *FB 2439*, *SG 461*); 41/1–2 1 br (*Cop 1848*, *FB 2439*, *SG 461*, *RISM 1538*^{9}); 42/1–2 lig (*RISM 1538*^{9}); 42/1–43/1 lig (*FB 2439*, *SG 461*); 45/1–2 1 f br err (*SG 461*); 47/1–2 1 br (*Cop 1848*, *FB 2439*, *SG 461*, *RISM 1538*^{9}); 48/1 miss err (*PBN 1596*); 50/1–2 lig (*RISM 1538*^{9}); 54/2–55/1 dot sbr, m (*Cop 1848*, *PBN 1596*, *RISM 1538*^{9}), lig (*SG 461*); 56/1 e sm, d sm (*FB 2439*, *PBN 1596*, *SG 461*); 61/1–63/1 lig (*Cop 1848*, *FB 2439*); 63 miss err (*PBN 2245*).

COMMENTARY:

The middle voice of no. 4 above transposed down a twelfth serves, with a few modifications, as the contra of this composition. In *PBN 2245*, the main source of the present edition, this voice is notated at its original pitch level and designated "Canon Royal." (In the manuscript, the inscription appears in connection with the superius, but it obviously applies to the contra.) Helen Hewitt has suggested[54] that this rubric refers to Louis XII of France and that the performer of the contra must infer from it the correct transposition of a twelfth lower. It should be pointed out, however, that at the time of Ockeghem's death in early 1497, the future king was still duke of Orléans. While it was widely supposed that Louis was first in line for the throne, Charles VIII and his wife, Anne of Brittany, still entertained hopes of presenting the realm with an heir. Under the circumstances, Louis probably could not allow himself to be styled "the twelfth" in any manner without leaving himself open to a charge of high treason.

It is possible, of course, that the idea for the canon originated not with the composer, but with the scribe who wrote the manuscript. One often reads in the literature that *PBN 2245* is dated "1496." These four digits, however, appear to be part of an obsolete shelf mark, which also includes, immediately below, the number "018" (fol. 1^r), rather than a date. Instead, the manuscript may have been compiled around 1498 when Louis ascended the throne (although admittedly the coat of arms on fol. 1^v is that of Louis as duke). The other sources, with the possible exception of *PBN 1596*, date from after 1500. All of them present the contra in transposed form, at the pitch level required for performance.

Otto Gombosi expressed doubts concerning Ockeghem's authorship of *Fors seullement contre*,[55] but there is no reason why Ockeghem could not have composed a new setting of his own melody. Three sources, none of them closely related, attribute the piece to him, including one (*SG 461*) that also contains his *Fors seulement l'actente* together with a number of *Fors seulement* settings by other composers.

Because the contra is borrowed from another piece where it serves as an upper voice, it inherently contains the same degree of melodic interest as do the superius and tenor. Although it does cross above the tenor in one passage (mm. 14–17), the contra occupies a low range (*F*–*b*-flat) throughout. Equality of the voices in the texture is more completely realized in this composition than in any of Ockeghem's other three-voice secular works. Imitation does not have a structural function, but is nevertheless present to a limited extent (for example, contra and superius, mm. 21–29). The style of the cadence formulas corresponds to what was current late in Ockeghem's career.

---

[54] *HewFS*, pp. 111–12.

[55] Cf. *GomO*, Notenanhang, p. 14.

6. IL NE M'EN CHAULT

SOURCE:

WLab, fol. lxxvj^{v}–lxxvij^{r}. *J. Okeghem*, t+xx.

TEXT AND TRANSLATION:

Il ne m'en chault plus de nul ame Fors de vous qui mon cueur enflame A vous bien loyaument amer, Sans jamais vous habandonner, A tousjours estre vostre dame.	Every soul now leaves me cold Save for you, who inflame my heart To love you most loyally, Never to abandon you, To be forever your lady.
Qu'on m'en loue ne qu'on m'en blame, Quoy qu'on en disoit, homme ou femme, Ilz en ont tous beau grumeller.	Whether people praise me or blame me, Whatever people say, men or women, They all grumble in vain.
Il ne m'en chault …	Every soul …
Car pour tout m'en vous tiens et clame Que tant je vueil et que tant j'ame Plus que nul sans riens excepter, S'ilz en devoyent tous crever Et deusse perdre du corps l'ame.	For I shall cleave to you forever and proclaim How much I want you and how much I love you More than any other without exception, Even if they all must burst from it, And I should lose the soul from my body.
Il ne m'en chault …	Every soul …

ERRORS IN SOURCE:

Superius: 36/2 m err.
Tenor: (none).
Contra: (none).

COMMENTARY:

It is likely that the scribe (or scribes) who copied the earlier portions of *Dij* also wrote a substantial part of *WLab*, including the opening that contains Ockeghem's *Il ne m'en chault*. Therefore, like *Dij*, *WLab* probably dates from the mid-1470s, but at present it is not possible to know whether it was compiled earlier or later than *Dij*. On account of their contents, it is assumed that the provenance of these two manuscripts, along with the apparently related sources *Cop 291* and *Wolf 287*, is Burgundian or more probably northern French.[56]

The style of this chanson, a *rondeau cinquain* setting, is similar to that of *Fors seulement l'actente*, but perhaps slightly more archaic. Here there are no duos or even delayed entries, except for that of the superius in m. 23. The superius and tenor voices cross in mm. 27–30, as do the contra and tenor in m. 15 and again in mm. 24–25. The contra even lies above the superius momentarily in m. 30, although it mostly occupies a bass tessitura otherwise. There are few hints of imitation, aside from the tenor m. 13 and superius m. 14, and the entries following the medial cadence.

The flat in the signature at the opening of the superius and tenor is evidently a preplaced accidental intended to apply to the *b* semibreves in mm. 2 and 4 only. It no longer appears at the heads of subsequent phrases of these voices, beginning with the second half of m. 9 of the superius and with m. 14 of the tenor in the present edition.

---

[56]See M. Gutiérrez-Denhoff, "Untersuchungen zu Gestalt, Entstehung und Repertoire des Chansonniers Laborde," *Archiv für Musikwissenschaft* XLI (1984), pp. 113ff.

7. J'EN AY DUEIL

MAIN SOURCE:

LonBL 20.A.xvi, fol. 23v–24r. Anonymous: Je nay dueil, t+ttt.

OTHER SOURCES:

Br 228, fol. 15v–16r. Anonymous: Je nay dueil, tttt.
Br IV.90/Tour 94, S, fol. 26r–27(28)r; T, fol. 25r–26r. Anonymous: Je nay deul, tt.
FB 2439, fol. XXXv–XXXIr. *Ockeghem*: Jen nay deuil, xxxx.
WLab, fol. 120v–21r. Anonymous: Je nay dueil, t+xxx.
RISM 1504[3], fol. 93v–94r. *Okenghem*: Je nay deul, xxxx.

TEXT ALONE:

PBN 1719, fol. 26v–27r.
VerChasse, fol. Qiiiir.

MUSIC PUBLISHED:

AmbG V, no. 2.
LitR, pp. 46–48.
MaldP XXI, no. 9 (erroneously attributed to Pierre de la Rue).
PickCA, pp. 226–28.

TEXT PUBLISHED:

FranAP, no. CXVII (refrain only) and pp. 267–68.
Wallis, no. CCXXXIX.

TEXT AND TRANSLATION:

J'en ay[1] dueil que je ne[2] suis morte; Ne doy je bien[3] vouloir morir?[4] Dueil a voulu mon cueur[5] saisir, Qui de tous biens me desconforte.[6]	I am in sorrow that I am not dead; Am I not right in wanting to die? Sorrow has wished to seize my heart, And of all things good deprives me.
Ma douleur est plus que trop forte, Car sans avoir aucun plaisir,	My pain is more than severe, For having no pleasure whatever,
J'en ay dueil …	I am in sorrow …
Je n'ay plus riens qui[7] me conforte; D'oeil ne voy plus[8] que desplaisir.[9] Mort est le plus de[10] mon desir, Car[11] quelque chose qu'on m'aporte,	I have nothing more to comfort me; My eye sees only displeasure. Death is my greatest desire, For whatever people bring me,
J'en ay dueil …	I am in sorrow …

[1]Je nay (*LonBL 20.A.xvi, Br 228, Br IV.90, PBN 1719, WLab, RISM 1504*[3])
[2]nen (*VerChasse*).
[3]pas (*Br 228, Br IV.90, VerChasse, WLab*).
[4]bien mort choisir (*VerChasse*); mourir (*PBN 1719, WLab*).
[5]mon cueur voulu (*Br 228*).
[6]Tant que de tous biens me depporte (*VerChasse*).
[7]rien qui plus (*PBN 1719, VerChasse, WLab*).
[8]fois (*PBN 1719*).
[9]Fors quennuy et tout desplaisir (*VerChasse*).
[10]Car iay perdu tout (*VerChasse*).
[11]Et (*VerChasse*).

VARIANT READINGS:

Superius: before 1/1 flat on top-line f in sig (*Br IV.90*, *RISM 1504*^{3}); 8/1 miss err (*WLab*); 8/2–9/1 2 sbr (*Br IV.90*); 9/2–10/1 lig (*FB 2439*, *WLab*); 19/1 2 sbr (*FB 2439*); 20/2–21/1 no mi col (*Br 228*, *FB 2439*, *RISM 1504*^{3}); before 26/1 flat on top line f in sig (*FB 2439*); 29/1 miss err (*WLab*); 31/1–2 no lig (*Br 228*, *Br IV.90*, *FB 2439*, *RISM 1504*^{3}); 33/1–2 no lig (*Br 228*, *FB 2439*); 37/2-3 no mi col, 2 m (*RISM 1504*^{3}); 37/3–4 no mi col (*Br 228*, *Br IV.90*, *FB 2439*, *WLab*), 2 m (*RISM 1504*^{3}); 37/4 m err (*Br IV.90*); 43/2–44/1 no lig (*Br 228*, *Br IV.90*, *FB 2439*, *WLab*, *RISM 1504*^{3}); 44/1–2 lig (*Br 228*, *Br IV.90*, *WLab*); 48/2 d sm, c sm (*Br 228*, *FB 2439*, *RISM 1504*^{3}); 51/5 b dot m, a sm (*FB 2439*); 51/5–52/1 no lig (*Br 228*, *FB 2439*, *RISM 1504*^{3}); 52/1–2 a dot m, g sm, g sm, f sm (*FB 2439*); 53/1 sig congr (*Br IV.90*).

Contra: labeled "Supranus" (*FB 2439*), labeled "Tenor" (*RISM 1504*^{3}); before 2/1 flat (for b) (*WLab*); before 6/1 flat (*Br 228*, *FB 2439*, *RISM 1504*^{3}); 8/2–9/1 no lig (*Br 228*, *FB 2439*, *RISM 1504*^{3}); 20/1–21/1 no lig (*FB 2439*, *RISM 1504*^{3}); 25/1 no sig congr (*RISM 1504*^{3}); 28/2–3 1 b m (*Br 228*, *FB 2439*, *WLab*); 30/1–2 lig (*Br 228*, *RISM 1504*^{3}); 31/1–2 no lig (*RISM 1504*^{3}); 32/1–2 1 a m (*Br 228*, *FB 2439*, *WLab*); 34/1–35/1 no lig (*Br 228*, *FB 2439*, *RISM 1504*^{3}); 43/1–2 no lig (*Br 228*, *FB 2439*, *WLab*, *RISM 1504*^{3}); 44/1–45/1 no lig (*RISM 1504*^{3}); 51/1–2 no lig (*Br 228*, *RISM 1504*^{3}).

Tenor: labeled "Contra" (*RISM 1504*^{3}); before 1/1 flat in sig (*Tour 94*); 1/1–3/1 no lig (*Tour 94*); 2/1–3/1 no lig (*RISM 1504*^{3}); 4/1–2 no lig (*RISM 1504*^{3}); 12/1 2 sbr (*Br 228*, *FB 2439*, *Tour 94*, *RISM 1504*^{3}); 15/1–2 no lig (*FB 2439*, *Tour 94*, *RISM 1504*^{3}); 15/2–16/2 br, 2 m err (*Tour 94*); 17/2–18/1 no mi col (*Br 228*, *FB 2439*, *Tour 94*, *RISM 1504*^{3}); 18/2–19/1 no lig (*Br 228*, *FB 2439*, *Tour 94*, *RISM 1504*^{3}); 23/2 br, sbr (*Tour 94*, *RISM 1504*^{3}); 23/2–25/1 no lig (*Tour 94*, *RISM 1504*^{3}); 25/1 no sig congr (*RISM 1504*^{3}); 33/1–2 no lig (*FB 2439*, *RISM 1504*^{3}); 34/1–2 no lig (*FB 2439*, *RISM 1504*^{3}); 34/2–35/1 lig (*Br 228*); 43/1–2 no lig (*FB 2439*); 44/1–2 no lig (*FB 2439*); 48/2–3 1 g sbr (*Br 228*, *FB 2439*, *Tour 94*, *WLab*, *RISM 1504*^{3}); 53/1 sig congr (*Tour 94*).

Bassus: labeled "Bazis" (*WLab*); before 1/1 no flat in sig (*Br 228*, *FB 2439*, *WLab*); before 17/1 flat (*Br 228*, *FB 2439*, *WLab*); 19/1–2 no lig (*RISM 1504*^{3}); 20/2–21/1 no lig (*RISM 1504*^{3}); 23/2–24/1 no lig (*RISM 1504*^{3}); 25/1 no sig congr (*RISM 1504*^{3}); 26/2 e (*RISM 1504*^{3}); 30/1–2 no lig (*RISM 1504*^{3}); 31/1–2 no lig (*RISM 1504*^{3}); 36/1–2 mi col (*FB 2439*); 38/1 br, 2 sbr (*Br 228*), 2 br (*FB 2439*); 38/1–40/1 no lig (*Br 228*, *FB 2439*, *RISM 1504*^{3}); 40/1–2 no mi col (*Br 228*, *RISM 1504*^{3}); 46/1–2 no lig (*RISM 1504*^{3}); 49/1–2 no mi col (*Br 228*, *FB 2439*, *RISM 1504*^{3}); 51/2–3 no lig (*Br 228*, *RISM 1504*^{3}).

COMMENTARY:

This composition survives in two versions. In the first, no. 7, the four voices occupy typical ranges corresponding to modern soprano, alto, tenor, and bass. The second voice, sometimes called contratenor in the sources, combines with the highest part to form a structural duo. Therefore it functions as a tenor in the usual sense, despite the prevailing nomenclatures of the sources. Conversely, the part most often designated tenor in the sources and printed here as the third voice actually functions as a contratenor. The two versions of the piece, the second being no. 7a here, have the superius and its partner in the structural duo in common. They also share the bassus except that it is written to sound an octave higher in no. 7a. The nature of the texture indicates that these three voices may constitute the chanson as it was originally composed by Ockeghem.[57]

It is in the remaining voice that differences between the two versions are most explicit. In the version printed here as no. 7a, this voice, like the bassus, lies an octave higher than in no. 7. The octave displacement alters the contrapuntal context in such a way that the rules of good part writing require certain changes in the melodic material in question. Litterick proposes that the character of these changes implies that no. 7 derives from no. 7a. Be that as it may, it is the version of the composition represented by no. 7 that is attributed to Ockeghem in two sources, *FB 2439* and *RISM 1504*^{3}. No. 7a comes down in only one source, *BQ 17*, where it is anonymous.

Litterick has speculated that "Ockeghem alone was responsible for all versions of the piece,"[58] although the evidence of the sources neither proves nor disproves her suggestion. Whether he wrote just three voices of the chanson, or one or both of the versions for four voices, cannot be determined with certainty. Therefore, it was thought advisable to publish both extant versions of the work in the present edition.

The two sources that attribute no. 7 to Ockeghem plus the two Brussels manuscripts date from the several decades following his death in 1497.[59] But two other sources that transmit this version of the chanson without attribution probably were compiled during his lifetime at or near the French court. These are *WLab* and the main source adopted for the present edition, *LonBL 20.A.xvi*, which was chosen, in part, because it transmits the full text along with the music. The main body of *WLab*, as has been pointed out above, was inscribed either in Burgundy or more probably in northern France in the mid-1470s. However, the same scribe who wrote substantial portions of the manuscript *FR 2794* entered *J'en ay dueil* near the end of *WLab* some years afterwards, perhaps at the French court in the late 1490s.[60] *LonBL 20.A.xvi* is also a French court source from the 1490s.[61] The central character of these two sources suggests at least that the version of *J'en ay dueil* they preserve, with its two low contratenors, derives from Ockeghem's own milieu. *BQ 17*, on the other hand, is a Florentine manuscript of the late 1490s.[62]

---

[57]See *PickCA*, p. 62, and *LitR*, p. 31.

[58]Op. cit., p. 33.

[59]*RISM 1504*^{3}, Venice; *FB 2439*, Hapsburg-Burgundian court circle, c. 1508, cf. *Census-Cat.* I, p. 234; *Br 228*, Brussels or Malines, 1516–23, cf. *PickCA*, p. 4; *Br IV.90/Tour 94*, Bruges, dated 1511 in an initial, cf. *Census-Cat.* I, p. 97.

[60]See *RifSC*, p. 319.

[61]See *LitR*, p. 38, n. 13.

[62]Cf. *Census-Cat.* I, p. 72.

Leaving aside the question of the authenticity of the contratenors and considering the style of *J'en ay dueil* on the basis of its superius, tenor (the second voice of no. 7), and bassus, the composition may be a later work. Here the bassus achieves true equality with the other voices in terms of both rhythmic and melodic content. Each phrase flows continuously into the next in the manner often associated with Ockeghem's motets. The work begins with relatively long note values and gains momentum by means of the gradual introduction of shorter rhythmic durations—the well-known drive to the cadence typical of the composer. Everything about *J'en ay dueil* suggests that Ockeghem was at the height of his powers when he composed it.

7a. JE N'AY DEUL

SOURCE:

BQ 17, fol. 72^{v}–73^{r}. Anonymous, xxxx.

TEXT ALONE:

(See no. 7 above.)

MUSIC PUBLISHED:

LitR, pp. 43–45.
PickCA, pp. 474–76.

TEXT PUBLISHED:

(See no. 7 above.)

TEXT AND TRANSLATION:

(See no. 7 above.)

ERRORS IN SOURCE:

(None.)

COMMENTARY:

(See no. 7 above.)

8. LA DESPOURVEUE

MAIN SOURCE:

WLab, fol. lxj^{v}–lxij^{r}. Anonymous, t+xx.

OTHER SOURCES:

FBNC 176, fol. 83^{v}–85^{r}. Anonymous, tx–.
PPix, fol. 155^{v}–56^{r}. *J. Ochghen*, txx.

TEXT ALONE:

BerRoh, fol. 185^{r}–85^{v}.

TEXT PUBLISHED:

LöpL, no. 580.

TEXT AND TRANSLATION:

La despourveue et la bannye	Destitute and banished
De cil qui m'a donné ma vie,	From him who gave me my life,

Seulement par ung faulx rapport.
Ha, Fortune, n'as tu pas tort[1]
D'avoir[2] sans[3] cause ainsi pugnie!

Le povre cueur ne pensoit mye
D'estre de luy si fort[4] haye;
Puis qu'il luy plaist, elle[5] est d'acord,

La despourveue …

Elle[6] ne veult[7] plus de compaignie,
Fortune l'a[8] trop esbaye
D'avoir esté tout[9] son confort.
Plus ne desire que la mort,
Puis qu'ainsi suis par sa faulce envie.[10]

La despourveue …

Solely on account of a false tale.
Ah, Fortune, have you not erred
To have punished [me] so without reason!

This poor heart never thought
It could be so utterly hated by him;
But since that pleases him, she accepts it,

Destitute …

She wants no further company,
Fortune has so appalled her
After having been her whole consolation.
I desire nothing more but death,
Since I am like this on account of her false envy.

Destitute …

[1]grant tourt (*PPix*).
[2]lavoir (*PPix*); mavoir (*BerRoh*).
[3]la (*WLab*).
[4]en tel (*WLab*).
[5]en (*BerRoh*).
[6]Si (*BerRoh*).
[7]veuls (*BerRoh*).
[8]ma (*BerRoh*).
[9]Car ung temps fus (*BerRoh*).
[10]Sil fault quelle soit faicte oublie (*WLab*).

VARIANT READINGS:

Superius: before 1/1 e-flat in sig throughout (*FBNC 176*, *PPix*); between 3/3 and 3/4 c sm err (*FBNC 176*, *WLab*); 7/6–8/1 lig (*PPix*); 11/4 f fu, e-flat fu (*PPix*); 17/4 e-flat sm, d sm (*PPix*); 30/2 fu err (*FBNC 176*); 30/4 f (*PPix*).

Tenor: before 1/1–18/1 e-flat in sig (*FBNC 176*); 10/3–4 mi col (*PPix*); 11/2–3 2 m (*FBNC 176*); 14/1 2 perf br (*PPix*); 16/2 e err (*FBNC 176*); 23/2 b–flat (*PPix*); before 28/1 no flat in sig (*FBNC 176*).

Conctra: before 2/3 flat (*PPix*); 3/4 a sm (*FBNC 176*), a fu, g fu (*PPix*); 3/5–4/1 dot m, sm (*PPix*); before 4/1 no flat (*PPix*); 4/5 b-flat sm, c sm (*FBNC 176*); 13/3–5 mi col (*PPix*); 13/6–7 dot m, sm (*WLab*); before 15/2 no flat (*FBNC 176*); 15/2 2 m (*PPix*); 17/1 dot miss err (*FBNC 176*); 17/2–4 mi col (*PPix*); before 21/2 flat (for b) (*FBNC 176*); 30/4–31/1 no mi col (*PPix*).

COMMENTARY:

This *rondeau cinquain* setting probably represents an earlier stage in the development of Ockeghem's style at a time when he still was composing more or less in the manner of Binchois. The texture is clearly treble-dominated and the lower voices cross repeatedly. In fact, at the conclusion of the piece, which appears to take the form of an old-fashioned double-leading-tone cadence, the contra lies above the tenor. As Binchois frequently did, Ockeghem employs *tempus perfectum* and sets a courtly *rondeau* text having eight-syllable lines.

Because the main source, *WLab*, preserves a somewhat inferior version of the poem, certain changes have been made in the text published here based on the reading in *BerRoh*. Editorial flats have been applied to many of the notes *e* in the present edition, since there is an *e*-flat in the signature throughout the superius in *FBNC 176* and *PPix*. Both of these sources are believed to be of Florentine origin.

VerChasse (fol. Qiiii^{r}) transmits a poem, under the title "Rondel d'une dame amoureuse," bearing a remarkable similarity to the text that accompanies Ockeghem's music in *WLab*:

La despourueue et la banye
De cil qui me tenoit unye,
Seullement par ung faulx rapport.
Delaisse a me donner support,
Dont i'ay grant angoisse infinye.

Mon poure cueur, point ne le nye,
Oncques ne pensa villenye,
Mais veue suis sans nul deport.

La despourueue …

De mes amours ie suis pugnie
Et de tristesse fort munye;
Helas! mais cest a tresgrant tort.
Plus ne desire que la mort,
Car on me tient par felonnye.

La despourueue …

9. L'AUTRE D'ANTAN

MAIN SOURCE:

Dij, fol. xvij^{v}–xviij^{r} (20^{v}–21^{r}). Anonymous, t+x–.

OTHER SOURCES:

BQ 16, fol. lxxx^{v}–lxxxi^{r} (93^{v}–94^{r}). Anonymous: La trentanta, xxx.
NHMel, fol. 25^{v}–26^{r}. *Jo. okeghem*: Laultre dantan, t+tx.
PCord, fol. 24^{v}–25^{r}. Anonymous, t+xx.
PPix, fol. 32^{v}–33^{r}. Anonymous: Laultre dantan, t+xx.
RCas 2856, 52^{v}–53^{r} (44^{v}–45^{r}). *Okeghem*: Lauter dantan, xxx.

MUSIC PUBLISHED:

AmbG V, no. 3.
DrozT, no. 17.
PerkMC, no. 20.

TEXT AND TRANSLATION:

L'autre d'antan l'autrier passa
Et en passant me transperça[1]
D'un regard forgé a Millan,
Qui m'a mis en l'arriere ban,[2]
Tant mauvais brassin me brassa.[3]

Par tel façon me fricassa
Que de ses gaiges me cassa,
Mais, par Dieu, elle fist son dan!

L'autre d'antan …

Puis apres nostre amour cessa,
Car oncques puis qu'elle dansa,
L'autre d'antan, l'autre
   d'antan,
Je n'eus ne bon jour ne
   bon an,
Tant de mal en moy amassa.[4]

L'autre d'antan …

Someone of yesteryear did pass yesterday
And in passing passed me through
With a glance forged in Milan,
Which knocked me into the back of the pack,
In so bad a brew did she stir me.

In such a fashion did she cook me
That she dismissed me from her service,
Oh, by God, she did her damage!

Someone of yesteryear …

Then after our love did cease,
Forever since has she danced on,
Someone of yesteryear,
   Someone of yesteryear,
I have had not one good day
   nor one good year,
So much ill has been heaped upon me.

Someone of yesteryear …

[1] trespassa (*Dij*).
[2] *PCord* does not transmit this line.
[3] *NHMel*, *PCord*, and *PPix* add a repetition of the opening line to the refrain as given here.
[4] The reading in *PPix* lacks this line and the two preceding it; *NHMel* fails to transmit the entire five-line strophe.

VARIANT READINGS:

Superius: before 1/1 ȸ3 in sig (*BQ 16*, *NHMel*), O3 in sig (*PCord*, *PPix*), ₵3 in sig (*RCas 2856*); 4/1–5/1 no col (*NHMel*); 4/1–5/2 no col (*BQ 16*, *PCord*, *PPix*, *RCas 2856*); 10/1–11/1 lig (*PCord*); 11/1–2 1 perf br (*BQ 16*, *Dij*); 15/1–16/2 col (*BQ 16*, *NHMel*, *PCord*, *PPix*, *RCas 2856*); 15/2–16/1 lig (*BQ 16*, *NHMel*, *PCord*, *PPix*, *RCas 2856*); 17/1 sig congr (*PCord*); 19/1–2 1 bl longa (*RCas 2856*); 20/1–3 g bl dot sbr, f bl m (*RCas 2856*); 21/1 bl (imperf) br err (*Dij*); 25/1–2 lig (*NHMel*, *PCord*); 25/1 d (*RCas 2856*); 29/1–2 1 dot sbr (*BQ 16*, *NHMel*, *PCord*, *PPix*, *RCas 2856*); 31/2 a dot sbr, g m (*BQ 16*, *NHMel*, *PCord*, *PPix*, *RCas 2856*); 35/1–2 lig (*BQ 16*, *NHMel*, *PPix*, *RCas 2856*); 35/1–36/1 lig (*PCord*); 35/2 a dot sbr, g m (*NHMel*, *RCas 2856*).

Tenor: before 1/1 ȸ3 in sig (*BQ 16*, *NHMel*), O3 in sig (*PCord*, *PPix*), ₵3 in sig (*RCas 2856*); 4/1–5/2 lig (*BQ 16*, *NHMel*, *PCord*, *PPix*); 9/1–2 1 perf br (*BQ 16*, *NHMel*, *PCord*, *PPix*, *RCas 2856*); 12/1–2 lig (*PCord*); 14/1 imperf br, sbr rest (*RCas 2856*); 15/1–2 lig (*RCas 2856*); 15/1–16/1 lig (*PCord*); 17/1 no col (*BQ 16*, *NHMel*, *PCord*, *PPix*, *RCas 2856*); 18/1–19/1 lig (*PCord*, *RCas 2856*); 19/1 perf br (*PCord*, *RCas 2856*); 21/1–2 lig (*RCas 2856*); 22/1–2 lig (*BQ 16*, *NHMel*, *RCas 2856*); 26/1–2 lig (*PCord*); 26/2 col (*NHMel*, *RCas 2856*); 27/1–2 1 perf br (*BQ 16*); 28/1 2 sbr (*PCord*); 31/1–2 1 perf br (*BQ 16*); 33/1–2 lig (*PCord*); 33/1–35/4 c imperf br, d sbr, c bl sbr-a bl sbr lig, g bl br, d bl sbr-g bl sbr lig (*RCas 2856*); 33/2–4 dot sbr, 2 sm (*BQ 16*, *NHMel*, *PCord*, *PPix*); 34/2–35/2 g dot sbr, f m (*BQ 16*, *NHMel*, *PCord*, *PPix*); 35/4 g (*BQ 16*, *NHMel*, *PCord*, *PPix*); 36/2–37/1 no lig (*RCas 2856*).

Conctratenor: before 1/1 ȸ3 in sig (*NHMel*), O3 in sig (*PCord*, *PPix*); 25/1–26/1 no lig (*PCord*); 35/1–2 lig (*NHMel*, *PCord*); *BQ 16* and *RCas 2856* transmit the following substantially different contra voices:

BQ 16

RCas 2856

COMMENTARY:

The sources of this composition collectively report four different mensuration signs. (See the list of VARIANT READINGS.) Taken literally, these various signs suggest a broad range of possible tempi for a performance of the piece. But in view of the well-known ambiguity of fifteenth-century mensural practice, it is likely that one of no more than two possible interpretations was intended.

Strictly speaking, the addition of a virgule to the basic sign should denote a duple proportion. In practice, however, the virgule appears to signify a quickening of the tempo by perhaps one third of the *integer valor* rather than a doubling. The significance of the virgule pales, or perhaps even disappears, when one considers that several chansons by Ockeghem and other composers survive with a C in one source and a ¢ in another. (See, for example, no. 11 below.) Therefore, assuming the speed of the semibreve in *integer valor* to be equal to approximately M.M. 72, it may be that the ¢ portion of the sign in *RCas 2856* indicates the same tempo (◇ = c. 72) as the C of *Dij*, or else one a third faster (◇ = c. 96). This is also true of the relationship between the O (*PCord* and *PPix*) and Φ (*BQ 16* and *NHMel*); here again the *integer valor* is ◇ = c. 72, and the virgule might have either no effect or else call for an increase of the tempo to ◇ = c. 96. The numeral 3 following the sign in all the sources could mean either a further triple proportion or three in the time of two (*proportio sesquialtera*), the latter interpretation being the more probable. *Proportio sesquialtera* (3:2) would then render the tempo ◇ = c. 108 in all mensurations, or else, in ¢3 and Φ3, a one-third faster ◇ = c. 144.

Alternatively, the signs ¢3 and Φ3 could be taken as standing for *proportio sesquialtera diminuta* (2:1 × 3:2 = 3:1), in effect *proportio tripla*, which results in the even faster tempo ◇ = c. 216. This, it will be seen, is equivalent to regarding either C3 (*Dij*) or O3 (*PCord* and *PPix*) as the triple proportion of C or O, where the *integer valor* is ◇ = c. 72, resulting again in the tempo ◇ = c. 216. This last tempo is perhaps the most appropriate of all those discussed above.

Although the explanation of the mensuration signs suggested here may prove satisfactory in practical terms, Johannes Tinctoris registered a theoretical objection to the usage O3 as found in *PCord* and *PPix*. He evidently considered the 3 too ambiguous, inasmuch as it could be construed as either *proportio sesquialtera* or *proportio tripla*, and he accused Ockeghem of having committed an "inexcusable error."[63] Tinctoris recommends *proportio sesquialtera* with a virgule; that is, it appears, the mensuration sign found in *BQ 16* and *NHMel*. Perkins has suggested that the emendation goes back to Tinctoris and that Gafori, who lived in Naples beginning in 1478, may have adopted it from him.[64] But it must be remembered that these two theorists were concerned more with the theoretically correct way of notating the mensuration than with practical results. From the practical point of view, all the different signs found in the various sources yield the same approximate tempo, ◇ = c. 216.

On account of the mensuration with its implied lively tempo, the style of *L'autre d'antan* does not lend itself easily to comparison with that of Ockeghem's other secular works. But his authorship can hardly be doubted, if only because of the way each phrase flows into the next without interruption. Since none of the sources transmits *signa congruentiae* for the medial cadence, one cannot even be certain where the first section of the refrain should conclude. For the purposes of the present edition, it was decided that the two lower voices should continue beyond the conclusion of the phrase in the superius, m. 17, to their cadence point in m. 19. When the first line of the text returns at the end of the refrain, something that does not usually occur in a *rondeau*, Ockeghem uses the music of the opening again but skillfully blends the beginning of the repeat (m. 31) with the end of the previous phrase.

The double-leading-tone final cadence and the frequent crossing of the contra above the tenor are somewhat old-fashioned. Nevertheless, the presence of clear-cut rhythmic patterns, a superius-tenor framework, and imitation identifies *L'autre d'antan* as a mature work. It was, of course, known to Tinctoris when he wrote his *Proportionale*, which is thought to date from 1473–74, and it may have been composed not long before then.

Howard Garey has pointed out that in numerous fifteenth-century chansons the meaning of the additional strophe appears to bring about an alteration of the sense of the subsequent refrain.[65] The text of Ockeghem's *Quant de vous seul* (no. 17 below) provides a convenient illustration of what Garey perceives: At the conclusion of the long strophe, the poem reads (in translation), "For I know well that I must be alone, deprived of all good things"; whereupon the final refrain begins, "When I lose sight of you alone, by whom I am held so dear," extending the meaning across the interval between the strophe and the refrain. Now, it would seem, according to the altered sense of the final refrain, that there ought to be a full stop after the word "dear," rather than the (editorial) comma implied by the original sense of the refrain: "When I lose sight of you alone, by whom I am held so dear, my pain then assails me ..."

On the basis of his study of similar poems associated with music in *NHMel* (not a source of *Quant de vous seul*), Garey concludes that "the quest of the one best or uniquely authentic reading of a poem could be a vain one, that a poet of that game-loving epoch was capable of devising a poem susceptible of anywhere from one to a dozen different readings." Therefore, Garey proposes ending a musical performance of a final refrain at the cadence nearest to where the revised sense of the poem seems to demand a full stop. In similar circumstances, such curtailments might also be applied to medial refrains. Howard Mayer Brown has brought forward additional evidence in support of Garey's suggestion.[66] These observations have led both Garey and Brown to propose various hypothetical ways of performing *L'autre d'antan* with shortened refrains.

---

[63]See *Proportionale musices* in *CouS* IV, p. 156.

[64]Cf. *PerkMC* II, p. 266, *MillerFG*, pp. 159–60, and *YoungG*, p. 173.

[65]See his "Can a Rondeau with a One-Line Refrain Be Sung?," *Ars Lyrica* II (1983), pp. 9–21.

[66]See "A Rondeau with a One-Line Refrain Can Be Sung," *Ars Lyrica* III (1986), pp. 27–35.

10. LES DESLÉAULX

MAIN SOURCE:

Dij, fol. viiij^{v}–x^{r} (12^{v}–13^{r}). *Okeghem*, t+xx.

OTHER SOURCE:

WLab, fol. 105^{v}–06^{r}. Anonymous: Les desloyaulx, t+xx.

TEXT ALONE:

BerRoh, fol. 79^{r}.
PBN 1719, fol. 61^{v} and 132^{r}.
VerJard, fol. Cxiiii^{r}–Cxiiii^{v}.

MUSIC PUBLISHED:

DrozT, no. 9.
HaarCM, pp. 141–42.

TEXT PUBLISHED:

DrozJP, no. 489.
LöpL, no. 121.

TEXT AND TRANSLATION:

Les desléaulx ont la saison
Et des bons nessun[1] ne tient compte,
Mais Bon Droit de trop se mesconte
De souffrir si grant[2] desraison.

Je ne sçais par quel achoison
Fortune ainsi[3] hault les[4] seurmonte;[5]

Les desléaulx …

Nul ne[6] doit parler sans moison[7]
De paour d'avoir reprouche ou[8] honte;
Pour ce me[9] tais, mais fin de compte
Tout[10] va sans rime et sans[11] raison.

Les desléaulx …

The disloyal are in season
And no one takes account of the good,
But Right has seriously miscalculated
To allow such great unreason.

I know not for what cause
Fortune thus raises them so high;

The disloyal …

No one should speak without measure
For fear of having reproach or shame;
Therefore I keep silent, but in the end
Everything is without rhyme or reason.

The disloyal …

[1]nully (*PBN 1719*, *VerJard*, *WLab*).
[2]telle (*PBN 1719*, *VerJard*).
[3]a point si (*BerRoh*).
[4]missing (*BerRoh*).
[5]Fortune a tort si hault monte (*VerJard*); monte (*BerRoh*, *PBN 1719*, *WLab*).
[6]Chascun (*VerJard*).
[7]De nommer prince ne maison (*PBN 1719*, *WLab*).
[8]Ce me seroit reproche et (*PBN 1719*, *WLab*); et (*VerJard*).
[9]Pourtant men (*PBN 1719*, *WLab*).
[10]Quant tout (*BerRoh*).
[11]missing (*BerRoh*, *VerJard*).

VARIANT READINGS (all from *WLab*):

Superius: 2/3–4 dot m, sm; 3/2–3 no mi col; 4/2 3; 4/3–4 no mi col; 13/1 no sig congr; 19/4–20/1 no mi col; 29/2–3 no mi col.

Tenor: before 1/1 C in sig; 3/1–2 no mi col; 3/1–4/2 a dot sbr, b sm, c sm, d m, b sbr; 13/1 no sig congr; 14/4–15/1 no mi col; 15/3–4 no mi col; 18/2–3 dot m, sm; 19/1–2 no mi col; 25/3–5 dot m, 2 fu.

Conctratenor: 2/4–5 1 d m; 4/2–3 sbr rest, c m; 13/1 no sig congr; 22/3–24/1 no mi col; 29/2–3 mi col; 30/3 m err.

COMMENTARY:

The texture of this *rondeau quatrain* setting does not seem quite as treble-dominated as, for example, that of *La despourveue*, no. 8. Nor can it be said without reservation that Ockeghem conceived it as a superius-tenor duo with accompanying contra. For one thing, the melody of the tenor is rather less vocal in character than that of the superius, as may be seen especially in mm. 17-18, where it leaps upward a diminished fifth. Also, neither source provides the tenor with more than the incipit of the text.

On the other hand, the counterpoint of the upper voices is self-contained with appropriate two-voice cadences throughout, crossing briefly only once, in mm. 22–24. The contra, however, begins above the tenor and crosses it again in mm. 6–13, 25–26, and 29. That the contra serves primarily as harmonic filler rather than as a fully independent bass voice is most apparent in the fauxbourdon-like approach to the medial cadence (mm. 11–13), where it moves in parallel thirds above the tenor.

Another early trait is the octave leap of the contra at the cadence in m. 6 and again at the final cadence. The presence of the mensuration sign C in both surviving sources may also point to an earlier date of composition. However, the imitation involving all three voices at the beginning of the second phrase and the less conspicuous imitation in mm. 13, 21, and 26 give the composition a somewhat more modern aspect. All things considered, *Les desléaulx* appears to represent a transitional stage between Ockeghem's earlier style and his mature style, as found, for example, in *Fors seulement l'actente* (no. 4).

11. MA BOUCHE RIT

MAIN SOURCE:

PNiv, fol. lij^{v}–liiij^{r}. *Okeghem*, t+xx.

OTHER SOURCES:

BerGlo, Discantus, fol. L vij^{v}; T., fol. M iij^{v}; Ct., fol. M viij^{r}. Anonymous: H., ---.
Cop 1848, p. 401. Anonymous: (*prima pars* only), ---.
Dij, fol. iiij^{v}–vj^{r} (9^{v}–10*bis*^{r}). Anonymous, t+x–.
FBNC 176, fol. 32^{v}–34^{r}. *Ocheghem*, xxx.
FR 2356, fol. 28^{v}–29^{r} (34^{v}–35^{r}). Anonymous: Ma boncherit, t–x.
MunSche, fol. 62^{v}–64^{r}. *Ockegheim*, ---.
NHMel, fol. 38^{v}–40^{r}. *Okeghem*: Ma bouce rit, txx.
PBN 4379, fol. 4^{v}–6^{r} (e5^{v}–e7^{r}). Anonymous: Ma bouce rit, t+xx.
PCord, fol. 42^{v}–44^{r}. Anonymous, t+tx.
PPix, fol. 30^{v}–32^{r}. Anonymous, txx.
RCas 2856, fol. 61^{v}–63^{r} (51^{v}–53^{r}). *Okeghem*: Ma bouce fijt, xxx.
RCG XIII.27, fol. 76^{v}–77^{r} (69^{v}–70^{r}). Anonymous: Ma boche rit, x––.
WLab, fol. xxxij^{v}–xxxiiij^{r}. Anonymous, t+xx.
Wol 287, fol. 29^{v}–31^{r}. Anonymous, t+xx.
RISM 1501, fol. 59^{v}–60^{r}. *Okenhem*, xxx.
RISM 1538^{9}, no. 86. Anonymous: Male bouche rit, –x–.

TEXT ALONE:

BerRoh, fol. 83^{v}–84^{r}.
PBN 1719, fol. 61^{r} and 132^{r}.
VerJard, fol. lxi^{r} (as a *rondeau cinquain*) and lxxi^{v}.

MUSIC PUBLISHED:

DiseM, pp. 29–31.
DrozT, no. 5.

EitWL, suppl., no. 8.
GomO, Notenanhang, no. 5.
HAM I, no. 75.
HewO, no. 54.
PerkMC, no. 30.
RingGL, no. 267.
WolfS, no. 14.

TEXT PUBLISHED:

DrozJP, nos. 10 and 103.
LöpL, no. 142.

TEXT[a] AND TRANSLATION:

Ma bouche rit et ma pensée pleure,
Mon oeil s'esjoye[1] et mon
cueur[2] mauldit l'eure
Qu'il eut le bien qui sa
santé deschasse
Et le plaisir que la mort me[3] pourchasse[4]
Sans resconfort qui m'aide[5] ne sequeure.

Ha,[6] cuer pervers, faulsaire[7] et mensonger,
Dictes comment avez osé songer
Que de[8] faulser ce que m'avez promis.

Puis qu'en ce point vous vous[9] voulez venger,
Pensez bien tost de ma vie abreger;
Vivre ne puis au point ou[10]
m'avez mis.

Vostre rigueur[11] veult doncques que je meure,
Mais Pitié[12] veult[13] que vivant je demeure;
Ainsi meurs vif et en vivant trespasse,
Mais pour celer le mal qui ne se passe
Et pour couvrir le dueil ou je labeure,

Ma bouche rit …

My mouth laughs, and my thoughts weep,
My eye looks merry, and my
heart curses the hour
When it acquired the benefit
that dissipates its health
And the pleasure for which death pursues me
Without comfort to aid or console me.

Ah, perverse, false, and deceitful heart,
Tell me how you dared to dream
Of lying about what you promised me.

Since in that respect you wish to avenge yourself,
Think soon of shortening my life;
I cannot live in the situation in which
you have placed me.

Your hardness, then, wills that I die,
But Pity wishes that I remain alive;
Thus alive I die and in living perish,
But to hide the pain that will not go away
And to conceal the sorrow under which I labor,

My mouth laughs …

[a]The readings of the text transmitted by *FR 2356* and, to a somewhat lesser extent, by *PPix* are notably corrupt.

[1]sejouit (*Wol 287*).
[2]brief (*Wol 287*).
[3]luy (*PBN 1719*, *PCord*, *Wol 287*, *VerJard*).
[4]entire line missing (*PBN 4379*).
[5]laide (*Wol 287*).
[6]O (*FR 2356*, *PPix*).
[7]faulx yeux (*PPix*).
[8]Vouloir (*BerRoh*); De ainsi (*PCord*).
[9]second "vous" missing (*Wol 287*).
[10]que (*WLab*).
[11]pitie (*BerRoh*, *Dij*, *PBN 1719*, *PBN 4379*, *VerJard*, *WLab*, *Wol 287*).
[12]rigueur (*BerRoh*, *Dij*, *PBN 1719*, *PBN 4379*, *VerJard*, *WLab*, *Wol 287*).
[13]missing (*Dij*).

VARIANT READINGS:

Superius: before 1/1 C2 in sig (*BerGlo*), ¢ in sig (*PBN 4379*, *RISM 1501*, *RISM 1538^9*); 2/1–2 1 br (*RCas 2856*); 3/1–2 1 br (*RCG XIII.27*); 5/1–2 c dot sbr, b m (*BerGlo*), 1 br (*RISM 1538^9*); 7/2–8/1 lig (*WLab*); 8/1–2 lig (*BerGlo*, *MunSche*, *PCord*, *Wol 287*, *RISM 1538^9*); 9/2–10/1 lig (*Cop 1848*, *PCord*, *RCas 2856*); 10/1–2 lig (*RISM 1538^9*); 10/2–11/1 lig (*PCord*); 12/2–13/1 1 br (*BerGlo*, *RCas 2856*, *RISM 1538^9*); 13/2 br err (*BerGlo*); 14/1–2 lig (*RCas 2856*, *RISM 1538^9*); 15/1 sbr, m (*BerGlo*); 16/1–2 lig (*MunSche*, *PCord*, *RISM 1538^9*); 16/2 miss err (*Wol 287*); 18/2–19/1 lig (*WLab*); 19/2–20/1 sbr rest err (*PNiv*); 22/2–3 mi col (*BerGlo*, *Cop 1848*, *FBNC 176*, *FR 2356*, *MunSche*, *NHMel*, *PBN 4379*, *PPix*, *RCG XIII.27*, *WLab*, *Wol 287*), 2 m (*RISM 1501*); 23/1 sm err (*NHMel*); 23/1–3 miss err (*MunSche*); 24/2–3 no lig (*RCas 2856*, *RISM 1501*); 31/1–32/2 d m, c sm, b sm, a sbr, g m, f m (*RISM 1538^9*); 31/3 m err (*Cop 1848*); 31/2–32/2 bl sbr, bl m, m (*RCG XIII.27*); 31/3–32/2 dot m, sm, m (*RISM 1501*); 32/1–2 1 g m (*FBNC 176*, *FR 2356*, *PPix*); 34/2–3 dot m, sm (*Dij*); 35/1–2 no mi col (*BerGlo*, *FBNC 176*, *FR 2356*, *NHMel*, *PPix*, *RCas 2856*, *WLab*, *RISM 1501*, *RISM 1538^9*); 38/1 miss err (*PNiv*); 39/1–2 bl sbr, bl m (*MunSche*); 41/1–2 mi col (*BerGlo*, *Cop 1848*, *Dij*, *FBNC 176*, *FR 2356*, *MunSche*, *NHMel*, *PBN 4379*, *PCord*, *PPix*, *RCG XIII.27*, *WLab*, *Wol 287*); 41/2 c fu, b fu (*RISM 1538^9*); before 42/1 sharp (*NHMel*); 42/3–43/2 bl sbr, 2 fu err (*MunSche*); 43/1–2 1 g m (*FBNC 176*, *FR 2356*, *PPix*, *RCG XIII.27*); 46/1 sig congr (*BerGlo*); before 47/1 C in sig (*Dij*, *FBNC 176*, *NHMel*, *PPix*, *RCas 2856*), ¢ in sig (*PBN 4379*, *WLab*); 50/1–2 1 br (*RCas 2856*, *RISM 1538^9*); 51/1–2 1 br (*BerGlo*, *RCas 2856*, *RISM 1538^9*); 52/1–2 lig (*RISM 1538^9*); 53/2–3 mi col (*BerGlo*, *FBNC 176*, *FR 2356*, *MunSche*, *NHMel*, *PCord*, *PPix*, *RCas 2856*, *RCG XIII.27*, *Wol 287*); 55/1–56/1 1 dot br (*FR 2356*, *PPix*); 55/1–56/2 1 longa (*RISM 1538^9*); 56/1 miss err(?) (*FBNC 176*, *RCG XIII.27*); 58/1–2 1 br (*MunSche*, *RISM 1538^9*); 59/1–2 lig (*MunSche*, *RCas 2856*, *RISM 1538^9*); 60/1–2 lig (*MunSche*, *RCas 2856*, *RISM 1538^9*); 60/2–61/1 lig (*NHMel*, *PNiv*); 61/1–2 no lig (*NHMel*, *PNiv*, *RCas 2856*, *RCG XIII.27*); 64/1–2 lig (*MunSche*, *RISM 1538^9*); 64/2 sbr rest (*PPix*, *RCG XIII.27*); 64/2–65/1 1 br rest (*FBNC 176*); 65/2 2 sbr (*RCG XIII.27*, *WLab*); 65/2–67/1 1 longa (*RISM 1538^9*); 66/1–67/1 1 br (*RCG XIII.27*); 68/2–3 dot m, sm (*BerGlo*, *PCord*, *RCas 2856*, *RISM 1501*, *RISM 1538^9*), bl sbr, bl m (*Dij*, *FBNC 176*, *FR 2356*, *MunSche*, *NHMel*, *PPix*, *RCG XIII.27*, *WLab*, *Wol 287*, *RISM 1538^9*); after 68/5 repeat sign (*MunSche*); before 69/1 sharp (*NHMel*); 69/1 no sig congr (*BerGlo*, *FBNC 176*, *RCG XIII.27*, *WLab*, *RISM 1501*, *RISM 1538^9*); 69/1–2 mi col (*Wol 287*); after 69/2 repeat sign (*NHMel*); 69/4–70/2 miss err (*Wol 287*); 70/1–2 1 b m (*PBN 4379*); 70/3 sm err (*MunSche*); 71/2–3 a dot m, g sm, g sm, f sm (*PCord*); 72/1 sig congr (*BerGlo*); after 72/1 repeat sign (*PBN 4379*).

Tenor: before 1/1 flat in sig (*WLab*), C2 in sig (*BerGlo*), ¢ in sig (*PBN 4379*, *RISM 1501*, *RISM 1538^9*); 4/1–2 1 br (*RCas 2856*); 5/1–2 1 br (*MunSche*); 7/2–4 a sm, b sm, c m, b sm, a sm (*RISM 1538^9*); 7/3–4 no mi col (*Cop 1848*, *Dij*, *FR 2356*, *PBN 4379*, *PCord*, *RCas 2856*, *RISM 1501*); 6/1–2 mi col (*BerGlo*, *FBNC 176*, *MunSche*, *PPix*, *RCG XIII.27*, *WLab*, *Wol 287*); 7/1–2 dot m, sm (*Cop 1848*), bl sbr, bl m (*NHMel*); 10/2–3 1 c m (*BerGlo*, *Cop 1848*, *Dij*, *FBNC 176*, *FR 2356*, *MunSche*, *NHMel*, *PCord*, *PPix*, *RCas 2856*, *RCG XIII.27*, *WLab*, *Wol 287*, *RISM 1501*, *RISM 1538^9*); 11/1–2 1 br (*MunSche*, *NHMel*, *Wol 287*, *RISM 1538^9*); 11/2–12/1 lig (*Cop 1848*); 13/2–14/1 lig (*NHMel*, *WLab*); 14/1–2 no lig (*BerGlo*, *Cop 1848*, *Dij*, *FBNC 176*, *MunSche*, *NHMel*, *PBN 4379*, *PCord*, *PPix*, *RCas 2856*, *RCG XIII.27*, *WLab*, *Wol 287*, *RISM 1501*); 16/1–2 no lig (*PBN 4379*, *RCas 2856*, *RCG XIII.27*, *WLab*, *RISM 1501*); 20/2–21/1 lig (*NHMel*); 22/1–2 no mi col (*Cop 1848*, *Dij*, *FR 2356*, *PCord*, *PPix*, *RCas 2856*, *RISM 1501*, *RISM 1538^9*); 22/3–23/1 lig (*NHMel*); 23/1–2 no mi col (*Cop 1848*, *Dij*, *FR 2356*, *PBN 4379*, *PCord*, *RCas 2856*, *RISM 1501*, *RISM 1538^9*); 23/3–24/1 lig (*BerGlo*, *FR 2356*, *MunSche*, *NHMel*); 24/1–2 lig (*RISM 1538^9*); 25/2–26/1 lig (*BerGlo*, *NHMel*); 27/2–28/1 no lig (*Dij*, *PBN 4379*, *RCas 2856*, *RCG XIII.27*, *WLab*, *Wol 287*, *RISM 1501*, *RISM 1538^9*); 28/1 d err (*Cop 1848*); 28/1–2 lig (*RISM 1538^9*); 29/3–30/1 lig(*NHMel*); 31/1–2 lig (*NHMel*, *RISM 1538^9*); 33/3 d err (*Cop 1848*); 34/3–35/1 no lig (*BerGlo*, *Cop 1848*, *Dij*, *FBNC 176*, *FR 2356*, *MunSche*, *PBN 4379*, *PCord*, *PPix*, *RCas 2856*, *RCG XIII.27*, *WLab*, *Wol 287*, *RISM 1501*, *RISM 1538^9*); 36/2 a bl sbr, g fu, f fu (*RCG XIII.27*), a dot m, g sm (*Cop 1848*, *PBN 4379*), a dot m, g fu, f fu (*BerGlo*, *FBNC 176*, *FR 2356*, *MunSche*, *NHMel*, *PCord*, *PPix*, *WLab*, *Wol 287*, *RISM 1501*, *RISM 1538^9*), a dot m, g sm, f sm err (*Dij*); 37/1–2 1 e sbr (*BerGlo*, *Cop 1848*, *Dij*, *FBNC 176*, *FR 2356*, *MunSche*, *NHMel*, *PBN 4379*, *PCord*, *PPix*, *RCas 2856*, *RCG XIII.27*, *WLab*, *Wol 287*, *RISM 1501*, *RISM 1538^9*); 38/1 m err (*MunSche*); 38/1–2 lig (*NHMel*, *RCG XIII.27*, *WLab*, *RISM 1538^9*); 39/3–4 mi col (*Cop 1848*, *FBNC 176*, *MunSche*, *NHMel*, *PBN 4379*, *PCord*, *PPix*, *RCG XIII.27*, *Wol 287*), 2 m (*WLab*); 42/1–2 lig (*NHMel*, *RISM 1538^9*); 42/2–43/1 lig (*FR 2356*, *PBN 4379*); 43/1 m rest, f m (*WLab*); 45/1–2 g, e (*MunSche*); 45/3 miss err (*Cop 1848*); 46/1 sig congr (*BerGlo*); before 47/1 C in sig (*FBNC 176*, *NHMel*, *PPix*, *RCas 2856*), ¢ in sig (*PBN 4379*, *WLab*); before 47/1–before 53/1 no flat in sig (*WLab*); 47/1–48/2 lig (*NHMel*); 48/1–2 1 br (*MunSche*, *NHMel*, *RCas 2856*, *RISM 1538^9*); 49/2 c sm, b sm (*RISM 1501*); 50/1–2 1 br (*MunSche*, *NHMel*, *RISM 1538^9*); 52/1–2 lig (*NHMel*); 52/2–3 mi col (*Dij*, *FBNC 176*, *FR 2356*, *MunSche*, *PPix*, *RCG XIII.27*, *Wol 287*); 52/3 b fu, a fu (*BerGlo*); 54/1 miss err(?) (*FBNC 176*, *RCG XIII.27*); 55/1–2 a m, 2 a sbr (*BerGlo)*; 55/2–57/1 1 longa (*NHMel*, *RISM 1538^9*); 55/2–57/2 lig (*NHMel*); 56/1–57/1 1 br (*BerGlo*); 56/1–57/2 lig (*BerGlo*); 58/1–59/1 lig (*BerGlo*, *MunSche*, *NHMel*, *RCas 2856*); 59/1–2 lig (*RISM 1538^9*); 59/2–60/1 (*MunSche*, *NHMel*, *PCord*, *RCas 2856*); 60/1–2 lig (*RISM 1538^9*); 60/2–61/1 lig (*BerGlo*, *MunSche*, *NHMel*, *PBN 4379*, *PCord*); 61/1–2 lig (*RISM 1538^9*); before 62/3–before 68/3 no flat in sig (*WLab*); 62/4–63/1 mi col (*RCG XIII.27*), 2 m (*FR 2356*), sbr, m err (*MunSche*), miss err (*Wol 287*); 64/1–2 no mi col (*Dij*, *RCas 2856*, *RCG XIII.27*, *RISM 1501*, *RISM 1538^9*); 2 m (*FR 2356*); 64/3–65/1 lig (*MunSche*, *NHMel*, *PCord*); 66/1 miss err (*FR 2356*); 67/1–2 lig (*RISM 1538^9*); 69/1 no sig congr (*BerGlo*, *Dij*, *FR 2356*, *RCG XIII.27*, *WLab*, *RISM 1501*, *RISM 1538^9*); after 69/1 repeat sign (*MunSche*, *NHMel*, *WLab*); 69/1–2 1 br (*RCG XIII.27*); 69/1–70/1 1 dot br (*RISM 1538^9*); 69/2–70/1 1 br (*BerGlo*, *WLab*); 72/1 sig congr (*BerGlo*); after 72/1 repeat sign (*PBN 4379*).

Contra: labeled "bassus" (*RCas 2856*, *RCG XIII.27*); before

1/1 flat in sig (*WLab*), ¢ in sig (*BerGlo, PBN 4379, RISM 1501, RISM 1538*^{9}), no C in sig (*Dij, MunSche*); 1/1–2 1 br (*Cop 1848, FR 2356, MunSche, NHMel, PBN 4379, PCord, RCas 2856, RCG XIII.27, WLab*); 1/1–2/1 1 dot br (*RISM 1538*^{9}); 2/1–2 lig (*NHMel, PBN 4379*); 3/2–3 mi col (*FBNC 176, NHMel, PCord, PPix, RCG XIII.27, Wol 287*); 4/1–5/1 sbr, br, m (*Dij*); 6/2–8/2 e m, f m, m rest, c m, e sbr–d sbr lig (*BerGlo*); 8/1–2 1 d m (*Cop 1848, RISM 1538*^{9}), 1 c m (*PBN 4379, RISM 1501*); 8/3–9/1 1 dot br (*BerGlo, Cop 1848, Dij, FBNC 176, FR 2356, MunSche, NHMel, PBN 4379, PCord, PPix, RCas 2856, RCG XIII.27, WLab, Wol 287, RISM 1501, RISM 1538*^{9}); 10/2–11/1 lig (*NHMel, WLab*); 11/1–2 longa-br lig err (*RCas 2856*), no lig (*NHMel, PBN 4379, RCG XIII.27, WLab, RISM 1501*); 11/2 dot sbr err (*MunSche*); 12/1 miss err (*MunSche*); 12/2–3 lig (*BerGlo*); 12/2–13/1 lig (*Dij, FBNC 176, FR 2356, MunSche, NHMel, RISM 1501*); 12/3–13/1 1 dot sbr (*Cop 1848, Dij, FBNC 176, FR 2356, MunSche, NHMel, PCord, PPix, RCas 2856, WLab, Wol 287, RISM 1501, RISM 1538*^{9}); 15/2–3 no lig (*Cop 1848, PBN 4379, PPix, RCas 2856, WLab, RISM 1501, RISM 1538*^{9}); before 16/2 flat for f (*RISM 1538*^{9}); 16/2–17/1 lig (*FR 2356, NHMel, PBN 4379, WLab, RISM 1538*^{9}); 17/3–18/1 no mi col (*BerGlo, FR 2356, RCas 2856, RISM 1501, RISM 1538*^{9}), 1 e sbr (*PBN 4379, RCG XIII.27, WLab*); 18/1 c (*Cop 1848, Dij, FBNC 176, FR 2356, MunSche, NHMel, PCord, PPix, Wol 287, RISM 1501*); 19/2–3 no lig (*Cop 1848, PCord, RCas 2856, RCG XIII.27, RISM 1501, RISM 1538*^{9}); 20/1 e err (*RISM 1538*^{9}); 21/2 m err (*RISM 1538*^{9}); 21/2–22/1 lig (*NHMel, WLab*); 22/1–2 mi col (*BerGlo, Cop 1848, FBNC 176, MunSche, NHMel, PBN 4379, PCord, PPix, RCG XIII.27, WLab, Wol 287*); 22/3–23/1 lig (*NHMel*); 23/1–2 a, g err (*Cop 1848*), no lig (*NHMel, PCord, RCas 2856, RCG XIII.27*); 24/1–3 no rest, e sbr, c m (*Dij, PCord*); 24/2–3 1 sbr e (*RCas 2856*), no mi col (*FR 2356, RISM 1501, RISM 1538*^{9}); 27/1–2 no mi col (*Cop 1848, FR 2356, RCas 2856, RISM 1501, RISM 1538*^{9}); 29/1–2 lig (*NHMel, RISM 1538*^{9}); 29/2–30/2 no lig (*BerGlo, NHMel, RCas 2856, RCG XIII.27, RISM 1538*^{9}); 30/1–2 no lig (*WLab, RISM 1501*); 32/3 a m, g sm, a m (*Cop 1848*); 33/2–3 2 m (*BerGlo, Cop 1848, Dij, FBNC 176, FR 2356, MunSche, NHMel, PBN 4379, PCord, PPix, RCas 2856, RCG XIII.27, WLab, Wol 287, RISM 1501, RISM 1538*^{9}); 34/2 m err (*FR 2356*); 35/1 b sm, a sm (*PCord*); 35/2 dot sbr err (*FR 2356*); 36/1 f err (*MunSche*); 36/3–37/1 1 c sbr (*FBNC 176, PPix, RCG XIII.27*); 37/2 f err (*Cop 1848, MunSche*), sbr err (*Wol 287*); 37/2–3 bl sbr, bl m (*BerGlo, Cop 1848, Dij, MunSche, NHMel, PBN 4379, PCord, RCG XIII.27, WLab, Wol 287*), g bl sbr, f bl m (*FBNC 176, PPix*), dot m, sm (*FR 2356, RCas 2856, RISM 1501, RISM 1538*^{9}); 38/1–2 lig (*MunSche, NHMel, WLab, RISM 1538*^{9}); 39/1–2 1 dot sbr (*RISM 1538*^{9}); between 40/1 and 41/1 c sbr err (*Wol 287*); 41/1–2 dot sbr err (*RISM 1538*^{9}); 42/1–2 dot m, sm (*FR 2356*); 42/3–44/1 lig (*NHMel*); 43/1–2 mi col (*Cop 1848, FBNC 176, MunSche, PBN 4379, PCord, PPix, RCG XIII.27, Wol 287*); 43/2 b fu, a fu (*RISM 1501*); 43/3–4 bl sbr, bl m (*FBNC 176, RCG XIII.27*), dot m, sm (*PPix*); 44/1 a err (*Cop 1848*); 44/3–5 m, 2 sm (*FR 2356, RCas 2856, RISM 1538*^{9}), mi col (*MunSche, RCG XIII.27, Wol 287*); 44/4–5 sm, m err (*Cop 1848*), 1 b m (*PBN 4379, PCord*); between 45/1 and 45/2 2 m rest err (*Cop 1848*); 45/2–3 b dot m, a sm, a sm, g sm (*Cop 1848, WLab*); 45/3 sbr err (*MunSche*); 46/1 sig congr (*BerGlo*); before 47/1 C in sig (*Dij, FBNC 176, NHMel, PPix, RCas 2856*), ¢ in sig (*PBN 4379, WLab*); 47/2 c sm, b sm (*BerGlo, RCas 2856, RISM 1501*); 48/1–2 1 br (*MunSche, NHMel, RCas 2856, RISM 1538*^{9}); 48/1–49/1 lig (*NHMel*); 50/1–2 mi col (*BerGlo, FBNC 176, MunSche, NHMel, PBN 4379, PCord, PPix, RCG XIII.27, WLab, Wol 287*), 2 m (*RISM 1501*); 50/3–51/1 lig (*MunSche, NHMel, WLab*); 51/1 c err (*MunSche*); 52/1–2 lig (*NHMel, WLab, RISM 1538*^{9}); 53/1 miss err (*RCG XIII.27*); 54/1–2 lig (*RISM 1538*^{9}); 55/1 sbr err (*RCG XIII.27*); 56/1–2 no lig (*PBN 4379, RCG XIII.27, RISM 1501, RISM 1538*^{9}); 56/2 2 m (*RCG XIII.27*); 57/2 2 sbr (*FR 2356*); 58/1–59/1 no lig (*RCas 2856, RISM 1501, RISM 1538*^{9}); 59/1–2 no mi col (*RCas 2856, RISM 1501, RISM 1538*^{9}); 59/3–60/1 lig (*MunSche, NHMel, WLab*); 60/1–2 lig (*BerGlo, PBN 4379, RCas 2856, RISM 1538*^{9}); 60/2–61/1 lig (*NHMel*); 61/1–2 no lig (*NHMel, RCas 2856, RISM 1501*); 64/1–2 lig (*BerGlo, NHMel*); 64/2–3 no mi col (*RCas 2856, RISM 1501, RISM 1538*^{9}); 65/1–2 lig (*MunSche, NHMel, RISM 1538*^{9}); 66/1–67/1 e sbr, c br (*FR 2356*); 66/2–67/1 no lig (*FBNC 176, FR 2356, MunSche, NHMel, PBN 4379, PPix, RCas 2856, RCG XIII.27, Wol 287, RISM 1501, RISM 1538*^{9}); 67/1–2 lig (*FBNC 176, MunSche, NHMel, PBN 4379, PPix, Wol 287, RISM 1538*^{9}); 69/1 no sig congr (*BerGlo, Dij, FR 2356, RCG XIII.27, Wol 287, RISM 1501, RISM 1538*^{9}); after 69/1 repeat sign (*MunSche, WLab*); 69/1–2 no mi col (*RCas 2856, RISM 1501, RISM 1538*^{9}), e sbr, f m err (*MunSche*); 69/1–70/1 e sbr, e m, g m, a m (*WLab*); after 69/2 repeat sign (*NHMel*); 72/1 a 8va bassa, sig congr (*BerGlo*), a (*PBN 4379, RISM 1501, RISM 1538*^{9}); after 72/1 repeat sign (*PBN 4379*).

COMMENTARY:

This *bergerette* setting, one of the most widely distributed and best liked of Ockeghem's day, has been preserved in no fewer than seventeen sources. Pierre de la Rue and Josquin des Prez were inspired to compose works drawing, respectively, on its tenor and superius. The main source of the present edition is *PNiv*, a French manuscript of 1460–65 that is perhaps the earliest and most central source of the piece. Another early source is the manuscript *MunSche*, much of which was written by Hartmann Schedel in the mid-1460s; but the musical text is defective there, as are the texts of many of the other pieces preserved in it.[67]

Most of the melodic interest in *Ma bouche rit* is centered in the superius, which dominates the texture. Unfolding in long flowing phrases, it is supported by two substantially more disjunct and somewhat more rhythmically active lower voices. Both of those voices occupy approximately the same range (tenor) and cross each other continually. There is even a passage in which the contra and the tenor both lie above the superius momentarily (m. 64).

[67]See H. Besseler, "Hartmann Schedel," *MGG* XI (1963), cols. 1609ff.

As in many of his works, Ockeghem avoids strong cadences and maintains the forward momentum by eliding the end of one phrase with the beginning of the next. In terms of its structure, the concluding cadence of the piece (mm. 45–46), with its suspensions in superius and contra, closely resembles a cadence of the double-leading-tone variety. It is, however, a Phrygian cadence, and one cannot really speak of leading tones. The cadence of the *clos* ending of the second section (mm. 71–72) also takes on an old-fashioned aspect on account of the octave leap in the contra. Imitation, although present, plays no important part in the formal design of the composition.

12. MA MAISTRESSE

MAIN SOURCE:

Wol 287, fol. 27^{v}–29^{r}. Anonymous, t+xx.

OTHER SOURCES:

Cam R.2.71, fol. 4^{v}. *Okeghem*: (S *prima pars* and part of T only), tx.
Esc IV.a.24, fol. 123^{v}–24^{r}. Anonymous: (*prima pars* only, transposed a fourth lower), –––.
PBN 4379/Sev 5–I–43, *prima pars* of S, fol. 42^{v} (o1^{v}); *secunda pars* of S, and the complete T and Ct, fol. 100^{r}–101^{r} (o2^{r}–o3^{r}). Anonymous, xxx.
Tr 93, fol. 375^{v}–76^{r}. Anonymous, –––.
WLab, fol. viiij^{v}–xj^{r}. Anonymous, t+xx.

TEXT ALONE:

BerRoh, fol. 100^{r}–100^{v}.
VerJard, fol. lxxi^{r}.

MUSIC PUBLISHED:

HAM I, no. 74.
OckCW I, p. 124.

TEXT PUBLISHED:

DrozJP, no. 99.
LöpL, no. 214.

TEXT AND TRANSLATION:

Ma maistresse et ma[1] plus grant[2] amye,
De mon desir la mortelle enemye,
Parfaicte en biens s'onques maiz[3] le fut femme,[4]
Celle seule de qui court[5] bruit et fame
D'estre sans per, ne vous verray je mye?

Helas, de vous bien plaindre me devroie,
S'il ne vous plaist que brefvement vous voye,[6]
M'amour, par[7] qui d'aultre aymer n'ay[8]
puissance.

Car sans vous voir, en[9] quelque part que[10] soye,
Tout ce que voys[11] me desplaist et ennoye,
Ne[12] jusqu'alors[13] je n'auray souffisance.

Incessamment mon dolent cueur larmye[14]
Doubtant qu'en vous pitié[15] soit[16] endormye.

My lady and my greatest love,
Of my desire the cruel enemy,
Perfect in qualities, if ever a woman was,
She alone whom rumor and fame hold
To be without peer, shall I not see you ever?

Alas, well should I complain of you,
If it does not please you that I see you shortly,
My love, because of whom I have no
power to love any other.

For without seeing you, wherever I may be,
Everything I see displeases and bores me,
Nor until then will I be satisfied.

Ceaselessly my sorrowing heart weeps,
Fearing that in you pity might be asleep.

Que ja ne soit, ma tant amée dame;
Maiz[17] s'ainsy est, si malheureux me clame,
Que plus ne quiers[18] vivre heure
ne demye.

Ma maistresse …

May that not be, my well-beloved lady,
But if it is so, I proclaim myself so unhappy
That I do not want to live one hour more,
nor even one half.

My lady …

[1]missing (*Cam R.2.71*).
[2]que aultre (*BerRoh*, *WLab*); quautre (*Cam R.2.71*, *VerJard*).
[3]missing (*WLab*); se jamaiz (*BerRoh*); tant que plus (*Cam R.2.71*).
[4]fist ame (*WLab*).
[5]lon (*BerRoh*); est (*VerJard*).
[6]revoye (*BerRoh*, *VerJard*, *WLab*).
[7]missing (*BerRoh*).
[8]na (*WLab*); je nay (*BerRoh*).
[9]missing (*BerRoh*, *VerJard*, *WLab*).
[10]que je (*BerRoh*, *VerJard*).
[11]quanque voy (*VerJard*); quancque voiz (*WLab*).
[12]missing (*WLab*).
[13]jusquez alors (*WLab*).
[14]fremye (*BerRoh*, *VerJard*, *WLab*).
[15]que priere (*WLab*).
[16]soit pitie (*VerJard*).
[17]Car (*BerRoh*).
[18]Je ne requier plus (*WLab*).

VARIANT READINGS:

Superius: before 1/1 no flat in sig throughout (*Tr 93*, *WLab*), temp perf sign (*PBN 4379*, *WLab*); 2/4 a err (*PBN 4379*; before 3/2 flat for f (*Cam R.2.71*); 4/4–5/1 no lig (*PBN 4379*, *WLab*); 6/2–3 one sm g (*Cam R.2.71*); before 12/3 C1 clef err for remainder of *prima pars* (*Tr 93*); before 16/1 flat (*Tr 93*); before 18/3 flat (for f) (*Tr 93*); 19/5 a err (*WLab*); 20/3–22/1 om err, but added in left margin (*Esc IV.a.24*); 20/3–22/2 repeated err (*Wol 287*); 23/2–4 dot m, sm, m (*WLab*); 24/4–5 1 m d (*PBN 4379*); 26/1 2 sbr (*WLab*); before 28/1 flat (*WLab*); 28/2–5 a sm, g sm, f sm (*Cam R.2.71*, *Esc IV.a.24*, *PBN 4379*, *Tr 93*, *WLab*); before 29/3 flat (*WLab*); 30/2–3 1 a (=d) sbr (*Esc IV.a.24*); 31/1–2 dot m, sm (*Cam R.2.71*, *Esc IV.a.24*, *Tr 93*, *WLab*); 31/4–5 dot m, sm (*WLab*); 33/5–6 c dot m, b sm, b sm, a sm (*WLab*); 47/1 2 sbr (*WLab*); 55/1–2 2 sbr (*WLab*); 58/1 2 sbr (*Tr 93*, *WLab*); 61/2–3 1 a m (*Sev 5–I–43*); 62/2 b sm, a sm (*WLab*); 63/1–2 no lig (*WLab*); 65/1–2 no lig (*Tr 93*, *WLab*); 65/2–66/1 1 a sbr (*WLab*); 66/2 a dot sbr, g m, g m, f m (*Sev 5–I–43*); 67/1 m err (*Tr 93*); 68 sig congr (*Sev 5–I–43*).

Tenor: before 1/1 flat in sig implies e-flat on account of transposition (*Esc IV.a.24*), no flat in sig throughout (*Tr 93*), temp perf sign (*Sev 5–I–43*); 1/1 imperf br, sbr (*Sev 5–I–43*, *WLab*); 2/1–2 lig (*Cam R.2.71*, *Sev 5–I–43*); 3/2 d err (*Sev 5–I–43*); 3/3–4 no lig (*WLab*); 4/2 d err (*Tr 93*); 5/2 c sm, b–flat sm (*Cam R.2.71*); before 7/2 no flat in sig throughout remainder of voice (*WLab*); 12/4–5 no mi col (*Cam R.2.71*, *Esc IV.a.24*, *Tr 93*, *WLab*); before 14/1 no flat in sig (*Esc IV.a.24*); 18/1 imperf br, sbr (*WLab*); between 20/1 and 20/2 b (=e) m crossed out (*Esc IV.a.24*); 20/1 c err (*Tr 93*); 20/4 d err (*WLab*); 21/4–5 dot m, sm (*Esc IV.a.24*, *Tr 93*, *WLab*); 22/1–2 no lig (*Sev 5–I–43*, *WLab*); 24/3–4 g dot m, f sm (*WLab*); 24/4 c (=f) m err (*Esc IV.a.24*); 25/2–3 1 e (=a) sbr (*Esc IV.a.24*), 1 a sbr (*WLab*); 25/2–3 no mi col (*Tr 93*); 26/2–3 1 c m (*Sev 5–I–43*); 26/4–5 2 m (*WLab*); 28/3–4 lig (*Sev 5–I–43*); 29/1 sbr, sbr rest (*Tr 93*, *WLab*); 30/4–31/1 no lig (*WLab*); before 31/5 flat (*Sev 5–I–43*, *Wol 287*); 31/5–32/1 no lig (*Esc IV.a.24*, *Sev 5–I–43*, *WLab*); before 35/1 flat in sig throughout remainder of voice (*Sev 5–I–43*); 37/1 imperf br, sbr (*Sev 5–I–43*); 39/1–2 lig (*WLab*); 41/1–42/1 lig (*Sev 5–I–43*); 42/1–43/1 no lig (*Sev 5–I–43*, *Tr 93*, *WLab*); 44/2 e (err?) (*Sev 5–I–43*, *Tr 93*); 45/1–46/1 lig (*Sev 5–I–43*, *WLab*); 47/1–2 1 br (*WLab*); 50/1–2 lig (*Sev 5–I–43*); 51/1–2 no lig (*Sev 5–I–43*, *WLab*); 51/1–53/1 1 lig (*Tr 93*); 52/1–53/1 no lig (*Sev 5–I–43*, *WLab*); 56/1–2 1 br (*WLab*); 56/1–57/1 lig (*WLab*); 61/1–62/1 no lig (*Sev 5–I–43*, *WLab*); 68/1 sig congr (*Sev 5–I–43*).

Contra: before 1/1 no flat in sig throughout (*Tr 93*), temp perf sign (*Sev 5–I–43*); 3/1–2 no lig (*Sev 5–I–43*); 4/1 2 sbr (*Esc IV.a.24*, *Tr 93*, *WLab*); 5/5–6 dot m, sm (*Sev 5–I–43*); 7/1 sbr, m rest (*WLab*); 7/3 g (*WLab*); before 9/5 flat (*Sev 5–I–43*); before 10/3 no flat in sig throughout remainder of voice (*WLab*); 10/3–4 2 m (*Sev 5–I–43*); 11/1 flat on line 5 (for b) (*Sev 5–I–43*); 11/4–5 bl sbr, bl m (*Sev 5–I–43*); 12/1–2 g dot m, f sm (*WLab*); 12/4–13/1 1 br (*Sev 5–I–43*, *WLab*); 16/3–17/1 lig (*WLab*); before 19/3 flat (for b) (*WLab*); 20/4 b err (*Tr 93*); 21/1–2 f (=b-flat) sbr, f (=b-flat)-d (=g) c.o.p. lig (*Esc IV.a.24*); 25/4 a (=d) sm, f (=b-flat) sm (*Esc IV.a.24*); 26/1–2 lig (*Tr 93*); 26/2–3 no lig (*Sev 5–I–43*, *Tr 93*); 30/4–31/1 sbr, imperf br (*Sev 5–I–43*); 31/1 d (=g) bl sbr, e (=a) bl m (*Esc IV.a.24*); 32/1 f err (*Sev 5–I–43*); 36/1 g err (*Tr 93*); 37/1–38/1 lig (*Sev 5–I–43*, *WLab*); 40/1–42/1 lig (*Sev 5–I–43*); 41/1–42/1 no lig (*Tr 93*); 41/1–43/1 no lig (*WLab*); 42/1–43/1 no lig (*Sev 5–I–43*); 44/1–2 lig (*Sev 5–I–43*, *WLab*); 45/1–47/1 lig (*Sev 5–I–43*, *WLab*); 46/1–47/1 no lig (*Tr 93*); 49/1–2 lig (*Tr 93*, *WLab*); 49/2 f err (*Tr 93*); 55/1 2 sbr (*Sev 5–I–43*, *WLab*); 57/1–59/1 no lig (*Sev 5–I–43*); 58/1 g err (*Tr 93*); 60/1–2 e sbr, d sbr, e br lig err (*Tr 93*); 63/2–64/1 no lig (*WLab*); 64/1 imperf br, sbr (*Sev 5–I–43*); 68/1 sig congr (*Sev 5–I–43*).

COMMENTARY:

Ockeghem's own *Missa Ma maistresse* is based on this composition.[68] Presumably the chanson was composed before *Au travail suis* (no. 23 below), which quotes from the opening of *Ma maistresse* beginning in its sixteenth measure. *Ma maistresse* was praised by Johannes Tinctoris in the eighth chapter of his *Liber de arte contrapuncti* of 1477.[69] Formerly, the piece, which is the only known musical setting from the period of a text beginning with those words, was ascribed to Ockeghem on the strength of Tinctoris's remarks. David Fallow's report of the discovery of binding fragments (*Cam R.2.71*) that include the superius and part of the tenor of *Ma maistresse* attributed to "Okeghem" now gives us confirmation of Tinctoris's testimony in a musical source.[70] The style of this setting of a *bergerette* is distinctly treble-dominated in the older manner and highly reminiscent of the style of Binchois's secular works. Virtually all the melodic interest belongs to the superius, which is supported by two meandering, angular lower voices. Because they occupy identical ranges (*f* to *c*''), the tenor and the contra cross repeatedly, and the overall tessitura is exceptionally high. Other archaic features include the double-leading-tone cadences in mm. 17–18, 28–29, and 52–53, and the octave-leap cadence that concludes the music of the refrain (mm. 33–34). One of the most impressive passages in the work is the long melodic sequence in the superius, mm. 9–11, which is carried one measure further by the tenor.

As in many *bergerette* settings by his contemporaries, Ockeghem employs a contrasting mensuration for the music of the *couplet* portion of the poem. In this section, the rhythmic activity decreases considerably, mostly owing to the relative absence of irregular accent. Here the rhythmic practice foreshadows that of Ockeghem's presumably later compositions.

13. MORT TU AS NAVRÉ

MAIN SOURCE:

Dij, fol. viij^{xx}iij^{v}–viij^{xx}v^{r} (166^{v}–68^{r}). Anonymous, t+xt–.

OTHER SOURCE:

MC 871, pp. 388–89 (fol. 158^{v}–59^{r}). *Oquegan*, x–––.

MUSIC PUBLISHED:

MarM, no. 54.
MoD, Appendice, no. III.
PopeMC, no. 107.
TrowIMM III, no. 4.

TEXT AND TRANSLATION:

Mort, tu as navré de ton dart
Le pere de joyeuseté,
En desployant ton estandart
Sur Binchois, patron de bonté,
Son corps est plaint et lamenté,
Qui gist soubz lame.
Helas, plaise vous en pitié
Prier pour l'ame.

En sa jonesse fut soudart
De honnorable mondanité,
Puis a esleu la milleur part
Servant Dieu en humilité
Tant luy soit en crestienté
Son nom est fame.

Death, you have wounded with your dart
The father of joyousness,
In spreading your banner
Over Binchois, model of goodness,
Who, his corpse mourned and lamented,
Lies beneath a tombstone.
Alas, may you for pity's sake
Pray for his soul.

In his youth he was a soldier
Of honorable worldliness,
Then he made the better choice,
Serving God in humility,
So much so that in Christendom
His name is famed.

---

[68]The mass is published in vol. I of the present edition, no. 8.
[69]*CouS* IV, p. 152.
[70]See *FallJO*.

Qui detient de grant voulenté, Priez pour l'ame.	Whoever has great goodwill, Pray for his soul.
Retoricque, se Dieu me gard, Son serviteur a regretée, Musicque, par piteux regard, Fait deul et noir a portée. Pleurez, hommes de feaulté . . . .[1] Vueillez vostre université [Prier pour l'ame].[2]	Rhetoric, as God preserves me, Has grieved for her servant; Music, with piteous gaze, Has mourned and dressed in black. Weep, O men of fealty, ... Ask that your community [Pray for his soul].
Miserere, pie [Jesu, Domine, dona ei requiem,][3] Quem in cruce redemisti precioso sanguine, Pie Jhesu, Domine, dona ei requiem.	Have mercy, compassionate [Jesus, Lord, grant him rest,] Whom Thou didst redeem upon the cross with Thy precious blood, Sweet Jesus, Lord, grant him rest.

[1]line missing.
[2]line missing (supplied from strophes 1 and 2).
[3]missing (supplied from *LU*).

VARIANT READINGS:

Superius: before 1/1 no mens sign (*MC 871*); before 1/1–14/2 b-flat in sig (*MC 871*); 9/1–2 1 br (*MC 871*); 10/2–11/1 perf br (*MC 871*); before 11/1 sharp (*MC 871*); before 13/1 flat (*MC 871*); 18/1–3 c sbr, b sbr (*MC 871*); 46/2–47/1 no lig (*MC 871*); 47/1–2 lig (*MC 871*); 47/2–48/1 no lig (*MC 871*); 50/1–53/1 miss err (*Dij*); 57/2–3 1 m b (*MC 871*).

Conctratenor: labeled "C" (*MC 871*); before 1/1 no mens sign (*MC 871*); 7/2–8/1 2 b sbr, 2 a sbr (*Dij*); 12/1–2 no lig (*Dij*); 12/2 sbr, m rest (*Dij*); 16/2 sbr, m (*MC 871*); 18/1–19/1 1 longa (*MC 871*); 21/1–22/1 lig (*MC 871*); 24/2–25/1 lig (*MC 871*); 25/2–26/1 no lig (*MC 871*); 36/2 a (*MC 871*); 49/2–3 1 sbr (*MC 871*); 52/3–53/1 1 sbr e (*MC 871*); before 56/1 flat (*MC 871*).

Tenor: before 1/1 no mens sign (*MC 871*); 3/2–4/1 2 sbr (*MC 871*); 4/1–2 lig (*MC 871*); 8/1–2 lig (*MC 871*); 9/1–2 2 e sbr, 2 d sbr (*Dij*); 9/1–10/1 no lig or col (*Dij*); 11/1 sbr, imperf br (*Dij*); 14/1 imperf br, sbr (*Dij*); before 17/4 flat (*MC 871*); 23/1 2 sbr (*MC 871*); 30/1–31/1 no lig (*MC 871*); 41/1–42/1 no lig (*MC 871*); 56/2–57/1 lig (*MC 871*).

Conctratenor Basis: labeled "Cb" (*MC 871*); 3/2 miss err (*Dij*); 19/2 d (*MC 871*); 31/1 2 sbr (*Dij*); 39/1–43/1 1 lig (*MC 871*); 42/1–43/1 1 longa (*MC 871*); 44/1–46/1 lig (*MC 871*); 56/1–57/1 lig (*MC 871*).

COMMENTARY:

Inasmuch as this piece is a *déploration* for Gilles Binchois (d. 1460), it may be that Ockeghem studied with the older composer at one time or at least considered him his mentor. *Mort tu as navré* is a setting of a *ballade*, Ockeghem's only known essay in that form.[71] Of the two extant sources, *Dij* transmits by far the more complete reading of the text. Nevertheless, two lines are missing from what will for present purposes be regarded as the third strophe. According to the rhyme scheme of the first two strophes, line six of strophe three should end with a word that provides the rhyme "-ame." The absence of this line is signaled in mm. 27–30 of the present edition by a row of dots. It is possible, however, to supply the other missing line editorially, for it is the refrain of the poem and therefore must be the same as the concluding lines of the complete strophes.

Dij is somewhat ambiguous concerning the order of the second and third strophes. The strophe beginning "Retoricque ..." is written on a blank staff under the superius of the first section of the *ballade* on fol. 166v, while the strophe beginning "En sa jonesse ..." appears similarly under the high contratenor voice in the second section on fol. 168r. This perhaps implies that the former is to be performed as strophe two, while the latter is strophe three. It was thought best, however, to reverse that order in this edition. The strophe underlying the music reproves Death for the loss of Binchois; the strophe given here as the second consists of a brief account of Binchois's life; the third strophe in the present edition describes how he is mourned by Rhetoric and Music. This ordering seems the more logical one.

A somewhat puzzling feature of the piece as it is transmitted in *Dij* is the presence, at the ends of the superius, tenor, and high contratenor voices, of what seem to be *rentrements* for the first and third lines of the first strophe. This appears to suggest that

[71]André Pirro proposed that the author of the poem might have been Ockeghem; see *PirH*, p. 102. At least one fact concerning Binchois derives solely from *Mort tu as navré*, that "in his youth he was a soldier."

the first section of music should be repeated with lines one through four of the poem before proceeding to the second strophe. Since no known setting of a *ballade* follows such a plan, the present edition does not adopt this procedure.

The text of the tenor consists of a troped paraphrase of part of the sequence from the Mass for the Dead, *Dies irae, dies illa.*[72] The phrase "Jesu, Domine, dona ei requiem" has been supplied editorially after "pie," because "Quem" in the succeeding line needs an antecedent ("ei"). Elements of the famous sequence melody are also present, in particular at the words "Pie Jhesu, Domine, dona ei requiem," mm. 35–40.

In *Dij*, the tenor voice bears a complete text, except for what has been provided, as explained above, in the latter portion of the first section. The contratenor bassus, as written in *Dij*, is wholly without text, but this voice does contain the concluding phrase of the plainchant in *MC 871*. It was decided, therefore, to provide the contratenor bassus with the Latin words throughout in this edition. In *MC 871*, the high contratenor is devoid of text, while in *Dij* its first section bears the incipit "Miserere." However, the opening of the second section of that voice in *Dij* is marked "son," which is the first word of the fifth line of the French *ballade* and would be the appropriate word for beginning the second section of the voice with the French text. The presence of the French incipit for the second section in *Dij* notwithstanding, it has been thought best to avoid the incongruity of changing from Latin to French in the contratenor altus. Therefore, for the purposes of the present edition, the Latin text underlies the voice in question from beginning to end.

14. ALIUS DISCANTUS SUPER O ROSA BELLA

SOURCE:

Tr 90, fol. 445^{r}. *Ockeghen*, x.

TEXT ALONE:

Fiore, Fol. bii^{v}–biii^{r}.
PBN 1035, fol. 34^{v}.

MUSIC PUBLISHED:

AdlerST, pp. 233–34.
TrowIMM IV, no. 1.

TEXT PUBLISHED:

AltaR, no. LXXIV.
FerraB II, p. 13.
MandaR, pp. 121–22.
RaphQ, p. 170.
RestC, no. 29.
WieseNL, no. 4.

TEXT[1] AND TRANSLATION:

O rosa bella, O dolce anima mia.
Non mi lassar morire in cortesia.
Ai lasso mi, dolente dezo finire
Per ben servire e lialmente amare.

O beautiful rose, O my sweet soul,
Do not let me die, for the sake of kindness.
Alas, must I end in sorrow
For having served well and loved loyally?

[1]after *DunstO*, no. 54.

ERRORS IN SOURCE:

Ockeghem's discantus: before 1/1–30/3 flat in sig in space for a err; 3/2 sm err; 11/1–2 2 m err; 17/1 sbr err; 40/4–5 2 m err; before 42/10–46/1 flat in sig on line for g err.

Dunstable's (Bedingham's?) discantus (after *Tr 90*, fol. 361^{v})**:** between 26/1 and 27/1 br rest; before 33/5 flat (for b); 41/2 f; before 42/1 flat; 46/1 longa, br, longa.

[72]See *Liber usualis*, pp. 1811–13.

COMMENTARY:

The "other descant over *O rosa bella*" immediately follows a three-voice arrangement by Hert in *Tr 90* of Dunstable's (Bedingham's?) setting of the well-known *ballata*. Hert's composition incorporates the original superius, to which are added a new tenor and contra. The editors of the Trent Codices took the rubric "Alius discantus ..." to mean that Ockeghem's voice should be combined with Hert's arrangement. However, Ockeghem's discantus and Hert's tenor, which occupy similar ranges, form frequent parallel unisons and obviously should not sound together. If Ockeghem's discantus is substituted for Hert's tenor, defective counterpoint also results between the former voice and the remaining two. Therefore, no relationship exists between Ockeghem's discantus and Hert's tenor and contra.

Ockeghem clearly intended, rather, for his new voice to be combined with the setting variously attributed to Dunstable and Bedingham—but again, not with the tenor and contra parts, which would result in poor counterpoint. The only remaining possible alternative is to combine Ockeghem's discantus with the superius of the setting by Dunstable (or Bedingham), which does result in more or less satisfactory counterpoint.[73]

For the present edition of this duo, it was decided to adopt the reading of the Dunstable/Bedingham superius provided in *Tr 90* on fol. 361^{v}, rather than the slightly different version of it belonging to Hert's nearby arrangement. It is evident that the two do not fit together where, for example, in m. 41 of Hert's superius the second note *f* clashes with the corresponding note in Ockeghem's discantus.

15. PRENEZ SUR MOI

MAIN SOURCE:

Cop 291, fol. 40^{v} (46^{v}). Anonymous, t.

OTHER SOURCES:

Dij, fol. i^{r}. Anonymous: Prenez sur moy (listed in index but now missing).
Mantua, intarsia. *Jo. Okenghem*: Canon Prendes sur moy, x.
RISM 1504^{3}, fol. 167^{v}. *Okenghem*: Prennes sur moy, x.
RISM 1590^{30}, no. XV. *Okenhemius*: Fuga trium vocum in epidiatessaron, –.
Heyden, p. 39. *Okeghem*: Fuga trium vocum in Epidiatessaron, –.
Glareanus, p. 454. *Okenheim*: Fuga trium vocum in Epidiatessaron, –.
Faber, pp. 152–53. *Okeghem*: Fuga trium partium, –.
Wilphlingseder, pp. 57–63. *ORenhemius* [sic] (index: *Okhenhemius*): Fugra [sic] trium vocum in Epidiatessaron cum Resolutione, –.

TEXT ALONE:

BerRoh, fol. 185^{r}.
LonBL 380, fol. 243^{v}.

MUSIC PUBLISHED:

AmbG V, Notenanhang, no. 6.
BocF, pp. 161–65.
BohnGD, p. 454.
Burney II, pp. 475ff.
Busby I, pp. 430ff.
DartIM, no. 6.
DiseFP, no. 1.

[73] *Tr 90*, which perhaps dates from the 1460s, is one of the earliest sources to transmit a work by Ockeghem. It may be that this *Alius discantus* is a student work.

DrozT, no. 1.
FétB VI, p. 363.
FétE, p. 28.
FinHM, p. 134.
ForkA II, pp. 528–33.
FröB II, pp. 122ff.
HawkH II, pp. 471ff.
JepK, no. 33.
KiesV, Anhang, pp. 22ff.
LeviO, pp. 450–51.
MillerG II, pp. 532–33.
MillerH, p. 52.
ReMC, pp. 84–85.
RieH II, pp. 236ff.
RittHM, Appendix, pp. 4ff.
ScherlMN, pp. 79–81.
WoolP II, pp. 65–66.

TEXT PUBLISHED:

LöpL, no. 578.
Wallis, no. CCXII.

TEXT[1] AND TRANSLATION:

Prenez sur moi vostre exemple amoureux:
Commencement d'amours est[2] savoureux,
Et le moyen plain de paine et tristesse.
Et la fin est d'avoir plaisant maistresse,
Mais au saillir sont les pas dangereux.

Servant Amours,[3] me suis trouvé[4] eureux
L'une des foiz, et l'autre malleureux;[5]
Ung jour sentant confort, l'autre destresse.

Prenez sur moi …

Pour ung plaisir cent pansers ennuieux,[6]
Pour ung solas cent dangiers perilleux,
Pour ung accueil cent regars par rudesse;
S'Amours sert doncques de telz mets a largesse,[7]
Et les[8] loiaux fait les plus doloureux.

Prenez sur moi …

Take from me your amorous example:
The beginning of love is savory,
And the middle full of pain and sorrow.
And the outcome is to have a pleasing mistress,
But breaking up is fraught with danger.

Serving Love, I have found myself delighted
At one time, and at another saddened;
One day feeling blissful, another distressed.

Take from me …

For one pleasure a hundred vexing thoughts,
For one consolation a hundred perilous dangers,
For one welcome a hundred severe glances;
Such dishes does Love serve generously
And makes the loyal the most sorrowful.

Take from me …

[1] *Additamenta* from *BerRoh*.
[2] et (*Cop 291*).
[3] Venus (*LonBL 380*).
[4] tenu (*LonBL 380*).
[5] line missing (*LonBL 380*).
[6] et mieux (*LonBL 380*).
[7] Sy treuve car icelle deesse (*LonBL 380*).
[8] Les plus (*LonBL 380*).

VARIANT READINGS:

Measure numbers refer to the lowest voice: before 1/1 (*Mantua*), err (*Glareanus*), (*RISM 1590*^{30}), O in sig (*Mantua, RISM 1504*^{3}, *RISM 1590*^{30}, *Heyden, Glareanus, Faber, Wilphlingseder*), (*Heyden*); before 1/1–8/3 (*Faber*); 2/1 sig congr (*Mantua, RISM 1504*^{3}, *Heyden, Glareanus, Faber, Wilphlingseder*); 3/1 sig congr (*Heyden, Faber, Wilphlingseder*); 3/1–3 mi col (*RISM 1590*^{30}); 4/2 sig congr err (*Glareanus*); 17/2 no sig congr (*Mantua, RISM 1504*^{3}, *RISM 1590*^{30}, *Heyden, Glareanus, Faber, Wilphlingseder*); 18/3 b-flat sm, a sm (*Mantua*); 19/2–3 lig (*RISM 1504*^{3}, *RISM 1590*^{30}, *Heyden, Glareanus, Faber, Wilphlingseder*); 20/5–21/1 bl sbr, bl m (*Mantua*), dot m, sm (*RISM 1504*^{3}, *RISM 1590*^{30}, *Heyden, Glareanus, Faber, Wilphlingseder*); 21/2–3 no mi col (*Mantua, RISM 1504*^{3}, *RISM 1590*^{30}, *Heyden, Glareanus, Faber, Wilphlingseder*); 21/3 f (*Mantua, RISM 1504*^{3}, *RISM 1590*^{30}, *Heyden, Glareanus, Faber, Wilphlingseder*); 24/3–6 1 d sbr (*Mantua*); 26/5–27/1 mi col (*Mantua*); 28/4 f fu, e fu (*RISM 1504*^{3}, *RISM 1590*^{30}, *Heyden, Glareanus, Faber, Wilphlingseder*); 29/4 c err (*Mantua, RISM 1504*^{3}, *RISM 1590*^{30}, *Heyden, Glareanus, Faber, Wilphlingseder*); 33/1 no sig congr (*Faber*); 34/1 no sig congr (*Faber, Wilphlingseder*); 35/1 c longa below and together with g longa (*RISM 1504*^{3}, *Heyden, Glareanus, Faber, Wilphlingseder*), c br below and together with g br (*RISM 1590*^{30}), sig congr (*RISM 1590*^{30}, *Wilphlingseder*).

COMMENTARY:

The "Fuga trium vocum in Epidiatessaron post perfectum tempus," as Heyden called this canon in *De arte canendi*, has been one of the most studied pieces in the history of Renaissance music. In the twenty-sixth chapter of Book III of his *Dodecachordon*, Glareanus remarks that Ockeghem's canonic chanson belongs to a species of composition known as a *catholicon*, a piece that can be performed in many modes.[74] In the same context, he also places in this category the composer's *Missa Cuiusvis toni* (or, as he reports the title, *Missa ad omnem tonum*).[75] Referring to the latter work, Glareanus observes that it can be sung in any of the modes beginning on *C*, *D*, or *E*; that is, Ionian (or transposed Lydian with a lowered fourth degree), Dorian, or Phrygian. With regard to the mass, he may well be correct, but experimentation will demonstrate that the final cadence of the "Fuga" excludes the possibility of performing it in the Phrygian mode. The application of the necessary flats, especially a flat to the penultimate *D* of the middle voice, results in a proscribed *mi contra fa* (in this instance, a diminished fifth) with the lowest voice in the vertical sonority immediately preceding the final cadence point. Therefore, although the contrapuntal ambience clearly indicates that the final cadence is of the authentic variety, no cadence of that type could be possible if the mode were Phrygian. For this reason, the piece cannot be a *catholicon* in the full sense evidently intended by Glareanus.

Nevertheless, adhering to Glareanus's description of it, Joseph Levitan published a composite transcription that presents two versions of the piece: one in *B*-flat Mixolydian with a key signature of three flats and the other in *G* Lydian with a key signature of two sharps.[76] Carl Dahlhaus subsequently argued against Levitan's interpretation of the canon as a piece that can be transposed in its entirety into different modes. Instead he proposes that Glareanus meant only to point out that, in deriving two or more voices from the single notated voice according to the principle "in epidiatessaron," each performer will render the melody, in effect, in a different mode.[77] He overlooks the fact, however, that Glareanus discusses the canon in conjunction with the *Missa Cuiusvis toni*, which is a genuine *catholicon* in the sense evidently intended by Glareanus and understood by Levitan. Dahlhaus also takes no notice of the fact that Glareanus consistently assigns different modes to the various voice parts of polyphonic pieces in analyzing them throughout the *Dodecachordon*. But at no time does Glareanus call any piece other than the "Fuga trium vocum" and the *Missa Cuiusvis toni* a *catholicon*. Perhaps he concluded that both works are *catholica*, a term that he may have invented himself,[78] because both are notated without clefs. With regard to the "Fuga trium vocum," Glareanus may well be mistaken.

But if *Prenez sur moi* is not a *catholicon*, it is in any event a puzzle canon, although no verbal inscription giving the rule for its solution appears in its oldest surviving source, the Copenhagen Chansonnier of c. 1475 (*Cop 291*). For the purposes of the present edition, it has been assumed that a group of performers was able to interpret the piece directly from this manuscript without recourse to explanations in theoretical treatises, since everything needed to solve the puzzle is already present there. A glance at the reading in *Cop 291* (see plate IX[a]) reveals the presence of two *signa* near the end of the single notated voice, which locate the conclusions of the

---

[74] Amauit autem καθολικὰ in cantu, hoc est, Cantiones instituere, quae multis cantarentur modis ad cantorum propemodum arbitrium, ita tamen, ut Harmoniae ac consonantiarum ratio nihilo secius obseruaretur (p. 454).

[75] Published in vol. I of the present edition, no. 4.

[76] *LeviO*, pp. 450–51.

[77] See *DahlO*. Dahlhaus proposes a different view of the pattern of accidentals. He sees the first two at the left as indicating that the starting note of the lowest voice is *A*, if they are read as *C*-fa and *F*-fa. In like manner, the next two accidentals represent *F*-fa and *B*-mi, indicating that the first pitch of the middle voice is *D*. Finally, the last two accidentals represent *B*-mi and *E*-mi, which makes the first note of the highest voice *G*.

This proposal is imaginative, but it has two possible flaws: (1) The accidentals do not necessarily function as normal hexachord signs despite their placement at the beginning of the notated voice; for example, a flat signature is not appropriate to the intervallic content of Hypoaeolian with an *A* final, which would be solmized in the natural and hard hexachords. (2) The accidentals are not aligned vertically in three pairs reading from left to right in any of the extant sources, and one must distort the appearance of the pattern considerably to perceive them that way (see plates IX[a] and [b]).

Assuming that the first note of the lowest voice is an *A*, then Dahlhaus considers that the three voices are, respectively, in *A* Hypoaeolian, *D* Hypodorian, and *G* Hypomixolydian, and the piece is a *catholicon* only in this limited sense.

[78] See vol. I of the second, corrected edition of the present publication, New York, 1959, p. xxvi.

derived voices, indicating that two further voices must be added to the written voice. In addition, they show with unmistakable clarity that the time interval of the canon is one perfect breve. Therefore, one can deduce that the breve is perfect despite the fact that no mensuration sign for *tempus perfectum* appears at the beginning of the notated voice, although the rhythm at the outset clearly conveys perfect time in any event.[79]

Since no clef is present, one must still determine the starting pitch of the notated voices, the interval at which the derived voices should enter above or below the leader, and the meaning of the peculiar pattern of accidentals at the beginning of the notation. Evidently these accidentals supply the key to the remaining elements of the solution. The first flat is positioned on the second line from the bottom of the staff, suggesting that this line is to be thought of as *fa* (*B*-flat in the soft hexachord). *B*-flat can occur on that line in only the bass clef. If one takes this line to represent *B*-flat in the bass clef, then the starting note of the written-out voice is *D* below middle *C*. The next two flats, which are both positioned on the second line from the top, refer to the second voice of the canon. They indicate that this line should now be construed as *fa*, *B*-flat, making the first note of the second voice *G*—not, as might be thought, the g' of the soprano clef, but *g* an octave lower, *G* below middle *C*; that is, *G* a fourth higher than the starting note of the first voice. Thus the canonic rule "in epidiatessaron (at the upper fourth)," which Heyden correctly recognized, can be determined from the pattern of accidentals and no verbal instruction is needed.

The rule having been established, it may be assumed that the third voice should follow suit and enter a perfect fourth higher than the second. One might expect to find, then, after the group of two flats representing the second voice, another group of three flats, by way of confirmation, all in the second space from the bottom of the staff, signifying that the starting note of the third voice is to be middle *C*, the c' of the alto clef. But no such group of three additional flats is present. Instead there are three "sharps" (not sharps in the modern sense, but symbols for *B*-mi, in effect something more like naturals) positioned in such a way that they apparently bring about the cancellation of the previous flats. In other words, the naturals substitute the hexachord degree *mi* for the degrees *fa* signified by the flats. The canonic principle "in epidiatessaron" has already been established by the flats, so there is no need for the pattern of accidentals representing the third voice to indicate a starting pitch. The three naturals indicate instead that at least some of the notes *B* in the third voice should be solmized in the hard hexachord, that is, without a flat in the signature.[80]

In effect, the pattern of accidentals calls for the most common variety of partial signature occurring in the late fifteenth century: no signature in the superius, a flat in the tenor, and a flat in the contra. It should be emphasized that in no instance does a partial signature absolutely obviate the need for the application of *musica ficta* accidentals in the top voice of such pieces that have them; it simply indicates the predominating hexachord or hexachords for the correct solmization of the part.

There is reason to believe that the sixteenth-century theorists who wrote about the canon were no longer conversant with partial signatures, which were already obsolescent by the first decade of the new century. However, Gregorius Faber still may have had some notion of what the accidentals meant when, in 1553, he called *Prenez sur moi* a "Fuga trium partium, quarum priores duae in molli cantu, ultima in duro fictas voces usurpat"; that is, "A canon in three parts, in which the first two are sung in the soft hexachord, [and] the last, in the hard hexachord, uses *ficta* [solmization] degrees." In writing this, Faber seems to be providing a clear-cut description of a partial signature.

Sebald Heyden reproduces the flats and sharps as they are given by Petrucci, but after the flats he supplies the syllables "re" on the bottom line, "la-re" on the middle line, and "la" on the top line. In like manner, the syllables "ut," "sol-ut," and "sol" appear after the sharps on the bottom, middle, and top lines respectively. (See the VARIANT READINGS above.) These syllables have no direct bearing on the solution of the canon, contrary to what Joseph Levitan thought,[81] but merely serve as a guide to the correct solmization of the voice parts. Heyden, in fact, provides similar guidance for most of the examples in his treatise, whether or not they are canonic. His syllables do, however, tend to confirm the solution outlined above, since they show that the first note, which is on the middle line, is solmized, at least part of the time, as "re" in the first and second voices and as "ut" in the third voice. In other words, the first and second voices (the two lower voices) are to be solmized mainly in the soft hexachord, while the third voice should be solmized largely in the natural hexachord.

It ought to be mentioned here that the Mantuan intarsia differs from the other sources with respect to its opening signature. (See the VARIANT READINGS above.) In the first place, a sign for *tempus perfectum* is provided. Also, the accidentals consist of a single "sharp" on the second line from the bottom and a single "flat" on the second line from the top. If the first sign is taken to represent *mi* in one of the hexachords, then the first note on the middle line of the staff could be *G*, *C*, or *D*, the implication being that the part should begin on one of these pitches and be solmized in predominantly the natural and hard hexachords. If the second sign,

---

[79]The figure of a woman belonging to part of the illuminated "P" that begins the text is holding a large circular object, perhaps a variety of frame drum, and this might represent a surreptitious means of stating *tempus perfectum*.

[80]It could be possible also that Ockeghem did not intend for the combination of the first flat and the first note to suggest a particular starting pitch on a specific line in a specific clef. If the first flat were taken simply as *F-fa* in the natural hexachord without reference to staff or clef, then the first note of the piece might be *A*. (See also n. 77 above.) The following pattern of two flats would then make the beginning note of the second voice *D*, and the pattern of three sharps would suggest *G* as the starting pitch of the third voice.

This may seem to represent a version in a different mode from the one proposed here, but in effect it is no more than a transposition. In keeping with the rules of *musica ficta*, Ockeghem's counterpoint demands the addition of accidentals that make a version having its first note as *A* differ only in very minor ways from one beginning on *D*, and the mode does not change.

[81]See *LeviO*, p. 445. Levitan demonstrates that *Prenez sur moi* has been poorly understood since as early as the mid-sixteenth century. See his discussion of all of the sources of the piece and editions of it dating from prior to 1937. Levitan's aim is to show how the piece is a *catholicon*, but he offers only two versions of it, one in *B*-flat Mixolydian (with a modern key signature of three flats) and the other in *G* Lydian (with a signature of two sharps). His application of *ficta* accidentals to the version in Lydian makes it hardly more than a transposition of the other version. Levitan makes no attempt to provide a Dorian or Phrygian reading of the canon.

the "flat," is to be thought of as *fa* in one of the hexachords, then the first note of the voice could be *D*, *G*, or *A*, suggesting that the part should begin on one of these pitches and be solmized mainly in the natural and soft hexachords.

What the signature of the intarsia does not make clear, however, is how many voices of the three[82] should be solmized in the natural and soft hexachords and how many in the natural and hard. Presumably one must use trial and error to discover that the "flat" calls for two parts to begin on *D* and *G* (or *A* and *D*?) respectively, and the "sharp" stipulates *C* (or *G*?) for the opening note of the third.[83] It should be borne in mind that, unlike the other sources, the intarsia is a work of art rather than material for performance or theoretical study. It is likely, however, that its reading derives in some way from a family of practical sources that is otherwise completely lost to us. Therefore, the evidence of the intarsia cannot be discounted, but it can do little more than confirm for us what the respective starting notes of the voices probably should be.

Of the thirty-three chansons in *Cop 291*, all of which are *rondeau* or *bergerette* settings, only two lack complete texts. The short strophe for the repetition of the first section of music is missing in no. 14, the *rondeau* entitled *Garison sçay*,[84] no doubt because of an oversight. *Prenez sur moi* (no. 33), which *BerRoh* and *LonBL 380* transmit as a complete *rondeau cinquain*, is lacking its entire *additamenta* in *Cop 291*. Perhaps the omission was deliberate in this instance. The very nature of the canon seems to preclude the formation of a smoothly functioning medial cadence, and without the point from which to return to the beginning, it is not possible to execute the complete *rondeau* form.[85] It may well be that Ockeghem intended to set only the refrain text, adopting it because it appears to enjoin the performers ("Take from me your example ...") to seek a solution in the notation.[86] The remaining lines of the poem, after *BerRoh*, have been provided above and at the conclusion of the edition, but they might not have a place in the performance of the canon.

Since *Prenez sur moi* is sui generis among Ockeghem's secular works, it does not lend itself to stylistic comparisons. It must have been composed, of course, before c. 1475, the date of *Cop 291*. The rhythmic practice, as may be seen for example in mm. 7–9 and 30 of the top voice, suggests a rather earlier date, as does the octave leap in the final cadence.

16. PRESQUE TRANSI

MAIN SOURCE:

WLab, fol. iiii^{xx}j^{v}–iiii^{xx}iij^{r}. Anonymous, t+x–.

OTHER SOURCE:

Dij, fol. lij^{v}–liiij^{r} (55^{v}–57^{r}). *Okeghem*, t+x–.

TEXT ALONE:

BerRoh, fol. 152^{v}.

MUSIC PUBLISHED:

DrozT, no. 48.

TEXT PUBLISHED:

LöpL, no. 439.

TEXT AND TRANSLATION:

Presque transi ung peu mains qu'estre mort,	Almost overcome, barely less than dead,
Vivant en dueil sans avoir nul confort,	Living in sorrow without having any comfort,
Veoir l'en[1] me peut es lienx de Fortune[2]	One can see that I am in the bonds of Fortune,

[82]The intarsia does not supply a rubric, such as "Fuga trium vocum," but there are two *signa* correctly placed at the end to show the concluding points of the first and second voices.

[83]See n. 80 above concerning the possibility of using the pitches *A*, *D*, and *G* as the respective starting notes of the parts.

[84]See *JepK*, p. xli.

[85]There is a rather tentative looking *signum* in *Cop 291* that could be taken to indicate the halfway mark of the notated voice. In transcription, it lies above the second note in m. 17 of the bottom voice, the second note in m. 18 of the middle voice, and the second note in m. 19 of the top voice, but none of these places represents a convincing medial cadence point. A method for making the repeat, nevertheless, is suggested in *ReMC*, but the solution, which involves beginning the repeat in the lowest voice before the upper voices have reached their conjectured medial cadences, seems doubtful if only because it is unprecedented.

[86]Something like this was suggested in *BesSMM*, p. 126. Besseler and Gülke's brief explanation of a facsimile reproduction of *Prenez sur moi* (after *Cop 291*) is based on an interpretation of the canon published by Carl Dahlhaus in *DahlO*. See n. 77 above.

Qui sans cesser pis[3] qu'autre
  me fortune
Et me combat de plus fort en plus fort.

Helas, je suis contre mon vueil en vie,
Et si n'est riens dont tant j'aye d'envie
Que de povoir veoir ma fin bien[4] prouchaine.

Morir ne puis et tousjours m'y convie,
Et m'est bien tart que du tout
  je desvie
A celle fin que je[5] soye[6] hors de paine.

Il m'est advis que la Mort me tient tort
Quant autrement elle[7] ne fait son effort
De moy vengier de ma vie importune;
Car je languis sans avoir joye aucune
Par mon maleur qui me
  devoure et mort.

Presque transi …

Who unceasingly casts my lot
  worse than anyone else's
And strives against me harder and harder.

Alas, I am alive against my will,
And there is nothing I long for so much
As to be able to see my end near at hand.

I cannot die yet am invited to always,
And it is rather late for me, since I am dead
  to everything
In order to be free of pain.

It seems to me that Death does me wrong
When otherwise she makes no effort
To avenge me for my troublesome life;
For I languish without any joy
On account of my unhappiness, which
  devours and torments me.

Almost overcome …

[1]lon (*BerRoh*).
[2]entire line missing (*Dij*).
[3]puis (*Dij*).
[4]mort (*BerRoh*).
[5]missing (*Dij*).
[6]soit (*Dij*).
[7]el (*BerRoh*).

VARIANT READINGS:

Superius: before 17/1 flat in sig (*Dij*); 17/1 sbr, m (*Dij*); 18/1 sig congr (*Dij*, *WLab*); 22/1–2 2 m (*Dij*); before 32/1 no flat in sig (*Dij*); 43/3 e bl sbr, c bl m (*Dij*); 48/4–49/1 mi col (*Dij*).
Conctratenor: 9/3 d corrected to c (*Dij*); 10/1–2 no mi col (*Dij*); 11/1–2 mi col (*Dij*); 26/3–4 no mi col (*Dij*); 29/4–5 no mi col (*Dij*); 31/1 sig congr (*WLab*); before 32/1 flat in sig (*Dij*).
Tenor: 30/4 f corrected to a (*WLab*); 50/4–6 g sbr, a sbr, g m, a sbr, f m, all err (*Dij*).

COMMENTARY:

Many of the remarks made above concerning the style of *Ma bouche rit* (no. 11) apply equally well to this *bergerette* setting. In this composition, however, there is no more than the merest hint of imitation, if that. Both the tenor and the contra occupy a relatively low tessitura, although the overall range (*A* to *g'*) of the contra is rather wide. The archaic character of *Presque transi* is underscored by the presence of two prominent double-leading-tone cadences (mm. 11–12 and 23–24). Taking these attributes of the composition into account, it is probably an early work dating from the same time as *Ma bouche rit*, or perhaps somewhat before it.

WLab was selected as the main source on account of defects in the readings of both the music and the text that occur in *Dij*. The latter source, for example, lacks the entire third line of the refrain.

17. QUANT DE VOUS SEUL

SOURCE:

Dij, fol. xxxiij^v–xxxiiij^r (36^v–37^r). *Okeghem*, t+xx.

TEXT ALONE:

VerJard, fol. lxxxxi^r.

MUSIC PUBLISHED:

DrozT, no. 32.

TEXT PUBLISHED:

DrozJP, no. 316.

TEXT AND TRANSLATION:

Quant de vous seul je pers la veue
De qui tant chiere suis tenue,
Mon mal lors si tresfort m'assault
Qu'a peu que[1] le cueur ne me fault,
Tant suis de douleur esperdue.

Pour estre vostre devenue
Plus que[2] nul qui soit soubz la nue,
Toute ma joie me default

Quant de vous seul ...

Dont je voi bien que je[3] suis nue
De tous biens comme beste mue,
A qui de plus riens[4] il ne chault;
Car je sçais bien qu'estre me fault
Seulle de tous biens despourveue,

Quant de vous seul ...

When I lose sight of you alone
By whom I am held so dear,
My pain then assails me so grievously
That my heart nearly breaks,
I am so overcome by sorrow.

Because I have become yours
More than anyone else's under heaven,
All my joy fails me

When I lose sight ...

Then well do I see that I am stripped
Of all good things, like a shedding beast,
For whom nothing is any longer warming;
For I know well that I must be
Alone, deprived of all good things,

When I lose sight ...

[1]Que presque (*VerJard*).
[2]qua (*VerJard*).
[3]ien (*VerJard*).
[4]riens plus (*VerJard*).

ERRORS IN SOURCE:

Superius: 6/2 m err.
Tenor: (none).
Conctratenor: (none).

COMMENTARY:

Many of the remarks made above concerning the style of *Les desléaulx*, no. 10, apply also to the style of this *rondeau cinquain* setting. It may be, however, that *Quant de vous seul* is a somewhat earlier work. The voices cross constantly, most notably in m. 22, where the contra lies above both the superius and the tenor. Imitation is present, but it is canonic and unusually strict for Ockeghem. (See the superius and tenor, mm. 7–11, 14–20, and 27–32.)

The conclusion of the piece, in which the contra ends where it began (above the tenor), takes the form of a double-leading-tone cadence. A similar cadence formula occurs in mm. 26–27. As in *Les desléaulx*, the mensuration sign is plain C.[87]

18. QU'ES MI VIDA PREGUNTAYS

MAIN SOURCE:

MC 871, pp. 256–57 (fol. 5^{v}–6^{r}). *Cornago—Oquegan*, t+xxx.

[87]See the commentary for *L'autre d'antan*, no. 9 above, for remarks concerning the text of *Quant de vous seul*.

OTHER SOURCE:

Sev 7–I–28, fol. xxiiij[v]–xxvj[r] (20[v]–22[r]). Anonymous, txxx.

TEXT ALONE:

PBN 226, fol. 35[v].

MUSIC PUBLISHED:

GerberC, pp. 69–71.
HabkWVS, no. 14.
PopeMC, no. 10.
PopeSC, pp. 703–05.
QuerolC, no. 14.
StevSM, pp. 220–23.

TEXT PUBLISHED:

MorelC, p. 191.
PopeME, p. 49.

TEXT AND TRANSLATION:

¿Qu'es mi vida, preguntays? Non vos la quiero[1] negar: Bien amar e lamentar Es la vida que me dais.	What is my life, you ask? I do not seek to deny it to you: To love well and to lament Is the life you give me.
¿Quien vos pudiera servir Tambien como yo[2] he servido?	Who could serve you As well as I have served?
¿Mi trabajado bevir[3] Quien pudiera aver sofrido?[4]	Who could have suffered My troubled life?
¿Para que me preguntays La pena que he[5] de passar, Pues amar e lamentar Es la vida che me days?[6]	Why do you ask me about The pain I have to endure, Since to love and lament Is the life you give me?
¿Qu'es mi vida, …	What is my life, …

[1]puedo (*Sev 7–I–28*).
[2]missing (*MC 871*).
[3]trabaxado vivir (*PBN 226*).
[4]This line and the preceding supplied from (*Sev 7–I–28*).
[5]missing (*MC 871*).
[6]This line and the preceding three missing (*Sev 7–I–28*).

VARIANT READINGS:

Superius: before 1/1 O in sig (*Sev 7–I–28*); 12/2–13/4 a third too high err (*MC 871*); 13/3 m err (*Sev 7–I–28*); 13/5–14/1 miss (owing to a tear) (*MC 871*); 14/2–25/1 a third too high err (*MC 871*); 20/4–21/1 mi col (*Sev 7–I–28*); 24/4–5 m, sm (*Sev 7–I–28*); 24/7 c sm, b sm (*Sev 7–I–28*); 44/1 no sig congr (*Sev 7–I–28*).

Contratenor altus: before 1/1 O in sig (*Sev 7–I–28*); 6/1–2 2 sbr (*Sev 7–I–28*); before 11/3 no flat (*Sev 7–I–28*); 13/5–14/1 sbr, m (*Sev 7–I–28*); 17/3 miss err (*MC 871*); 33/3 e err (*MC 871*); 34/2 g err (*Sev 7–I–28*); 35/3 sbr err (*MC 871*); 36/2–3 sbr, m (*Sev 7–I–28*); 38/4 a err (*Sev 7–I–28*); 39/1 e (*Sev 7–I–28*); 42/2–3 no lig (*Sev 7–I–28*); 44/1 no sig congr (*Sev 7–I–28*).

Tenor: 13/5 a (*Sev 7–I–28*); 14/1–3 no lig or col (*Sev 7–I– 28*); 15/3 miss (owing to a tear) (*MC 871*); before 17/2 no flat (*Sev 7–I–28*); 35/1 1 perf br (*Sev 7–I–28*); 44/1 no sig congr (*Sev 7–I–28*).

Contratenor bassus: before 7/3 no flat (*Sev 7–I–28*); 11/3 a err (*MC 871*, *Sev 7–I–28*); before 19/1 no flat (*Sev 7–I–28*); before 32/1 no flat (*Sev 7–I–28*); 34/1–2 no lig (*MC 871*); 44/1 no sig congr (*Sev 7–I–28*).

COMMENTARY:

Undoubtedly, no. 18 is a revision for four voices by Ockeghem of a three-voice *canción* by Johannes Cornago, *Qu'es mi vida preguntays* (no. 18a). In January 1470, Ockeghem received payment "pour un voyage de Tours au royaume d'Espagne."[88] He may well have encountered Cornago's composition for the first time on this trip to the Iberian peninsula.

In recasting Cornago's work, Ockeghem retains the original framework of superius and tenor unchanged. He discards the original contratenor, substituting two new contras in its place, although the new contratenor altus begins with the old contra's first eight notes. The contratenor bassus is especially interesting because it descends to *d* below the bass staff numerous times, lower than any other voice in a secular work by Ockeghem, with the exception of the bassus of *Baisiés moy*, no. 2. This low contra takes over the role of the original in the point of imitation that begins the music for the *copla* (m. 26). Thus both new contras quote from Cornago's original. Stevenson has pointed out that the delayed cadence at the conclusion of the second ending (m. 45) is characteristic of Ockeghem.[89]

18a. [QU'ES MI VIDA] PREGUMTAYS

SOURCE:

MC 871, p. 380 (fol. 151^{v}). *Cornago*, t+xx.

TEXT ALONE:

(See no. 18 above.)

MUSIC PUBLISHED:

GerberC, pp. 51–53.
HabkWVS, no. 102.
PopeMC, no. 103.
PopeSC, pp. 710–12.

TEXT PUBLISHED:

(See no. 18 above.)

TEXT AND TRANSLATION:

(See no. 18 above.)

ERRORS IN SOURCE:

Superius: 36/4–5 miss.
Tenor: (none).
Contra: 23/2–3 2 m; 23/5 dot miss.

COMMENTARY:

(See no. 18 above.)

19. S'ELLE M'AMERA—PETITE CAMUSETE

MAIN SOURCE:

PNiv, fol. lv^{v}–lvj^{r}. *Okeghem*, t+ttx.

OTHER SOURCES:

BR 11239, fol. 20^{v}. Anonymous: Petitte camusette (S and T only), tt.

[88] See *BrenV*, p. 39.

[89] *StevSM*, p. 219. Cf. *Tant fuz gentement*, no. 21 below.

Dij, fol. viij^{xx}j^{v}–viij^{xx}ij^{r} (164^{v}–65^{r}). Anonymous: Selle mamera—Petite camusecte, t+ttt.
FB 2439, fol. XXXI^{v}–XXXII^{r}. *Ockeghem*: Petite camusette, xxtx.
MC 871, p. 392 (fol. 160^{v}). Anonymous: Petite camusette, x–––.
Mun 1516, no. 11. Anonymous: Petite camusete, xxxx.
NHMel, fol. 4^{v}–5^{r}. *J. okeghem*: Petitte camusette, tttt.
Sev 7–I–28, fol. cj^{v}–cij^{r} (92^{v}–93^{r}). Anonymous: De la momera—Petit le camiset, txxx.
Wol 287, fol. 61^{v}–62^{r}. Anonymous: Selle maymera—Petite camusette, t+ttt.
RISM 1504^{3}, fol. 1026^{v}–1023^{r} (*recte* 124^{v}–25^{r}). *Okenghem*: Petite camusete, xxxx.

TEXT ALONE:
PBN 1719, fol. 87^{r} (Selle maymera).
PBN 7559, fol. 66^{v} (Selle maymera).
VerChasse, fol. Piiii^{v} (Selle maymera).

MUSIC PUBLISHED:
GomO, Notenanhang, no. 6.
HabkWVS, no. 87.
PerkMC, no. 4.
PickCA, pp. 437–39.
PopeMC, no. 110.

TEXT PUBLISHED:
Bancel, p. 7.
FranAP, no. XCI (Petitte camusette only).

TEXT AND TRANSLATION:

S'elle m'amera[1] je ne scay,
Mais je me mettray[2] en essay
D'acquerir quelque peu sa[3] grace.[4]
Force m'est que par la je passe;
Ceste fois j'en feray l'essay.

L'aultre jour tant[5] je m'avençay[6]
Que presque[7] tout mon cuer lassay
Aler[8] sans que luy demandasse[9]

S'elle m'amera …

Puis apres le[10] coup me[11] pençay
Que long temps a que ne cessay,
Ne ne fut que je ne l'aimasse;[12]
Mais c'est ung jeu[13] de passe passe,
J'en suis comme je commençay.

S'elle m'amera …

Petite camusete,
A la mort m'avez mis.
Robin et Marion
S'en vont au bois joly,[14]
Ilz s'en vont bras a bras,

If she will love me I do not know,
But I shall make an attempt
To obtain, in some measure, her favor.
I am obliged to go that route;
This time I will give it a try.

The other day I went so far
That I almost let my heart
Go without having asked her

If she will love me …

Then after the fact I thought to myself
That for a long time I had not ceased,
Nor was it that I did not love her;
But it is a game of sleight of hand:
I am where I was when I began.

If she will love me …

Little snubnose,
You have brought me to death's door.
Robin and Marion
Are going to the greenwood,
They are going off arm in arm,

Ilz s'en sont endormis.	They have fallen asleep.
Petite camusete,	Little snubnose,
A la mort m'avez mis.	You have brought me to death's door.

[1]De la momera (*Sev 7–I–28*).
[2]prior to this point: Petitte camusette, j'ay / Proposé me mettre (*NHMel*); the remainder follows the refrain of the other sources.
[3]vo (*NHMel*).
[4]Que son corps ung peu ie compasse (*VerChasse*).
[5]missing (*Dij*).
[6]men advisay (*PBN 7559*); Ses facons, si bien ie ses scay (*VerChasse*).
[7]Qua peu que (*PBN 7559*, *VerChasse*).
[8]daller (*Wol 287*).
[9]de mansse (*Wol 287*); Vers elle aller, ains que trespasse (*VerChasse*).
[10]a (*VerChasse*).
[11]je (*VerChasse*).
[12]De laymer, sans que la trompasse (*VerChasse*).
[13]tour (*PBN 7559*); Mais tout me fist (*VerChasse*).
[14]jouer (*NHMel*, *Wol 287*).

VARIANT READINGS:

Superius: before 1/1 no flat in sig (*Dij*, *FB 2439*, *MC 871*, *Mun 1516*, *NHMel*, *Sev 7–I–28*, *Wol 287*, *RISM 1504[3]*), ₵ in sig (*BR 11239*, *Dij*, *Mun 1516*, *Sev 7–I–28*, *RISM 1504[3]*), no mens sign (*Wol 287*); 1/1–2 1 br (*Br 11239*, *FB 2439*, *MC 871*, *Mun 1516*, *NHMel*, *Sev 7–I–28*, *RISM 1504[3]*); 2/1–2 lig (*NHMel*); 4/1–2 no lig (*BR 11239*, *FB 2439*, *Mun 1516*, *Sev 7–I–28*, *Wol 287*, *RISM 1504[3]*); 5/2–3 mi col (*BR 11239*, *Dij*, *Wol 287*); 7/1–2 mi col (*BR 11239*), 2 m (*FB 2439*); 7/3–5 m, 2 sm (*BR 11239*, *FB 2439*, *Mun 1516*, *RISM 1504[3]*); 8/2 g err (*Dij*); 8/2–3 1 sbr (*BR 11239*); before 9/1 no flat in sig (*BR 11239*); 12/1–2 mi col (*BR 11239*), 2 m (*FB 2439*, *MC 871*, *NHMel*, *Sev 7–I–28*), b m, a sm, b sm (*Mun 1516*, *RISM 1504[3]*); 12/4 b dot m, a sm (*Sev 7–I–28*); 12/4–13/1 no lig (*BR 11239*, *FB 2439*, *Mun 1516*, *Sev 7–I–28*, *RISM 1504[3]*); 16/1 2 sbr (*FB 2439*); 18/2–3 no mi col (*FB 2439*, *MC 871*, *Mun 1516*, *NHMel*, *Sev 7–I–28*, *RISM 1504[3]*); 19/2–3 mi col (*BR 11239*, *MC 871*, *NHMel*); 20/1–2 1 f sbr (*BR 11239*, *MC 871*), dot m, sm (*FB 2439*, *Mun 1516*, *Sev 7–I–28*, *RISM 1504[3]*); bl sbr, bl m (*NHMel*); 22/3 e sm, d sm (*BR 11239*, *FB 2439*, *Sev 7–I–28*), d (*Dij*, *MC 871*, *Mun 1516*, *NHMel*, *Wol 287*, *RISM 1504[3]*); 23/1–2 lig (*MC 871*, *Mun 1516*, *NHMel*, *Sev 7–I–28*, *RISM 1504[3]*); 23/2–24/1 no lig (*Dij*, *FB 2439*, *MC 871*, *Mun 1516*, *NHMel*, *Sev 7–I–28*, *Wol 287*, *RISM 1504[3]*); 24/1–2 lig (*Dij*, *MC 871*, *Mun 1516*, *NHMel*, *Sev 7–I–28*, *Wol 287*, *RISM 1504[3]*); 29/1–30/1 c br-b br lig (*Mun 1516*, *RISM 1504[3]*); 32/1–2 no lig (*BR 11239*, *FB 2439*, *Sev 7–I–28*); 33/1–2 lig (*BR 11239*, *MC 871*, *NHMel*, *Sev 7–I–28*); 34/2 miss err (*MC 871*); 34/2–35/1 no lig (*BR 11239*, *FB 2439*, *MC 871*, *Mun 1516*, *Sev 7–I–28*, *RISM 1504[3]*); 35/1–2 lig (*BR 11239*, *MC 871*); 35/2–36/1 no lig (*BR 11239*, *FB 2439*, *MC 871*); 37/2–3 mi col (*BR 11239*); 38/2–3 b dot m, a sm, a m (*Mun 1516*, *RISM 1504[3]*); 39/2–4 dot m, sm, m (*FB 2439*); 42/1–2 no lig (*BR 11239*, *FB 2439*, *Wol 287*); 42/2–43/1 lig (*Wol 287*); 43/1 m, sbr (*BR 11239*); 44/1–2 no lig (*BR 11239*, *FB 2439*); 44/2 sbr, m rest (*Mun 1516*, *RISM 1504[3]*); 45/1–2 1 d m (*BR 11239*), 1 e m (*Mun 1516*, *RISM 1504[3]*); 46/1 c sm, b sm (*FB 2439*); 46/1–3 b m, c sbr (*MC 871*), c sbr, b sm, c sm (*Mun 1516*, *RISM 1504[3]*); 46/2–3 2 m (*BR 11239*, *Dij*, *NHMel*, *Sev 7–I–28*, *Wol 287*); 47/1 sig congr (*Mun 1516*).

Contra: before 1/1 ₵ in sig (*Dij*, *Mun 1516*, *Sev 7–I–28*, *Wol 287*, *RISM 1504[3]*); 4/1–2 dot sbr, m (*Dij*, *Wol 287*); 7/1–2 1 br (*FB 2439*); 9/2-3 d m, c m, b sm, c sm (*NHMel*); 16/1–2 1 dot sbr (*Dij*, *MC 871*, *Mun 1516*, *Sev 7–I–28*, *RISM 1504[3]*); 16/3 c sm, b sm (*MC 871*, *Mun 1516*, *NHMel*, *Sev 7–I–28*, *RISM 1504[3]*); 18/1–19/1 br rest err (*NHMel*); 19/1 d sbr (*Mun 1516*, *RISM 1504[3]*); 20/1 2 sbr (*Mun 1516*, *RISM 1504[3]*); 21/1–2 1 d sbr (*Mun 1516*, *RISM 1504[3]*); 22/1–2 1 dot sbr (*Dij*, *Mun 1516*, *RISM 1504[3]*); 22/1–3 d bl br, c bl sbr (*Sev 7–I–28*); 29/1–2 mi col (*Dij*, *Wol 287*); 30/1–2 g dot sbr, f m (*Dij*); 30/2 g m, f m (*FB 2439*), f m, e m (*Wol 287*); 31/2 e (*FB 2439*); 32/1–3 sbr, 2 m (*Dij*, *Mun 1516*, *NHMel*, *Sev 7–I–28*, *Wol 287*, *RISM 1504[3]*), f sbr, f m, d m (*MC 871*); 39/1–2 1 br (*Sev 7–I–28*); 42/1–2 no lig (*Mun 1516*, *RISM 1504[3]*); 44/1–2 2 m (*FB 2439*, *Mun 1516*, *Wol 287*, *RISM 1504[3]*); 44/3–5 dot m, 2 fu (*MC 871*, *Sev 7–I–28*), 1 b sbr (*Wol 287*); 44/4–5 1 a m (*NHMel*); 46/1–47/1 br, longa (*Dij*, *FB 2439*, *Mun 1516*, *Wol 287*, *RISM 1504[3]*); 47/1 sig congr (*Mun 1516*).

Tenor [I]: before 1/1 flat in sig throughout (*BR 11239*), ₵ in sig (*BR 11239*, *Dij*, *Mun 1516*, *Sev 7–I–28*, *RISM 1504[3]*), no mens sign (*Wol 287*); 8/1–2 dot sbr, m (*FB 2439*); 11/1–3 sbr, 2 m (*Sev 7–I–28*); 11/2–3 1 e m (*BR 11239*); 24/1 br rest (*Mun 1516*, *RISM 1504[3]*); 25/1–2 1 br (*Mun 1516*, *RISM 1504[3]*); between 27/1 and 28/1 b sbr err (*Sev 7–I–28*); 28/2–29/2 b sm, a sm, g sbr, g sbr all err (*NHMel*); 29/1–2 1 br (*MC 871*); 30/1–2 1 br (*FB 2439*, *MC 871*); before 31/1 flat (*FB 2439*); 45/1–46/1 no lig (*FB 2439*); 45/2–46/1 no lig (*Mun 1516*, *Sev 7–I–28*, *RISM 1504[3]*); 46/1–47/1 lig (*Br 11239*, *MC 871*, *Mun 1516*, *NHMel*, *Sev 7–I–28*, *Wol 287*, *RISM 1504[3]*); 47/1 sig congr (*Mun 1516*).

Tenor [II]: labeled "Bassus" (*FB 2439*, *RISM 1504[3]*), labeled "Contratenor" (*NHMel*), labeled "Contra" (*Wol 287*); before 1/1 no mens sign (*Dij*, *Wol 287*), ₵ in sig (*Mun 1516*, *Sev 7–I–28*, *RISM 1504[3]*); 6/1 miss (*Dij*); 12/1–2 dot sbr, m (*FB 2439*); 14/1 2 sbr (*FB 2439*); 14/1–15/1 no lig (*FB 2439*); 14/1–16/1 no lig (*Mun 1516*, *RISM 1504[3]*); 21/1–2 g dot sbr, f sm, e sm (*Mun 1516*, *RISM 1504[3]*); 23/2–3 1 e m (*FB 2439*); 24/1–2 no lig (*FB 2439*, *Mun 1516*, *RISM 1504[3]*); 25/2–26/1 1 dot br (*Mun 1516*, *RISM 1504[3]*); 28/2–29/1 sbr, br (*MC 871*, *Sev 7–I–28*); 29/1–30/1 lig (*Sev 7–I–28*); 30/1–2 mi col (*Dij*, *MC 871*, *NHMel*, *Sev 7–I–28*, *Wol 287*); 31/1–3 mi col (*MC 871*, *NHMel*, *Sev 7–I–28*); 31/2–3 1 fm (*FB 2439*); 32/1–2 no lig (*FB 2439*, *Mun 1516*, *RISM 1504[3]*); 32/2–33/1 lig (*Dij*, *NHMel*, *Sev 7–I–28*, *Wol 287*); 33/1–3 mi col (*Dij*, *FB 2439*,

MC 871, *NHMel*, *Sev 7–I–28*, *RISM 1504*[3]); 35/1–2 no lig (*FB 2439*, *MC 871*, *Mun 1516*, *NHMel*, *Sev 7–I–28*, *RISM 1504*[3]); 35/2–36/1 lig (*MC 871*, *NHMel*); 36/1–2 no lig (*FB 2439*, *MC 871*, *Mun 1516*, *NHMel*, *RISM 1504*[3]); 46/1–47/1 lig (*Dij*, *MC 871*, *Wol 287*); 47/1 sig congr (*Mun 1516*), sbr rest, d sbr, d and f longa together (*Sev 7–I–28*).

COMMENTARY:

This double chanson appears to be the only one of Ockeghem's surviving secular works that was conceived as a four-voice composition from the outset.[90] The tenor presents what is probably a *chanson rustique*, a popular melody of the day, the text of which begins "Petite camusete." All of the oldest sources of the piece (*Dij*, *PNiv*, and *Wol 287*) transmit the superius with a complete courtly *rondeau cinquain*, "S'elle m'amera je ne sçay." This raises the question of how the piece is to be performed as a *rondeau*. None of the sources provides *signa* for the medial cadence, although it is plain that the third phrase of the superius concludes in m. 26 of the present edition. A *signum* has been supplied in square brackets at that point. It should be possible to return from there to the beginning after the short strophe and short refrain, especially if the lower voices are performed on instruments. Alternatively, if an all-vocal performance in *rondeau* form is preferred, the *c* in the superius might be held, while the second voice proceeds to the *e* in m. 28 and the two bottom voices hold at m. 27, as suggested in *PerkMC* I, p. 45.

The remaining sources omit the *rondeau* poem and provide all the voices with the text of "Petite camusete" or its incipit, with the following exceptions: *Sev 7–I–28* gives a highly corrupt reading of the refrain of the *rondeau* plus incipits of the other text; *MC 871* has the incipit of "Petite camusete" in the superius, but the three lower voices are completely textless; *NHMel* substitutes a refrain-like combination of the rustic text and "S'elle m'amera" in the superius, which reads:

Pettite camusette, j'ay
Proposé me mettre en essay
De acquerir quelque peu vo grace.
Force m'est que par la je passe.
Ceste foys j'en feray l'essay.

There is a distinct difference between the rhythmic character of the highest voice and that of the lower voices, as though Ockeghem had intended to demonstrate a contrast between the courtly style and the style of popular melody. This chanson contains more imitation than is generally found in Ockeghem's secular works. All four voices participate in the opening series of entries, and again in mm. 14–18. One interesting touch is the repetition of the melodic material of the superius (mm. 7–9) that occurs at the conclusion of the contra.

Throughout the composition, one phrase joins the next without any interruption of the textural flow. Even the almost literal repetition of the opening fourteen measures of the three lower voices begins so unobtrusively (m. 34) that it avoids calling attention to itself. This "seamlessness," together with the four-voice texture and imitation, calls to mind the composer's style of motet composition.

20. SE VOSTRE CUER

MAIN SOURCE:

PPix, fol. 158^{v}–59^{r}. *J. Okeghen*, txx.

OTHER SOURCE:

RCas 2856, fol. 17^{v}–18^{r} (14^{v}–15^{r}). *Okeghem*: Se uostre ceur, xxx.

MUSIC PUBLISHED:

AmbG V, no. 5.

TEXT PUBLISHED:

PlamR, p. 324 (facsimile of *PPix*, p. 323).

---

[90]No. 13, *Mort tu as navré*, incorporates a sacred cantus firmus; *J'en ay dueil* comes down in two versions for four voices, nos. 16 and 16a, but both may well be revisions of a three-voice original.

TEXT AND TRANSLATION:

Se vostre cuer eslongne de moy a tort	If your heart should wrongly withdraw from me
Et que de vous ie n'ay[e] plus de confort,	And if I should have no encouragement from you,
Ie prendray lors sur Dieu et sur mon ame	I shall then predict, on God and on my soul,
Qu'en ce monde vous ne trouverés ame	That in this world you will not find a soul
Qui mains [que moy] vous voulsit faire tort.	Who wishes to wrong you less [than I].

VARIANT READINGS:

Superius: before 1/1 high b-flat in sig (*RCas 2856*); 4/1–7/1 a lig (*RCas 2856*); 9/1–2 lig (*RCas 2856*); 10/1–11/2 br-br lig (*RCas 2856*); 13/1–3 1 f sbr (*RCas 2856*); 15/1–2 1 br (*RCas 2856*); 18/1–2 lig (*RCas 2856*); before 19/1 flat (*PPix*); before 25/1 flat (for b) (*PPix*); 37/1–2 lig (*RCas 2856*); 38/1–2 lig (*RCas 2856*); before 38/2 flat (for b) (*PPix*); 39/1–2 lig (*RCas 2856*); 40/1–2 dot m, sm (*RCas 2856*).

Tenor: before 1/1 no high b-flat in sig (*RCas 2856*); 1/1–/1 1 dot br (*RCas 2856*); 3/1–2 lig (*RCas 2856*); before 10/1 flat (*PPix*); 10/1 sbr rest (*RCas 2856*); before 10/2 flat (*PPix*); 11/1–2 lig (*RCas 2856*); 12/1–2 1 b-flat sbr (*RCas 2856*); 16/1–2 lig (*RCas 2856*); before 23/1 flat (*PPix*); 23/1 m rest (*RCas 2856*); 33/1–2 d m, m rest (*RCas 2856*); 43/1–2 no lig (*RCas 2856*).

Contra: labeled "Bassus" (*RCas 2856*); before 1/1 no e-flat in sig (*RCas 2856*); before 8/2 flat (for b) (*PPix*); 11/1–12/1 no lig (*RCas 2856*); before 13/1 flat (*PPix*); 17/2–18/1 lig (*RCas 2856*); before 18/1 flat (*PPix*); 18/2–4 1 d sbr (*RCas 2856*); 20/1–2 no lig (*RCas 2856*); 20/2–3 no mi col (*RCas 2856*); 25/1–26/2 1 longa (*RCas 2856*); before 27/1 flat (*RCas 2856*); 28/2–29/1 no lig (*RCas 2856*); before 37/3 no e-flat in sig (*PPix*); 41/3–4 1 m d (*RCas 2856*); 43/1–2 no lig (*RCas 2856*).

COMMENTARY:

The complete text of this *rondeau cinquain* no longer survives. *RCas 2856* supplies only an incipit at the beginning of each of the three voices. Although the superius of *PPix* bears the complete refrain of the poem, it is evident that the Italian scribe of the manuscript possessed a poor knowledge of French. Therefore, it was necessary to emend the text as preserved in *PPix* considerably.[91]

With its quasi-homophonic texture, rich sonorities, and straightforward rhythms, *Se vostre cuer* sounds like a comparatively late work. Both the tenor and the contra lie in low ranges and cross relatively often, in mm. 8–10, 23, and 33–35. However, the tenor crosses the superius only momentarily in m. 12. Perhaps because the texture is so chordal, there is almost no imitation to speak of, although one might point to the strong similarity of melodic material shared by the superius and tenor in mm. 30–34.

21. TANT FUZ GENTEMENT

SOURCE:

PNiv, fol. lvj^{v}–lviij^{r}. *Okeghem*, t+xx.

TEXT AND TRANSLATION:

Tant fuz gentement resiouy	So much was I gently delighted
… par amours jouy	… I rejoice, for love's sake,
Me tenir au vueil davant tous	To keep myself, before all, at the behest
De vostre gentil cuer tresdoulx,	Of your noble, sweet heart,
Qu'oncques puis sur moy ne jouy	So that nevermore can my most grievous
Le mien tresdouloureux courroux.	Wrath triumph over me.
Si haultement avez party	So grandly have you shared with
Celuy qui de vous n'a party	Him who has not taken from you
Son cuer de vous amer tousjours,	His heart, loving you always,
Par cy tresgracieux party	By this most gracious sharing,
L'avez plaisaument departy	You have pleasantly deflected him

[91] For details concerning the emendations, see *PlamR*, pp. 322ff.

— C —

Du mal qu'il eust mis au dessoubs.

Mon leal cuer de dueil nercy,
Taint en des[es]peré soucy
Aloing de toute joye escoux,
M'avez comme a force rescoux
De Mort dont sans nulle mercy
Actendoye les dangereux coupx.

Tant fuz gentement …

From the pain that he had borne secretly.

My loyal heart, black from sorrow,
Tinted by desperate anguish,
Far from all joy, maltreated,
You have rescued me, as by force,
From Death, whose perilous blows
Without mercy I awaited.

So much was I gently …

ERRORS IN SOURCE:

Superius: (none).
Tenor: before 58/1 sharp (to cancel preceding flat).
Contra: (none).

COMMENTARY:

This *bergerette* setting, which survives in a single source, may postdate Ockeghem's other chansons in that form. Here, the restless, asymmetrical rhythms and old-fashioned cadences are absent, and the melody of the tenor is considerably less angular. The basic structure is that of a superius-tenor duo supported by a contra. The superius and tenor cross briefly just once, in m. 13, although the contra crosses the tenor rather frequently, lying above it at one point for nearly an entire phrase (mm. 27–35). Imitation between the superius and tenor is present in mm. 7–9 and again in mm. 27–32.

The equivalent of three syllables of text is missing at the beginning of the second line of the refrain. *PNiv*, the only source of the poem, shows no trace of any writing where the syllables should appear.

The mensuration sign, which is C at the outset, changes to ₵ at the beginning of the music for the *couplet* of the poem (m. 42). Assuming that the change was deliberate, it is unlikely that a strict proportion of 2:1 was intended, since the note values are substantially alike in the two sections. Depending on the tempo chosen for performance, taking the second twice as fast as the first would make either the first seem far too slow or the second much too fast. If the change has any actual significance, it may indicate that the tempo of the second section should be only somewhat faster, perhaps by one third.

22. UNG AULTRE L'A

MAIN SOURCE:

FR 2794, fol. 64^{v}–65^{r}. *De okeghem*: (Rondeau royal), t+xx.

OTHER SOURCE:

RCG XIII.27, fol. 17^{v}–18^{r} (10^{v}–11^{r}). *Okagem*: Dung aultrela, x−−.

MUSIC PUBLISHED:

AtlasCG II, pp. 3–4.

TEXT PUBLISHED:

PlamR, p. 322 (facsimile of *FR 2794*, p. 321).

TEXT AND TRANSLATION:

Ung aultre l'a, n'en querés plus;
Car dorenavant je conclus
De garder en tout temps mon droit.
Chascun se garde en son endroit,
Car bien peu me chault du surplus.

Je ne vueil pas estre forcluz

Another has it, seek no further;
For from now onward I resolve
To protect my rights at all times.
Let everyone look out for himself
For precious little do I care about the rest.

I do not wish to be prevented

D'acorder ou faire reffuz,
Mais ce que voulez orendroit

Ung aultre l'a …

Jamais en ce propos ne fuz
Que mon vouloir fust si confuz
D'entendre a tout ce qu'il voudroit;
De ce faire on me reprendroit
Congnoissant que seroit abuz.

Ung aultre l'a …

From giving or refusing,
But what you want, as of now

Another has it …

Never in this matter was
My will so confused
About attending to all it would like;
To do so, people would reproach me,
Knowing that it would be wrong.

Another has it …

VARIANT READINGS (all from RCG XIII.27):

Superius: 23/1 dot miss err; 30/1 c.

Tenor: 42/2–43/1 no lig.
Contra: labeled "Bassus"; 17/2–3 mi col; 23/2–3 mi col; 25/6–26/1 mi col; 32/2–3 mi col; 38/1–2 mi col; 41/2–3 mi col.

COMMENTARY:

In the manuscript *RCG XIII.27*, the superius bears no more than the a text incipit, "Dung aultrela," whereas the lower voices lack any text. The full poem survives, however, in the main source of the present edition, *FR 2794*. In that manuscript, a gap precedes the first syllable of the text, "Ung," suggesting that a letter was to be added at some later time by an illuminator. Modern commentators have assumed that the apparently missing initial in *FR 2794* must be the "D" in *RCG XIII.27*, but this assumption appears to be incorrect. In *FR 2794*, the *rentrement* written under the superius twice reads "Ung aultre la." Furthermore, the incipits of the two lower voices are given as "[T]enor Ung aultre la" and "[C]ontra Ung aultre la." In all probability, the scribe of *RCG XIII.27* had an imperfect knowledge of French and may have prefixed a "D" to the first word of the text, remembering the incipit of Ockeghem's *D'ung aultre amer*, a piece he had copied into the same manuscript.

In *FR 2794*, the words "Rondeau royal" appear above the superius, while the ascription "De okeghem" occupies, unusually, the lower left-hand corner of the same page.[92] It is possible that the author of the poem, the sense of which seems to refer to a specific event, was a member of the royal family.[93]

The resemblance of *Ung aultre l'a* to *Fors seulement l'actente* goes beyond their sharing very much the same opening rhythms. They are also alike in terms of the degree of imitation present, the overall smoothness of the rhythmic flow, the general lack of voice crossing, and the progressive style of cadence formulas. It seems probable that both were composed at about the same time, when Ockeghem had achieved full maturity as a composer.

[92]See the facsimile reproduction in *PlamR*, p. 321.
[93]The text of *Fors seullement contre*, no. 5 above, contains similar sentiments.

DOUBTFUL WORKS

23. AU TRAVAIL SUIS

MAIN SOURCE:

PNiv, fol. lxix^{v}–lxx^{r}. *Okeghem*, t+xx.

OTHER SOURCES:

Dij, fol. lix^{v}–lx^{r} (62^{v}–63^{r}). *Barbinguant*: Au traueil suis, t+xx.
Wol 287, fol. 62^{v}–63^{r}. Anonymous: Au traueil suis, t+––.

MUSIC PUBLISHED:

BarbO II, pp. 12–13.
OckCW I, no. 3a.

TEXT AND TRANSLATION:

Au travail suis que peu de gens croiroient;
On le peut bien qui veult aparcevoir,
Maiz c'est pour ce que je[1] ne puis veoir
Ma maistresse ainsi qu'aultres feroient.

Bien envieux certes aucuns seroient
Se de sa grace du[2] bien povoie avoir.

Au travail suis ...

S'il m'avenoit grant douleur
porteroient,
Car voir mon bien leur feroit recevoir
Mal si tresgrant que s'il duroit pour voir
Je suis tout seur que de
dueil creveroient.

Au travail suis ...

I am in such torment that few would believe it;
Those who want can easily perceive it,
For it is because I cannot see
My lady, as others may.

Some surely would be very envious,
If I could have the advantage of her favor.

I am in such torment ...

If that should happen, they would feel
great anguish,
For to see me receive my boon would give them
Such great pain that, if it truly lasted,
I am quite certain that they
would burst from sorrow.

I am in such torment ...

[1]missing (*Dij*, *Wol 287*).
[2]ung (*Wol 287*).

VARIANT READINGS:

Superius: 3/1–2 no mi col (*Dij*); 4/2–3 no mi col (*Dij*); 8/6–9/1 mi col (*Dij*, *Wol 287*); 9/1 a (*Wol 287*); 9/2–4 miss err (*Wol 287*); 9/7–10/1 mi col (*Dij*); 10/2 f sm, e sm, e sm (*Wol 287*); 10/3–5 d sm, e m, d dot m, c sm (*Dij*, *Wol 287*); 12/1–2 lig (*Wol 287*); 13/1–2 1 sbr f (*Wol 287*);13/3–4 mi col (*Dij*, *Wol 287*); 14/3–4 mi col (*Wol 287*); 14/5–15/1 mi col (*Wol 287*); 18/1–2 2 m (*Wol 287*); 20/6–21/1 mi col (*Dij*, *Wol 287*); 21/2–3 mi col (*Wol 287*); 21/4–5 no mi col (*Wol 287*); between 22/4 and 5 e sm, d sm (erased) (*Dij*); 22/5–23/1 a third too low (*Dij*).
Tenor: before 1/1 flat in sig err (*PNiv*); 7/1–2 lig (*Wol 287*); 8/5–9/1 lig (*Wol 287*); 10/4–11/1 no lig (*Wol 287*); 12/1–2 1 sbr

f (*Wol 287*); 12/1–3 lig (*Wol 287*); 12/4 f sm, e sm (*Wol 287*); 13/1–2 lig (*Wol 287*); 14/2 a bl sbr, g bl m (*Wol 287*); 14/4 m err (*Wol 287*); 15/3–4 lig (*Dij*); 16/3–17/1 lig (*Wol 287*); 18/3–4 no mi col (*Dij*); 21/1–2 no mi col (*Dij*); 21/3–4 mi col (*Wol 287*); 21/5–6 mi col (*Wol 287*).

Contra: 4/2 dot err (*Wol 287*); 4/2–3 no lig (*Wol 287*); 5/3–4 1 g bl m (*Dij, Wol 287*); 7/1–2 lig (*Wol 287*); 10/2–3 lig (*Wol 287*); 10/3–4 sbr, m (*Wol 287*); 11/1–2 lig (*Wol 287*); 11/4–12/1 lig (*Dij*); 12/1–12/2 no lig (*Dij*); 12/1–14/2  (*Wol 287*); 12/2–3 1 b sbr (*Dij*); 13/2–3 lig (*Dij*); 15/1–2 no lig (*Wol 287*); 15/3–16/1 lig (*Wol 287*); 16/2–3 mi col (*Wol 287*); 18/1–2 mi col (*Wol 287*); 20/2 e err (*PNiv*); 20/3 g err (*Dij, Wol 287*); 20/5–6 mi col (*Wol 287*); 21/3–4 mi col (*Wol 287*); 22/2 miss err (*PNiv*); 22/3 g sm, f sm (*Wol 287*).

COMMENTARY:

This composition is the original setting that served as a basis for other chanson settings and for Ockeghem's *Missa Au travail suis*.[94] The *rondeau quatrain* is ascribed to Barbingant in *Dij* and survives anonymously in *Wol 287*, but it is attributed to Ockeghem in *PNiv*. This attribution should be particularly noted, since the composition immediately preceding *Au travail suis* in *PNiv*, *Esperant que mon bien vendra*, is ascribed to "Barbingant." Evidently the compiler of *PNiv* had a degree of familiarity with Barbingant's work. It is possible, however, that he confused Ockeghem's mass with the chanson, so the latter is published here as a work of dubious authenticity.

There is nothing in the style of the chanson to preclude its having been written by either composer.[95] The opening of Ockeghem's *Ma maistresse* (no. 12 above) is quoted humorously in the superius and tenor of *Au travail suis* at the words "Ma maistresse" in the refrain, mm. 16–18 of the present edition.

24. DEPARTÉS VOUS

MAIN SOURCE:

PPix, fol. 133ᵛ–34ʳ. *Ochghen*, xxx.

OTHER SOURCES:

BQ 16, fol. xxvᵛ–xxviʳ (37ᵛ–38ʳ). Anonymous, xxx.
MC 871, p. 270 (fol. 12ᵛ). *Dufay*, txx.

MUSIC PUBLISHED:

DufayO VI, no. 93.
PopeMC, no. 21.

TEXT[1] AND TRANSLATION:

Departés vous, Malebouche et Envie,	Be off with you, Gossip and Envy,
Fuiés vous ent, vous et vostre maisnie.	Away with you and your group.
N'aprochiés du manoir de Noblesse.	Do not approach the house of Nobility.
L'Aysance y maint avec dame Jonesse,	Ease dwells there with Lady Youth,
Qui n'ont cure de vostre companye.	Who care not for your company.

[1]after *MC 871*.

VARIANT READINGS:

Superius: 3/1–2 1 br (*BQ 16*); before 4/2 flat (*MC 871*); 13/1–2 1 br (*BQ 16*); 16/1–2 lig (*PPix*); 18/2–19/1 a dot sbr, g m, g m, f m (*BQ 16, MC 871*); 30/2 d err (*PPix*); 31/2–3 e dot m, d sm, d sm, c sm (*BQ 16, MC 871*); 35/1–2 1 br (*BQ 16*); 38/2–39/1 lig (*BQ 16*); 39/2–40/1 lig (*BQ 16*); 42/3–43/1 1 a br (*BQ 16, MC 871*).

Tenor: between 4/1 and 5/1 superfluous sbr rest (*PPix*); 6/1–2 no lig (*MC 871*); 6/2–7/1 no lig (*BQ 16*); 11/1–12/1 lig (*BQ 16, MC 871*); 19/1–20/1 no lig (*MC 871*); 27/1–2 lig (*BQ 16, MC 871*); 29/2 b err (*BQ 16*); 50/4–51/1 no lig (*BQ 16, MC 871*); 51/1–2 lig (*BQ 16, MC 871*); 52/2–53/1 no lig (*BQ 16*).

Contra: 4/1–2 lig (*BQ 16*); 6/1–2 dot m, sm (*BQ 16*); 7/1–8/1 dot sbr-sbr lig, m (*BQ 16*); before 12/1 no flat (*BQ 16*);

[94]Published in vol. I of the present edition, no. 3. The chanson is printed there also, after *Dij*, as no. 3a.
[95]As Charles Warren Fox pointed out, Barbingant is not to be confused with Jacques Barbireau, a composer whose works are in a later style; see *FoxB*.

12/3–4 dot m, sm (*BQ 16*); 19/1–21/1 no lig (*BQ 16*); before 22/1 no flat (*BQ 16*, *MC 871*); 22/1–2 lig (*BQ 16*, *MC 871*); 22/2–23/1 1 a dot sbr (*BQ 16*); 24/1–4 bl sbr, 2 flagged sm, dot sbr (*BQ 16*); 30/2 b err (*BQ 16*); before 30/3 flat for b (*PPix*); 30/3–31/1 dot m, sm (*BQ 16*); 32/1 longa err (*MC 871*); 33/3–34/1 no lig (*BQ 16*, *MC 871*); 34/1–35/1 1 c br-g br lig (*BQ 16*, *MC 871*); 35/1–36/1 no lig (*BQ 16*); before 38/1 no flat (*BQ 16*, *MC 871*); 39/1–2 lig (*BQ 16*, *MC 871*); 41/3 a err (*BQ 16*, *PPix*); between 47/1 and 48/1 superfluous br rest (*BQ 16*); before 48/1 no flat (*BQ 16*, *MC871*).

COMMENTARY:

With reference to the attribution to Dufay in *MC 871*, H. Besseler proposed that *Departés vous* "is clearly inauthentic"[96] and published it as an *opus dubium*. He was apparently not aware, however,[97] that the work also survives in *BQ 16* anonymously and in *PPix* attributed to Ockeghem. In their study of *MC 871*, I. Pope and M. Kanazawa concur with Besseler, but they also express doubts concerning the validity of the ascription to Ockeghem in *PPix*.[98]

The style of the composition, in fact, does not bear much resemblance to that of Ockeghem's other chansons, even if one allows for his strong individuality. On the other hand, nothing about *Departés vous* is so out of the ordinary that it cannot be compared with works in Ockeghem's more conventional style as represented by, for example, *D'un autre amer* or *Fors seulement l'actente*. Imitation plays a rather more prominent role in *Departés vous* than in either of the last-named chansons. All three voices participate in a point of imitation at the outset and again at the start of the third phrase, and the superius and tenor engage in strict imitation from m. 45 to m. 51 in the last phrase. While the attribution of *Departés vous* to Dufay in *MC 871* might be questionable, there is little reason to accept the ascription to Ockeghem in *PPix* without hesitation. It is in *PPix* that one finds *D'un autre amer* attributed to Busnois, almost certainly incorrectly. For the purposes of the present edition, *Departés vous* must be considered a doubtful work.

No complete text survives, although the presence of signa in m. 32 and the structure of the extant lines of the poem suggest that it was originally a *rondeau cinquain*. The fundamental texture of the work is that of a superius-tenor duo with supporting contra, but none of the sources reports more that a text incipit for the tenor voice. Therefore, no text underlies the tenor in the edition provided here.

25. MALHEUR ME BAT

MAIN SOURCE:

RISM 1501, fol. 68^{v}–69^{r}. *Okenghem*: Malor me bat, xxx.

OTHER SOURCES:

BQ 16, fol. viii^{v}–viiii^{r} (20^{v}–21^{r}). Anonymous: Dieu damors, xxx.
BQ 18, fol. 73^{v}–74^{r}. Anonymous: Malur me bat, xxx.
FBNC 229, fol. 10^{v}–11^{r}. *Jannes Martini*, –––.
RCas 2856, fol. 57^{v}–59^{r} (48^{v}–50^{r}). *Malcort*: Mal heure me bat, xxx.
RCG XIII.27, fol. 72^{v}–73^{r} (65^{v}–66^{r}). *Jo. Martini*: Malior me bat, x––.
SG 461, pp. 52–53. *Ockenghem*: Malor me bat, xx–.
RISM [c. 1535]^{14}, part III, no. LVIII. Anonymous (S only), x.
RISM 1538^{9}, no. 91. Anonymous, –x–.

MUSIC PUBLISHED:

BrownFC, no. 11.
EvansM, no. 25.
GiesS, pp. 60–61.
HewO, no. 63.
JosqMS VIII, p. 66.
ObrO, *Missen* I, pp. 226–27.
ObrW I, pp. 189–92.

---

[96] *DufayO* VI, p. xiv.
[97] Ibid., p. lxix.
[98] See *PopeMC*, p. 594.

VARIANT READINGS:

Superius: before 1/1 no mens sign (*RCG XIII.27*); 4/1–2 1 br (*RISM [c. 1535]*[14], *RISM 1538*[9]); 4/1–5/1 lig (*RISM 1538*[9]); 5/1–2 1 br (*RCG XIII.27, RISM [c. 1535]*[14], *RISM 1538*[9]); 6/1–2 lig (*RISM 1538*[9]); 7/1–2 1 br (*BQ 16, RCG XIII.27, RISM [c. 1535]*[14], *RISM 1538*[9]); 8/1–10/3 (see below) (*RCG XIII.27*); 12/1–2 lig (*RISM 1538*[9]); 12/2–13/1 no lig (*BQ 16, BQ 18, FBNC 229, RCas 2856, RCG XIII.27, RISM [c. 1535]*[14], *RISM 1538*[9]); 13/1–2 lig (*RISM 1538*[9]); 13/2 m rest, m (*BQ 16*); 13/2–14/1 no lig (*BQ 16, BQ 18, FBNC 229, RCas 2856, RCG XIII.27, RISM [c. 1535]*[14], *RISM 1538*[9]); 16/3 c err (*BQ 16*); 19/4–20/1 1 c sbr (*BQ 16, BQ 18, FBNC 229*); 21/2–3 mi col (*BQ 18, FBNC 229, RISM [c. 1535]*[14]); 21/3 a (*RCas 2856*); 21/4 dot miss err (*RISM 1501*); 21/4–22/1 mi col (*FBNC 229*), 1 d sbr (*BQ 18*); 24/3–25/1 no lig (*BQ 18, FBNC 229, RCas 2856, RCG XIII.27, RISM [c. 1535]*[14], *RISM 1538*[9]); 28/1 no sig congr (*BQ 16, BQ 18, FBNC 229, RCG XIII.27, RISM [c. 1535]*[14], *RISM 1538*[9]); 28/1 2 g sbr (*SG 461, RISM 1501*); 29/2–30/1 1 br (*BQ 16, FBNC 229*); 29/2–30/2 1 dot br (*RISM 1538*[9]); 30/1–2 1 br (*BQ 18, RCG XIII.27*); 32/1–2 1 br (*BQ 18, RCG XIII.27, RISM [c. 1535]*[14], *RISM 1538*[9]); 33/1–2 1 br (*BQ 16, BQ 18, FBNC 229, RCG XIII.27, RISM [c. 1535]*[14], *RISM 1538*[9]); 34/3 miss err (*BQ 16*); 37/1–2 lig (*RISM 1538*[9]); 37/2–38/1 no lig (*BQ 16,BQ 18, FBNC 229, RCas 2856, RCG XIII.27, RISM [c. 1535]*[14], *RISM 1538*[9]); 39/2–40/1 lig (*BQ 16*); 40/1–2 no lig (*BQ 16, BQ 18, FBNC 229, RCas 2856, RCG XIII.27, RISM [c. 1535]*[14]); 44/2–45/1 1 dot sbr (*BQ 16, BQ 18, RISM 1538*[9]); 46/1–53/2 (see below) (*RCG XIII.27*); 46/2–47/1 mi col (*FBNC 229*); 50/4–51/1 mi col (*BQ 16, FBNC 229*); 57/4–58/1 mi col (*BQ 16, BQ 18*); 57/4–58/3 f sbr, e sbr, d m (*RCas 2856*); 58/2 d sm, c sm (*BQ 16, RCG XIII.27*).

Contra: labeled "Bassus" (*RCG XIII.27*); 2/1–3 mi col (*FBNC 229*); 3/1–2 1 br (*BQ 16, BQ 18, RCas 2856, RCG XIII.27, RISM 1538*[9]); 4/2–3 mi col (*BQ 18, FBNC 229, RCG XIII.27*); 4/3 b (*SG 461, RISM 1538*[9]); 4/4–5/1 mi col (*FBNC 229*); 5/4 a (*FBNC 229*); 5/4–6/1 no lig (*BQ 16, BQ 18, FBNC 229, RCas 2856, RCG XIII.27, RISM 1538*[9]); 6/1–2 lig (*RCas 2856, RISM 1538*[9]); 8/1–2 mi col (*BQ 18, FBNC 229*); 8/1–11/2 (see below) (*RCG XIII.27*); 8/4–9/1 2 m (*BQ 16*); 11/1–2 b n, c m, b m (*BQ 16, FBNC 229*); 11/3–12/1 mi col (*RCG XIII.27*); 16/2–3 mi col (*FBNC 229, RCG XIII.27*); 17/1 sbr err (*FBNC 229*); 17/2–3 1 e sbr (*BQ 18*); 18/1–2 mi col (*FBNC 229*); 18/3–6 1 b sbr (*BQ 18*); 19/4 m err (*FBNC 229*); before 21/3 flat (*BQ 18, RCas 2856*); 23/1 f sm, e sm (*FBNC 229*); 28/1 no sig congr (*BQ 16, BQ 18, FBNC 229, RCG XIII.27, RISM 1538*[9]); 28/1–2 br (*FBNC 229, RCG XIII.27*); 28/1–29/1 1 longa (*BQ 18, RCas 2856*); 28/1–30/1 a dot longa (*BQ 16, RISM 1538*[9]); 29/1 2 sbr (*FBNC 229, RCG XIII.27*); 32/1–2 1 br (*BQ 16, BQ 18, RISM 1538*[9]); 33/1–2 mi col (*FBNC 229*); 33/4–34/1 mi col (*BQ 18, FBNC 229*); 37/1–3 g dot m, f sm (*BQ 16*); 38/1–2 lig (*RCas 2856, RCG XIII.27, RISM 1538*[9]); 39/4–40/1 2 m (*BQ 16, BQ 18, FBNC 229, RCas 2856, RCG XIII.27, RISM 1538*[9]); 43/1–44/1 e dot sbr, c m, g sbr (*BQ 18*); 43/1–52/2 (see below) (*RCG XIII.27*); 44/2–3 mi col (*BQ 18, FBNC 229*); 45/2–3 mi col (*FBNC 229*); 49/2–3 1 a sbr (*RCas 2856*), mi col (*BQ 18, FBNC 229*); 50/3–51/3 a dot sbr, c sbr (*RCas 2856*); 50/4–51/1 mi col (*BQ 18, FBNC 229*); before 51/4 flat (*RISM 1538*[9]); 57/1–2 1 d m (*RCas 2856*); 57/4–58/2 mi col (*FBNC 229*); 55/2–3 1 sbr rest (*RCas 2856*); 57/4–58/3 bl sbr, 2 bl sm, m (*FBNC 229*); 57/4–58/4 c sbr, b sbr, a m (*RCas 2856*); 58/1–3 2 fu, m (*FBNC 229*); 58/2–3 1 g m (*BQ 18, RCG XIII.27, RISM 1538*[9]).

Tenor: 2/1–2 1 br (*RISM 1538*[9]); 2/1–3/1 lig (*RISM 1538*[9]); 3/1–2 1 br (*BQ 16, RCG XIII.27, RISM 1538*[9]); 4/1–2 lig (*RISM 1538*[9]); 4/1–5/2 lig (*BQ 16*); 5/1–2 1 br (*BQ 16, RCG XIII.27, RISM 1538*[9]); 6/1–2 1 dot sbr (*BQ 16, RISM 1538*[9]); 7/1–2 1 br *RCG XIII.27, RISM 1538*[9]); 8/1–10/1 (see below) (*RCG XIII.27*); 8/4–9/1 mi col (*FBNC 229*); 14/2–15/1 no lig (*BQ 16, BQ 18, FBNC 229, RCas 2856, RCG XIII.27, RISM 1538*[9]); 19/4–20/1 mi col (*FBNC 229*); 21/1–3 e sbr, d m (*RCG XIII.27*); 21/2–3 mi col (*BQ 16*), 1 e sbr (*BQ 18*); 23/1 c m (*RCG XIII.27*); 28/1 no sig congr (*BQ 16, BQ 18, FBNC 229, RCG XIII.27, RISM 1538*[9]); 28/1–2 1 dot sbr (*BQ 16, RCas 2856, RCG XIII.27, RISM 1538*[9]), m, sbr (*BQ 18, FBNC 229*); 29/4–30/1 mi col (*FBNC 229*); 33/1–2 mi col (*FBNC 229*); 33/3–34/3 e dot m, d sm, b m, c m, b sm, a sm, b m (*BQ 16*); 35/1–2 1 br (*RCas 2856, RCG XIII.27*); 35/1–36/1 1 dot br (*BQ 16*); 35/2–36/1 1 br (*BQ 18*); 36/2–37/1 no lig (*BQ 16, BQ 18, FBNC 229, RCas 2856, RCG XIII.27, RISM 1538*[9]); 38/2–39/1 lig (*BQ 16*); 39/1–2 no lig (*BQ 16, BQ 18, FBNC 229, RCas 2856, RCG XIII.27, RISM 1538*[9]); 40/2 a sm, g sm (*FBNC 229*); 42/1–2 lig (*BQ 16*); 42/2 a sbr (*BQ 16, BQ 18, FBNC 229, RCas 2856, RCG XIII.27, RISM 1538*[9]); 43/1–2 lig (*BQ 16, FBNC 229*); 43/1–53/1 (see below) (*RCG XIII.27*); 44/2 sbr, m (*BQ 18, FBNC 229, RCas 2856*); 46/1 sbr, m (*FBNC 229, RCas 2856*); 46/2–47/1 mi col (*BQ 18, FBNC 229*); 47/2 b sm, a sm (*BQ 16*); 49/2–50/1 no lig (*BQ 18, FBNC 229, RCas 2856, RISM 1538*[9]); 50/1–2 lig (*RCas 2856*); between 50/2 and 51/1 c dot m, d sm, e sbr err (*BQ 16*); 51/1–2 2 m (*BQ 16*); 51/4–52/1 mi col (*BQ 18, FBNC 229*); 57/4–58/1 mi col (*FBNC 229*); 58/2 f sm, e sm (*BQ 16, FBNC 229*).

RCG XIII.27, mm. 8–11

RCG XIII.27, mm. 43–53

COMMENTARY:

Malheur me bat is attributed to Ockeghem in *RISM 1501* and *SG 461*, and Pietro Aron refers to it as the composer's work in his *Trattato della natura et cognitione di tutti gli tuoni di canto figurato*, Venice, 1525.[99] However, two further sources, *RCG XIII.27* and *FBNC 229*, attribute it to Johannes Martini, and another, *RCas 2856*, gives it to "Malcort." No information exists concerning the identity of Malcort, whose name—if there was such a person—does not occur in any other connection. The ascription might represent a confused scribe's corruption of the first word of the poem. Martini's style resembles Ockeghem's mature manner so closely that it is not possible to make a secure determination based on the music alone.

A consideration of the sources does not resolve the question of who composed the piece, but several hypotheses emerge. Since Aron regularly took his attributions from Petrucci prints, and since the reading of the piece in *SG 461* undoubtedly derives from *RISM 1501* (cf. the list of VARIANT READINGS), the theorist, the printer, and the compiler of *SG 461* (Fridolin Sicher?) must together count as only a single witness in Ockeghem's favor. *FBNC 229* and *RCG XIII.27* both originated in Florence in the early 1490s, but, while the reading in *FBNC 229* largely agrees with what is found in the other sources, *RCG XIII.27* transmits an independent version of the piece. Allan Atlas has suggested that the version in *RCG XIII.27* represents Martini's revision of a chanson by Ockeghem (or Malcort?), which survives in its original form in all the other sources; whoever compiled *FBNC 229* was aware of the existence of a revision by Martini but mistakenly applied his name to the original version.[100]

Howard Mayer Brown, on the other hand, favors the attribution to Martini, pointing out, as did Atlas, that the scribe of *FBNC 229* must have known Martini's music well.[101] In *FBNC 229*, *Malheur me bat* is the eleventh work in the opening series of nineteen in which compositions by Martini alternate with pieces by Isaac. One might expect the scribe of *FBNC 229* to have taken special care to avoid a misattribution under the circumstances; if his apparent plan has full validity, then the piece ought to have been composed by Martini. However, as both Atlas and Brown recognize, *RCas 2856* was compiled in Ferrara during Martini's tenure there and contains almost two dozen chansons by him. Therefore, the attribution to "Malcort" in *RCas 2856*, whatever its meaning, would appear to weaken substantially Martini's claim to the piece. Nevertheless, the attribution to Ockeghem must remain at least questionable.

None of the sources preserves a text for *Malheur me bat*, although the structure of the music suggests that the original poem was a *rondeau quatrain*. The style of the music most closely resembles that of genuine chansons by Ockeghem such as *Fors seulement l'actente* and *Se vostre cuer* in terms of its texture. The tenor and superius, which never cross, constitute a duo supported by the contra. The melodic lines of the contra and tenor interweave constantly, and they occupy very nearly identical ranges. From m. 54 to the end, all three voices engage in imitation, a feature of the work that seems relatively progressive. The rhythmic practice, however, has an older aspect, as does the sequential, *fauxbourdon*-like approach to the final cadence. If it is Ockeghem's, *Malheur me bat* may represent, like *Les desléaulx*, a transitional stage between the composer's early and late styles.

---

[99]See *StrunkSR*, p. 214.
[100]*AtlasCG* I, pp. 149–55.
[101]*BrownFC* I, p. 88f and p. 211.

26. PERMANENT VIERGE

SOURCE:

Dij, fol. viii^{xx}ij^{v}–viii^{xx}iij^{r} (165^{v}–66^{r}). Anonymous, t+xttx.

MUSIC PUBLISHED:

AmbG II, pp. 355–57.
MoD, Appendice, no. IV.

TEXT AND TRANSLATION:

Permanent vierge, plus digne que nesune,
Femme couverte du soleil de justice,
Chief couronné par divin artifice
De douze estoilles supeditant la lune,

Esmerveillant nature et loy commune,
Tu enfantas par supernel office,

Permanent vierge, …

Preordonnée sans differance aucune,
Du Redempteur fille, mere et nourrice,
Soiez pour nous advocate propice,
Toy supplions, tres belle, clere, brune,

Permanent vierge, …

Pulchra es et decora, filia
 Jherusalem:
terribilis ut castrorum acies ordinata.

Sancta Dei genitrix, virgo semper, Maria,
intercede pro nobis ad Dominum Jhesum Christum.

Mulier amicta, sole et luna
 sub pedibus eius.

Permanent virgin, more worthy than anyone else,
Woman clad in the sun of justice,
Head crowned by the divine device
Of twelve stars suspended above the moon,

Confounding nature and common experience,
Thou gavest birth by means of a supreme causality,

Permanent virgin, …

Preordained without any disparity,
Daughter, mother, and nurse of the Redeemer,
Be for us a kindly advocate,
We beseech thee, most beautiful, pure, and radiant,

Permanent virgin, …

Thou art beautiful and comely, O daughter
 of Jerusalem:
terrible as an army set in array.

Holy mother of God, ever virgin, Mary,
intercede for us with Lord Jesus Christ.

Beloved woman, the sun and
 the moon beneath her feet.

ERRORS IN SOURCE:

Superius: 12/1–2 miss err.
Contratenor I: (none).
Tenor I: (none).
Tenor II: (none).
Contratenor II: (none).

COMMENTARY:

Permanent vierge bears no attribution in its only source, but it occupies an opening in *Dij* between two anonymous works that can be identified, through concordances, as compositions by Ockeghem: *S'elle m'amera—Petite camusete* and *Mort tu as navré.* For this reason, Ambros proposed Ockeghem as the composer.[102] Subsequently, Wolfgang Stephan accepted the suggestion without hesitation.[103] While there is little reason to reject Ockeghem's authorship on stylistic grounds, bibliographical evidence fails to confirm it, and the work must be considered doubtful.

[102] *AmbG* II, p. 534.
[103] *SteB*, p. 44.

This five-voice motet-chanson has two cantus firmi. The tenor part on the third staff of the present edition consists of the melody and words (from Song of Songs 6:3) of the antiphon *Pulchra es et decora.*[104] A second tenor voice sings the melody and words of the antiphon *Sancta Dei genitrix virgo.*[105] In the right margin of fol. viii^{xx}iij^{r} (166^{r}), written sideways from bottom to top next to the second tenor, one finds the rubric-like inscription "Mulier amicta sole et luna sub pedibus eius." This is the incipit of the text of yet another antiphon,[106] the melody of which strongly resembles that of *Sancta Dei genitrix virgo.* It is not certain how the text "Mulier amicta …" should be performed with the music, if at all. Perhaps the scribe, who was apparently responsible for all of the writing on the opening, merely intended to point out the resemblance; or else the composer deliberately chose a melody that could be performed with either text. On the other hand, it is possible that "Mulier amicta …" should be sung as the words of the second tenor during one or another of the repetitions that would result from a complete musical performance of the French *rondeau,* although *Dij* provides us with no information concerning precisely which ones. This *rondeau,* which is sung by the superius and presumably also by the contratenors, reflects the meanings of the three Latin texts. In particular, the poem glosses the text of the antiphon *Mulier amicta,* which is taken from the Apocalypse of St. John, chapter 12 ("And there appeared a great wonder in heaven; a woman clothed with the sun, and the moon under her feet, …").

It is apparent from the counterpoint that all five voices are essential to the composition. This is made obvious by the relationship of the first tenor to the other parts in m. 14 and the similar relationship between the second tenor and the other parts in m. 28.

[104] *Antiphonaire … de Worcester, Pal mus* XII, p. 358, and elsewhere.
[105] Ibid., p. 353.
[106] *AR,* p. 630, and *LU,* p. 1380.

SUPPLEMENT

SUPPLEMENT

ERGONE CONTICUIT (Johannes Lupi?)

SOURCE:

RISM 1547^{5}, fol. vi^{r}–vii^{v}. *Io. Lupi*: “In Ioannem Okegi Musicorum principem, Naenia.”

TEXT ALONE:

ErasA, no. 44 (“Iohanni okego musico summo: Epitaphium”).

MUSIC PUBLISHED:

LenE, pp. [97]–[108].

TEXT PUBLISHED:

ErasP, pp. 223–24.

TEXT AND TRANSLATION:

Ergone conticuit vox illa quondam
nobilis, aurea vox Okegi?
Sic musicae extinctum decus?
Dic age, dic fidibus tristes Appollo
naenias.
Tu quoque, Calliope pullata
cum sororibus, funde pias lachrymas;
Lugete, quotquot musicae dulce rapit
studium virumque ferte[1] laudibus.
Artis Appollineae sacer ille
foenix occidit.

Quid facis, invida mors?
Obmutuit vox aurea Okegi per
sacra tecta sonans.
Demulsit aures caelitum terrigenumque simul
penitusque movit pectora.
Quid facis, invida mors?
Sat erat tibi promiscue tollere res
hominum;
Divina res est musica;
numina cur violas?

Has then that once noble voice become silent, the
golden voice of Ockeghem?
Is the glory of music thus extinguished?
Go speak then, Apollo, and express sad
dirges with your lyre.
Also you, Calliope, clothed in black with
your sisters, shed compassionate tears;
Lament, whosoever sweetly partakes of the
study of music, and praise the man.
A priest of the Apollonian art,
the Phoenix is dead.

What have you done, O invidious Death?
The golden voice of Ockeghem has ceased to sound
throughout sacred temples.
It caressed the ears of the celestial and earthborn
alike and moved the heart deeply.
What have you done, O invidious Death?
It was enough for you to carry off
the person heedlessly;
Music is a divine thing; why
do you outrage the gods?

[1] forte (*RISM 1547*^{5}).

ERRORS IN SOURCE:

(None).

COMMENTARY:

Presumably within a few months of Ockeghem's death on February 6, 1497,[107] his memory was honored by several of the foremost literary figures of his time. Guillaume Crétin penned his "Deploration sur le trepas de feu Okergan Tresorier de Sainct Martin de Tours," mentioned above in connection with no. 5, *Ut heremita solus*. Jean Molinet wrote two such memorial poems, one in Latin, "Famosissimi musici Johannis Okghem regis Franciae capellani Epitaphium,"[108] and another in French, "Epitaphe de venerable seigneur de bonne memoire Okgam, tresorier de Tours."[109] The latter is the text of Josquin's well-known "Deploration de Iohan. Okeghem," which begins, "Nymphes des bois."[110]

A memorial poem was also written by Erasmus of Rotterdam and published as "Joanni Okego musico summo epitaphium" some ten years after the composer's demise.[111] This elegy represents the only recognition Erasmus afforded a specific musician in all of his voluminous writings.[112] Although it cannot be shown that Erasmus and Ockeghem ever met, the sense of the poem suggests that its author drew upon personal experience. It is curious, however, that Erasmus seems to refer to Ockeghem only as a singer ("Aurea vox Okegi"), not as a composer.[113]

A musical setting of Erasmus's memorial tribute was published in 1547 by Tielman Susato, attributed to "Io. Lupi," titled "In Ioannem Okegi Musicorum principem, Naenia." There is good reason to doubt that the best-known of the several musicians named Johannes Lupi was the composer, for he served as a choirboy at the cathedral of Cambrai until 1521.[114] Obviously he was not yet born when Ockeghem died, and it seems unlikely that he would have had a reason to set Erasmus's verses to music in the late 1520s or 1530s.

Two other musicians named Johannes Lupi, one from Nivelles and one from Antwerp, have been traced, but neither of them is known to have composed.[115] It is possible that "Io. Lupi" refers to the composer of a motet, *Esto nobis, Domine*, in the so-called Medici Codex of 1518 (where he is called only "Lupus").[116] That piece was probably written when Johannes Lupi from Cambrai was still a young boy. Edward Lowinsky is of the opinion that *Esto nobis, Domine* and *Ergone conticuit* have many stylistic traits in common and that both differ substantially in terms of style from the works of the younger Johannes Lupi.[117] No direct connection between Ockeghem and any of the composers named Lupus (or Lupi) has come to light.

---

[107]See *VaccJO*, p. 60.

[108]Paris, Bibliothèque nationale, Ms. f. fr. 19165, fol. 20^r; and Tournai, Bibliothèque communale, Ms. 105, fol. 310^r.

[109]Paris, Bibliothèque nationale, Ms. f. fr. 24315, fol. 96^r.

[110]Mod. eds. *JosqWW* II, pp. 56–58; and *LowMCE*, no. 46.

[111]*ErasA*, no. 44; mod. ed. *ErasP*, pp. 223–24.

[112]See *MillerE*, p. 341.

[113]Ibid., p. 342. As Miller points out, the expression "golden voice" could be a metaphor for both singer and composer.

[114]See Bonnie J. Blackburn, "Johannes Lupi," *Grove VI* 11, p. 334.

[115]*ReMR*, p. 306.

[116]See *LowMCE*, no. 53.

[117]Ibid. III, pp. 235–36. See also *BlackLP*, pp. 355–57.

LIST OF PLATES

I. Intemerata Dei mater (initial opening)

II. Gaude Maria (opening of the Bassus voice)

III. Salve regina [II] (initial opening)

IV. Aultre Venus

V. Fors seulement l'actente

VI. Il ne m'en chault

VII. J'en ay dueil

VIII. L'autre d'antan

IX(a). Prenez sur moi (after *Cop 291*)

IX(b). Prennes sur moy (after *RISM 1504*^{3})

X. Departés vous

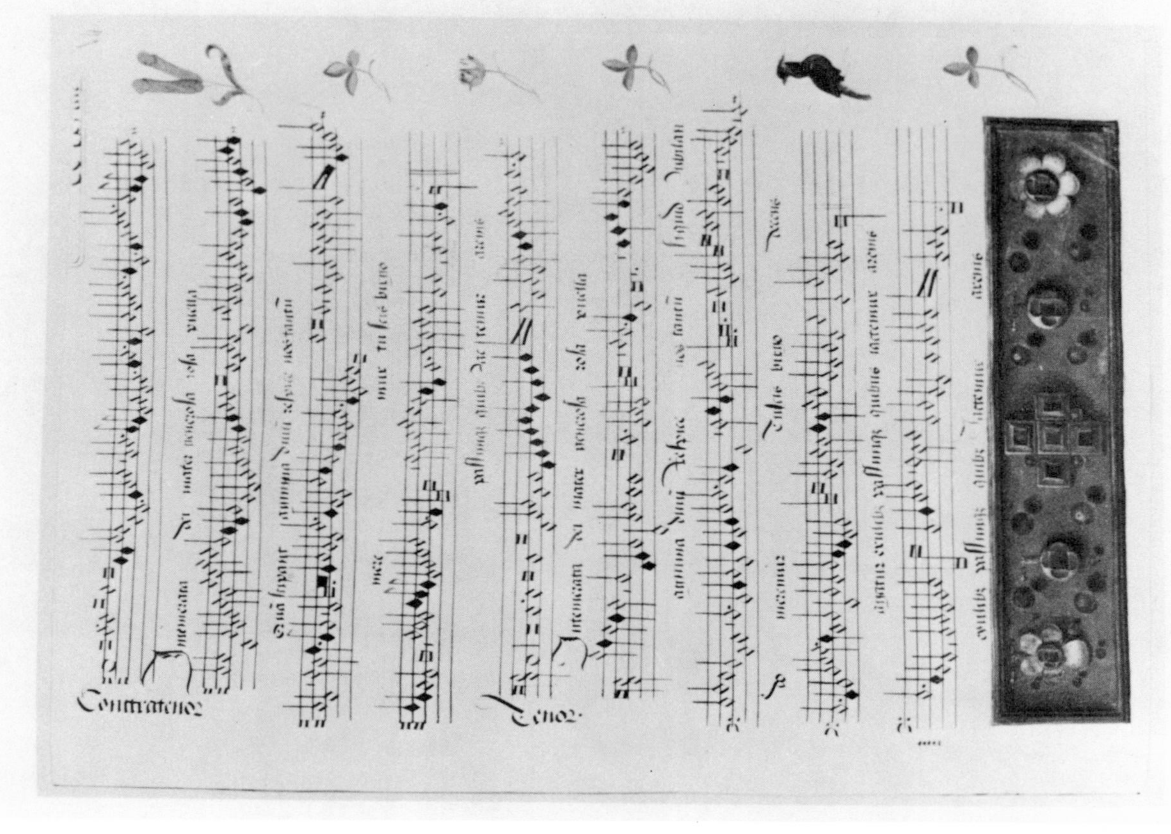

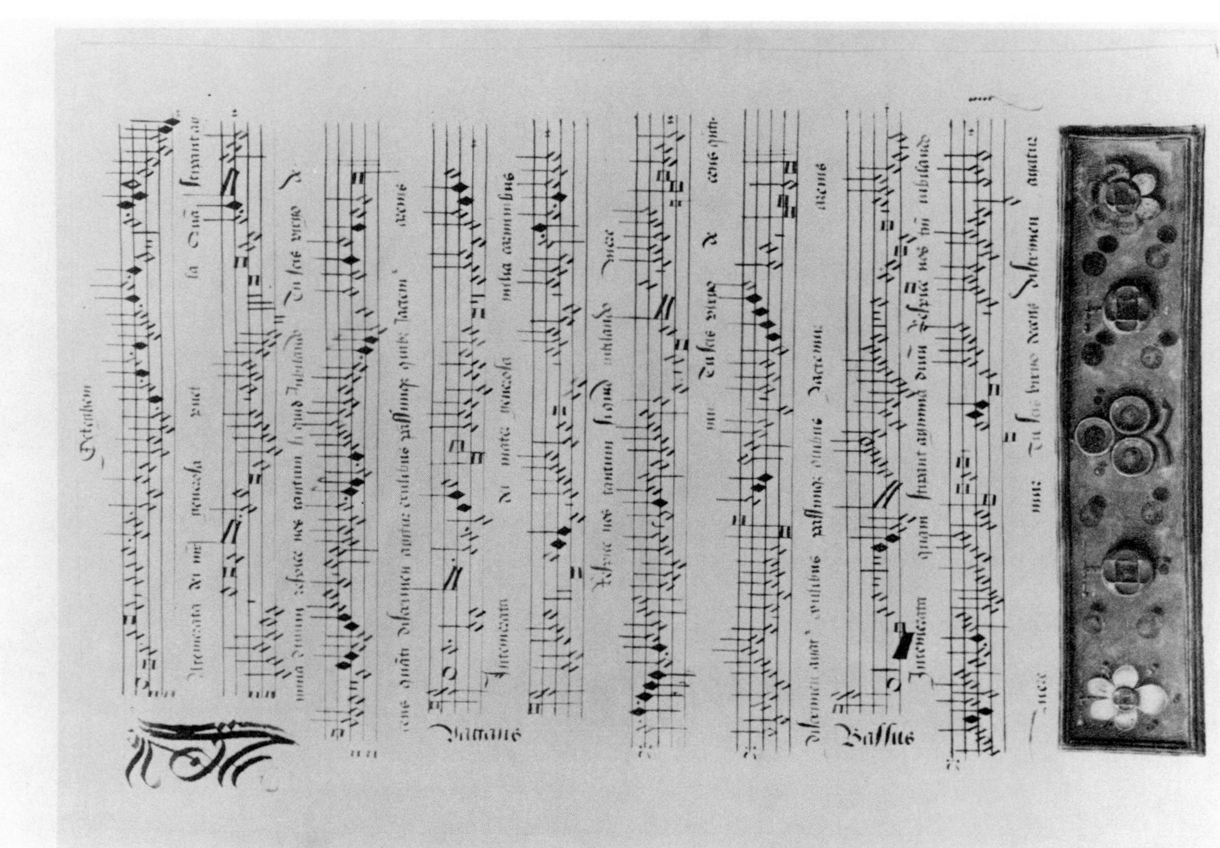

Intemerata Dei mater (initial opening)
(*RChigi*, fol. 276^{v}–77^{r} [CCLXVIII^{v}–CCLXVIIII^{r}])

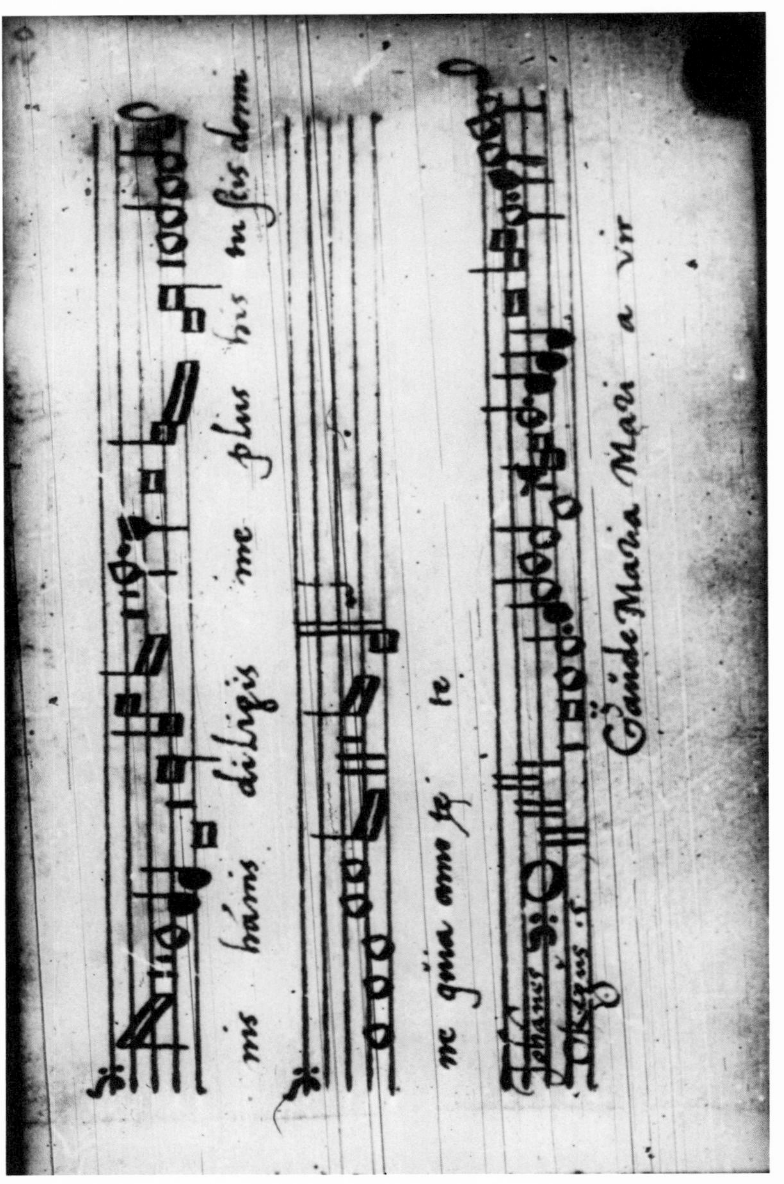

Gaude Maria (opening of the Bassus voice)
(*RegB 211–215*, no. 11)

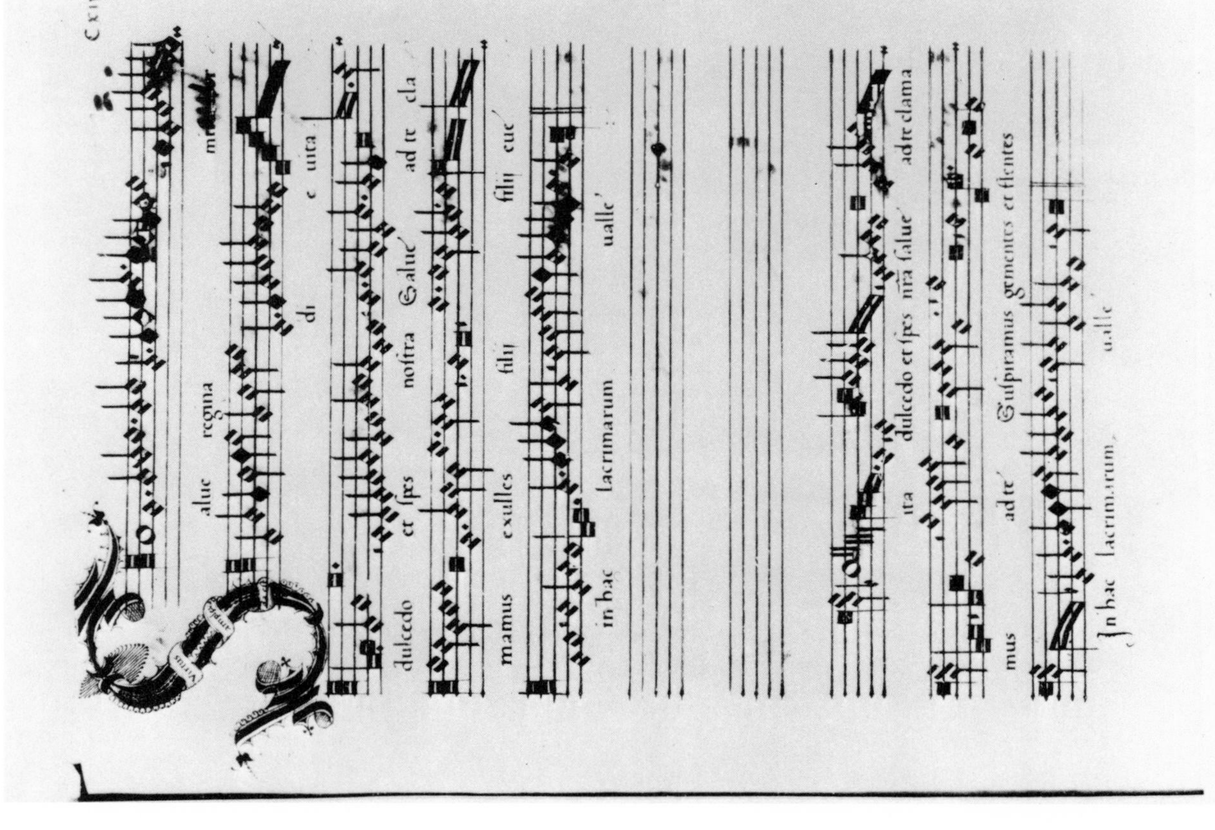

Salve regina [II] (initial opening)
(*RCS 46*, fol. CXVIII^{v}–CXVIIII^{r})

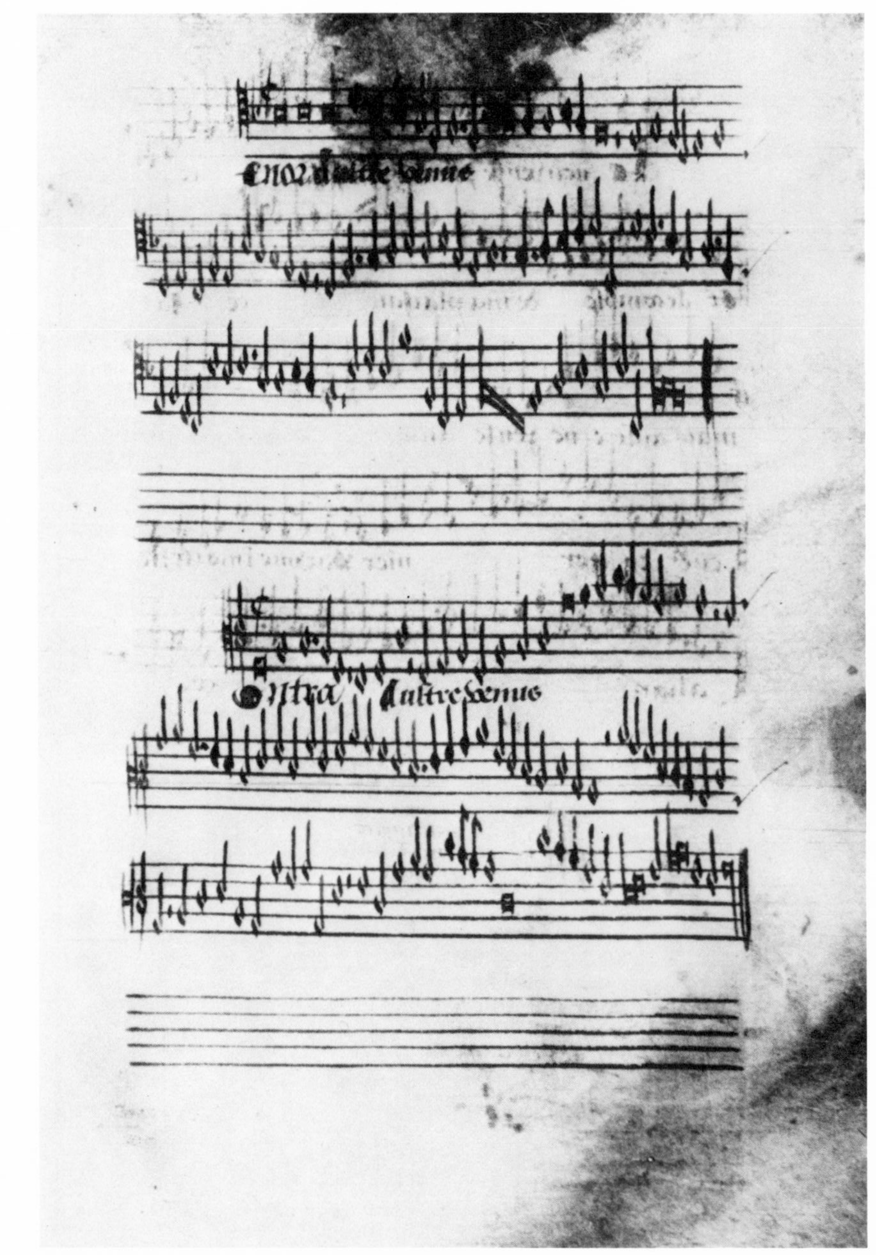

Aultre Venus
(*FR 2794*, fol. 39^{v}–40^{r})

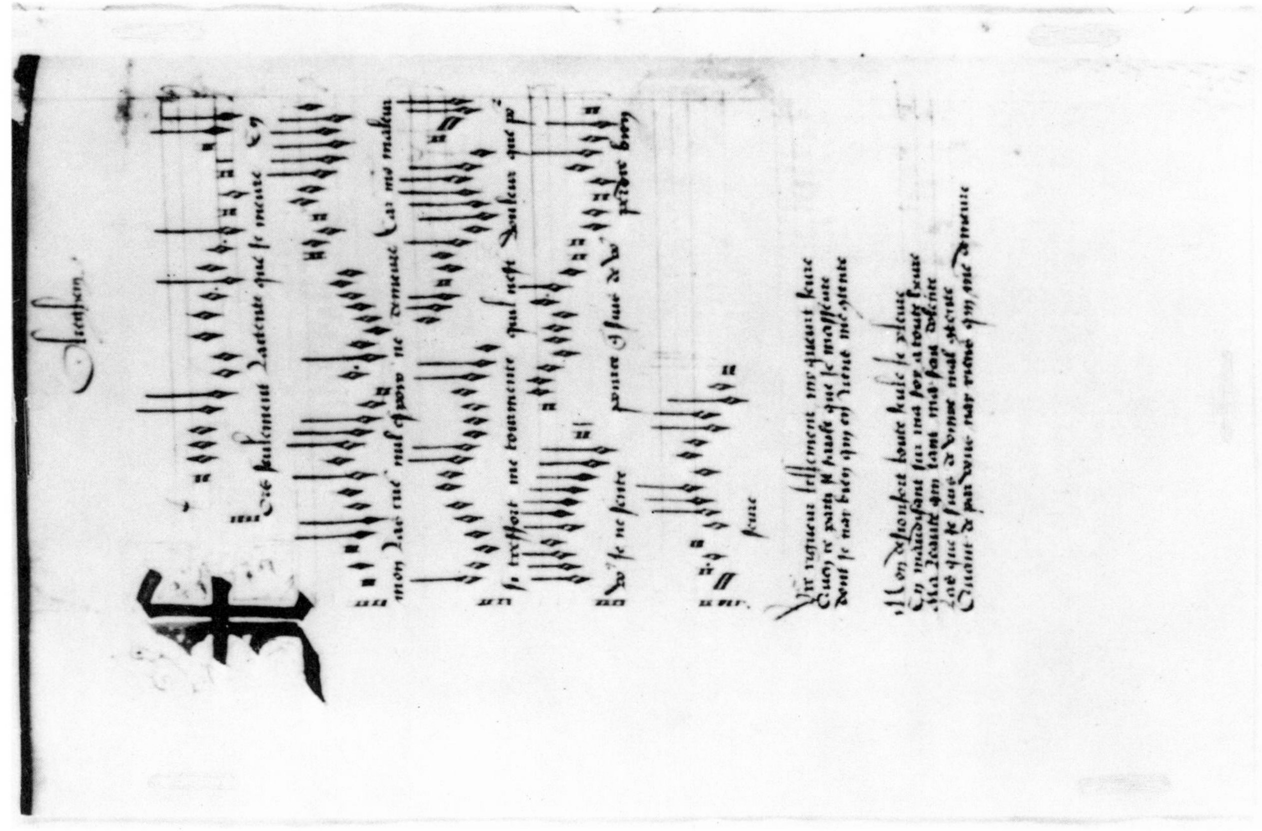

Fors seulement l'actente
(*Dij*, fol. xxv^{v}–xxvj^{r} [28^{v}–29^{r}])

PLATE VI

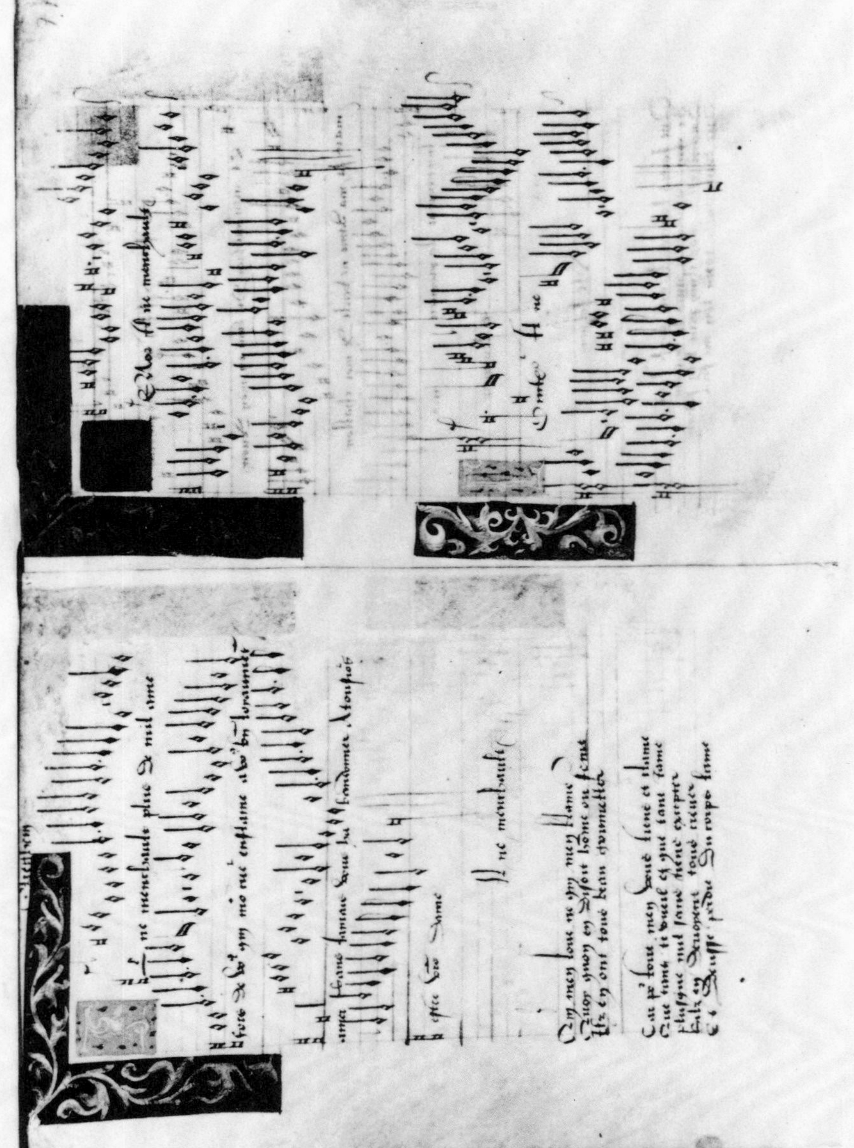

Il ne m'en chault
(*WLab*, fol. lxxvj^{v}–lxxvij^{r})

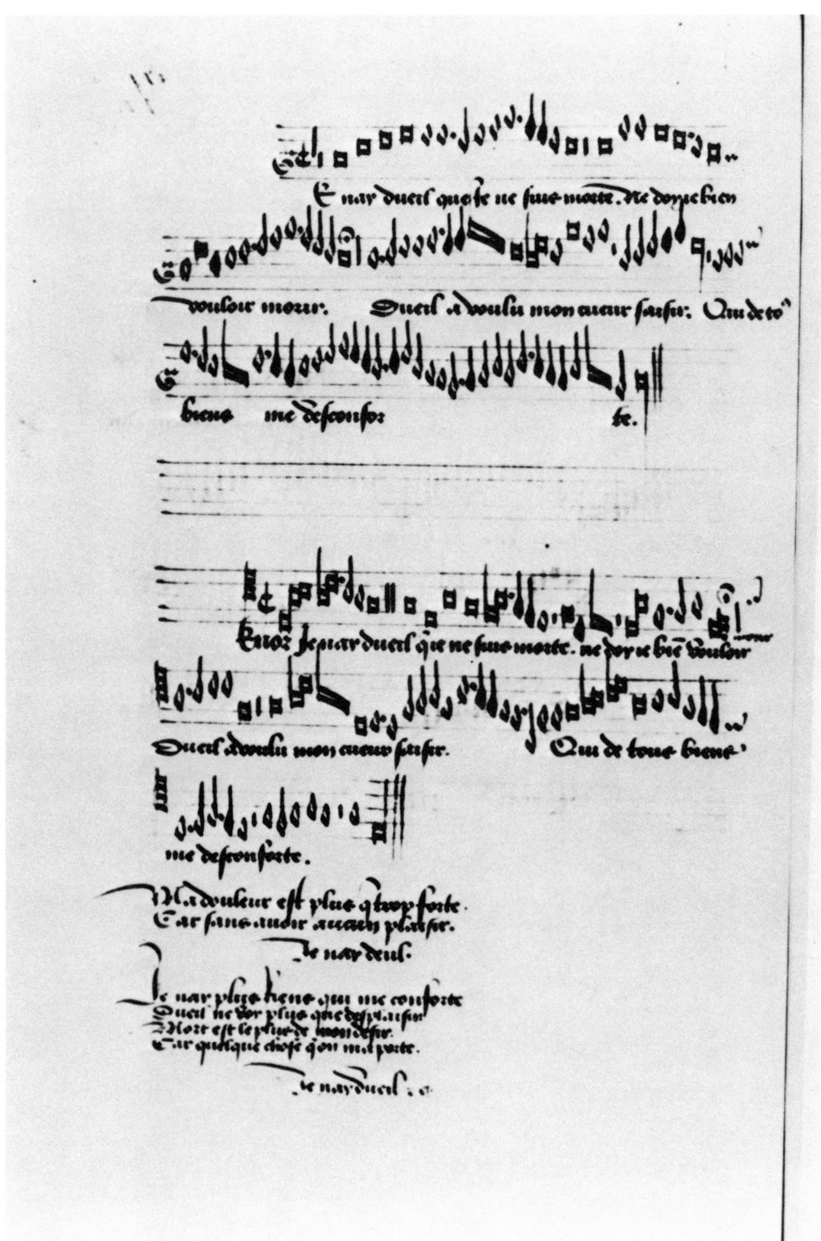

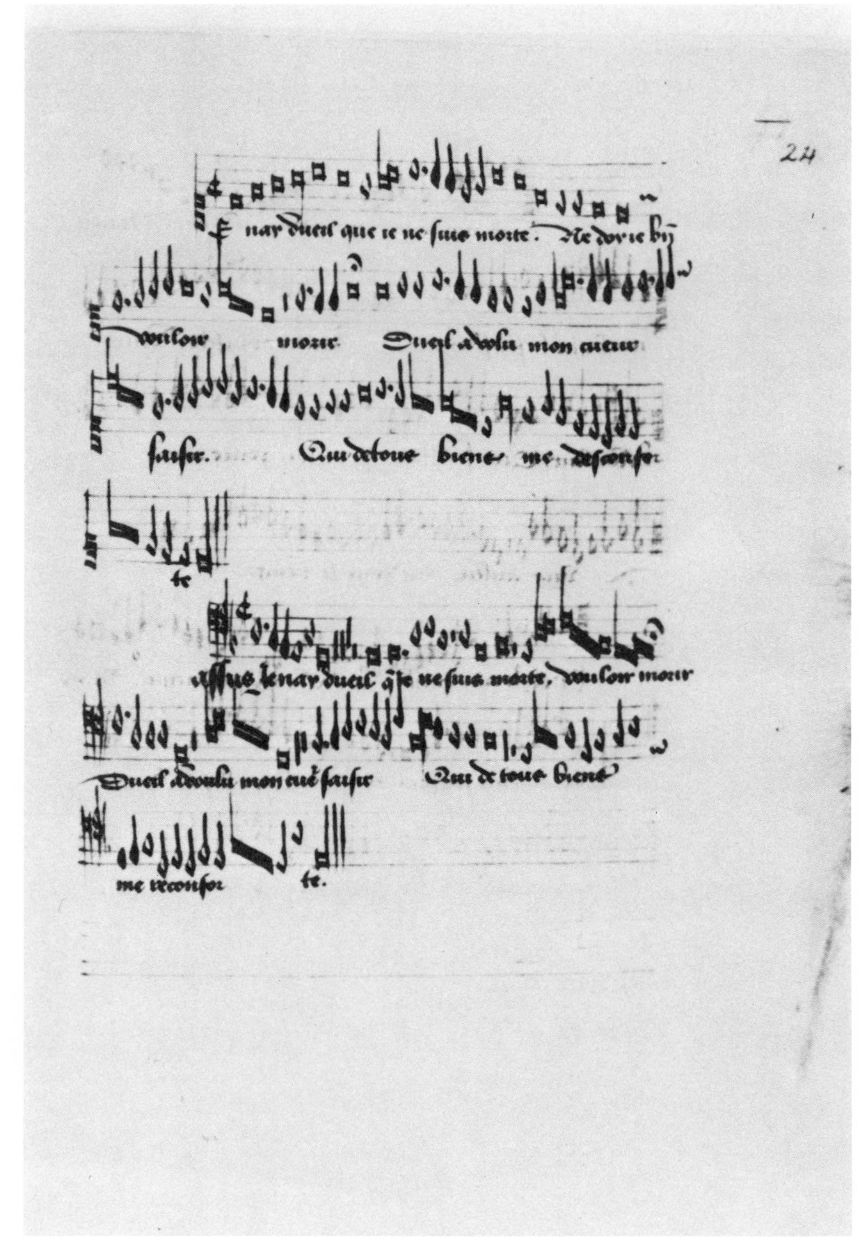

J'en ay dueil
(*LonBL 20.A.xvi*, fol. 23^{v}–24^{r})

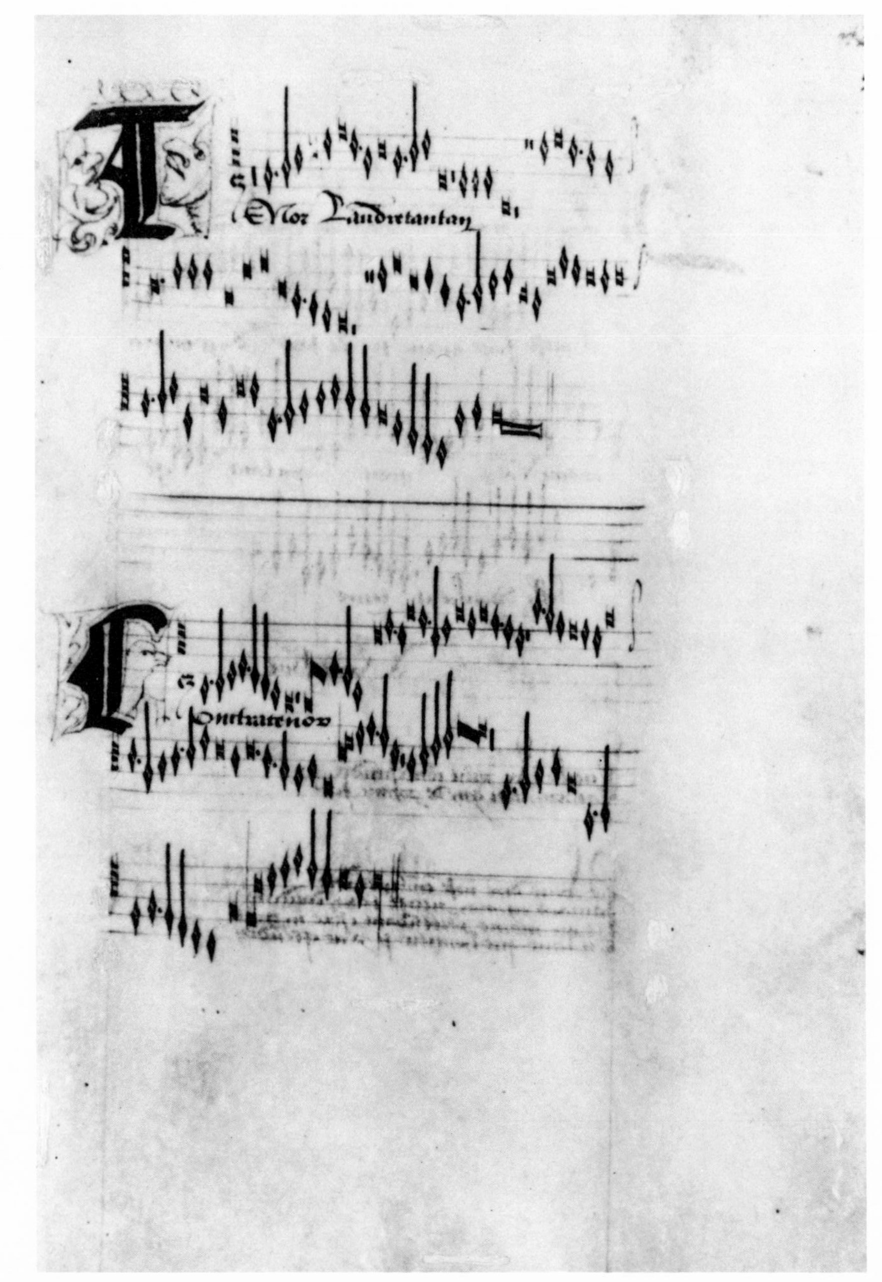

L'autre d'antan
(*Dij*, fol. xvij^{v}–xviij^{r} [20^{v}–21^{r}])

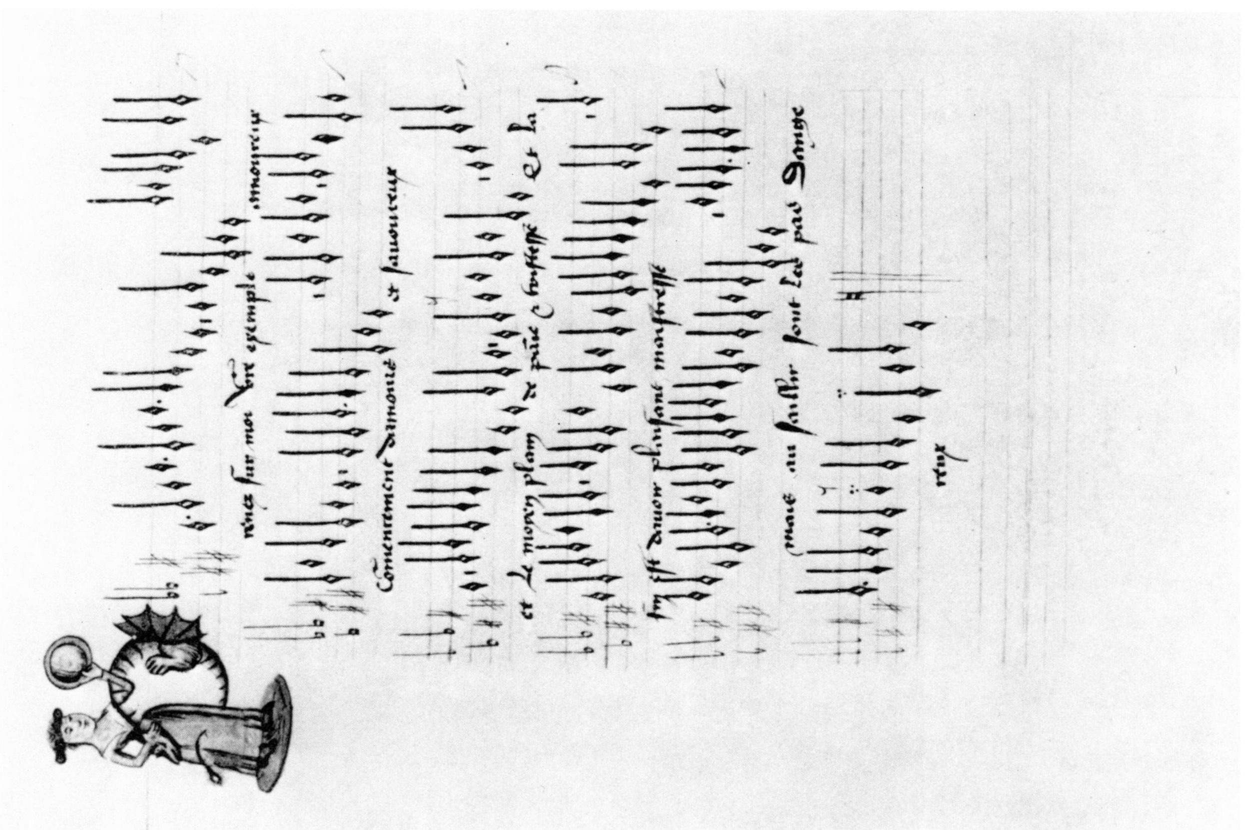

Prenez sur moi
(*Cop 291*, fol. 40^{v} [46^{v}])

PLATE IX(b)

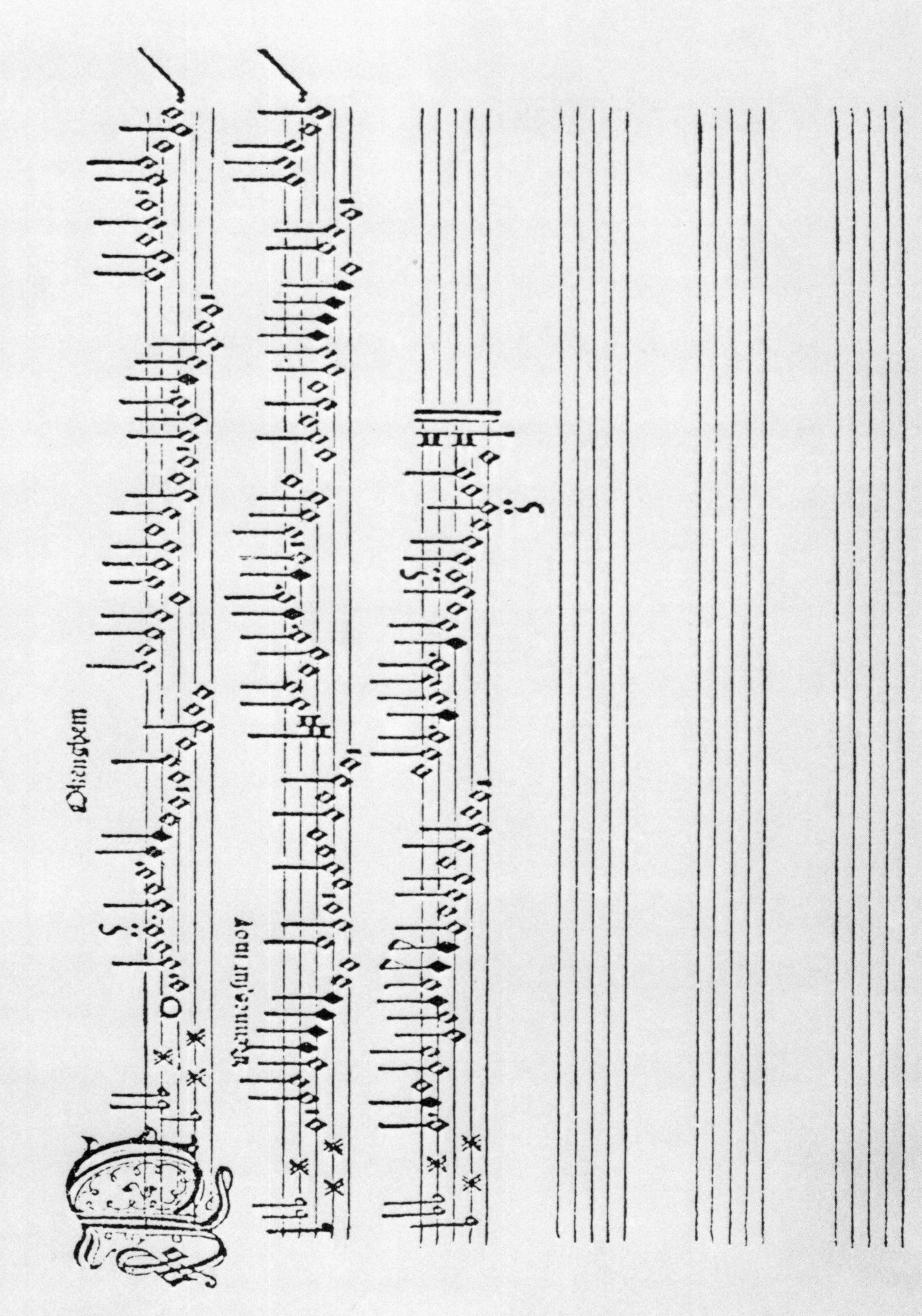

Prennes sur moy
(*RISM 1504*[3], fol. 167[v])

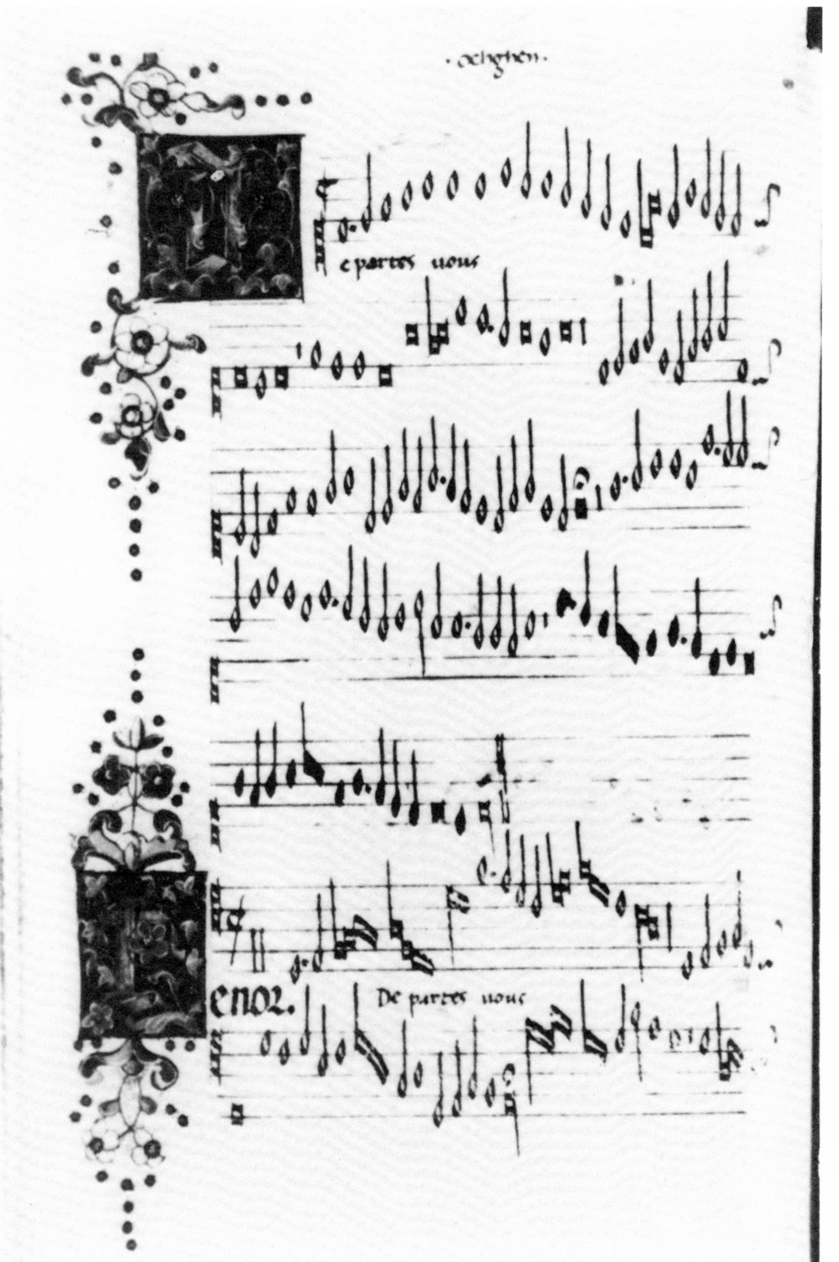

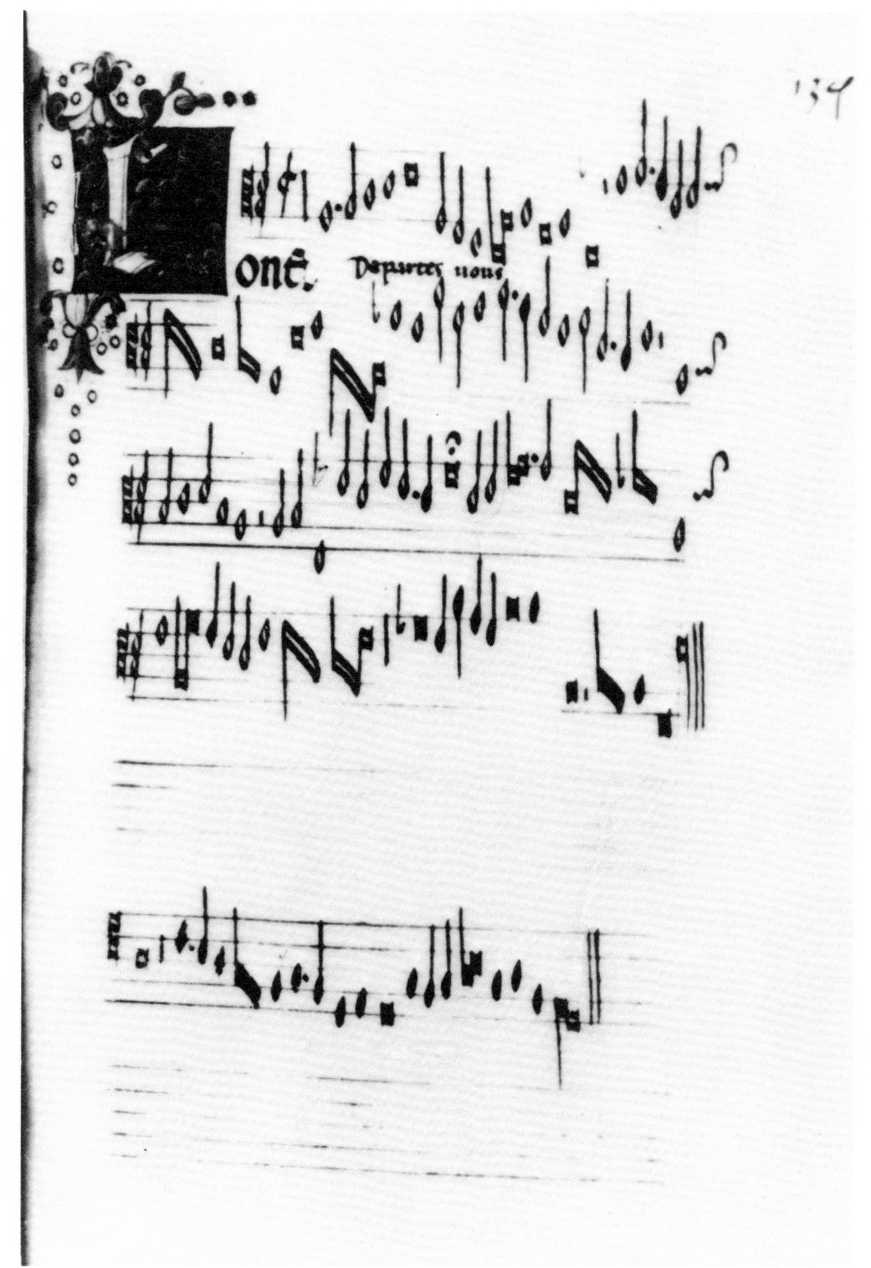

Departés vous
(*PPix*, fol. 133^{v}–34^{r})

EDITION
MOTETS

1.

Alma Redemptoris mater

den - - ti sur - ge-re qui cu-rat po - pu - lo.
- den - ti sur - ge - re qui cu - rat po - - pu - lo. Tu
den - ti sur - ge - re qui cu - rat po - - pu - lo.
- re ca - den - - - - ti sur - - ge - re
na -
quae ge - - nu - - - - - i - sti, na -
Tu quae ge - nu - - - i - sti,
na -
- tu - ra mi - ran - - te, tu - um san - ctum
tu - - - ra mi - ran - - - te, tu - um san - ctum
na - tu - ra mi - ran - te, tu - - - um san - - ctum Ge -
tu - - - - ra mi - - - - ran - te, tu - um san -
Ge - - - - - ni - to - - - rem. Vir - - -
Ge - - ni - to - - - rem. Vir - - -
- - ni - to - rem, Ge - ni - - to - - rem.
- - ctum Ge - ni - to - rem, Ge - ni - to - - rem.
- - - - go, pri - - us
- go, Vir - - go, pri - - - us ac
ac po -
pri - - - - - us

70
75
ac po- ste- ri- us. Ga- bri- e- lis ab
po- ste- ri- us, Ga- bri- e-
ste- ri- us, Ga- bri- e-
ac po- ste- ri- us, Ga- bri-
80
85
o- re su- mens, su- mens
lis ab o- re su- mens
lis ab o- re su- mens il-
e- lis ab o- re su-
90
95
il- lud A- ve, pec-
il- lud A- ve,
lud A- ve, pec- ca-
mens il- lud A- ve,
100
105
ca- to- rum, pec- ca- to- rum
pec- ca- to- rum, pec- ca- to- rum
to- rum pec- ca- to- rum
pec- ca- to-
110
115
mi- se- re- re, mi- se- re- re.
mi- se- re- re, mi- se- re- re.
mi- se- re- re, mi- se- re- re.
rum mi- se- re- re, mi- se- re- re.

2.
Ave Maria

A - - - - - ve Ma - ri - a, Ma -
A - ve Ma - - - ri - - -
A - ve Ma - - - ri - - - - a,
A - ve Ma - ri - - - - a, gra -
- - - ri - - - a, gra - - ti - a ple -
- - - a, Ma - - ri - - - a, gra -
gra - - ti - a ple - - - -
- - - ti - a ple - - - na,
- - - na, Do - mi - nus te - - - - -
ti - a ple - - na, Do - mi - nus te - cum, te -
- - - na, Do - mi - nus te - - - -
ple - - - - na, Do - mi - nus te - - -
- - - cum; be - - ne - di - - - cta
- cum, te - - - - cum; be - ne -
- - cum; be - ne - di - cta, be - ne - - di -
- - cum, te - - cum; be - ne - - di - cta

25
tu tu in mu - - li - e - - ri - bus, et
di - cta tu in mu li - e - - - - ri - bus, et
cta tu in mu - - - - li - e - - - -
tu in mu - li - e - ri - bus, mu - li -
30
be - ne - di - ctus, et be - - ne - di -
be - - ne - di - ctus fru - - ctus ven - - - -
- ri - bus, et be - ne - di - ctus fru - ctus ven - tris
e - - ri - bus, et be - ne - di - - ctus fru -
35
- - ctus fru - ctus ven - tris, ven - tris tu - i, Je -
tris tu - - - - - i, Je - - - - sus Chri -
tu - - i, fru - ctus ven - tris tu - i, Je - - - sus
ctus ven - tris tu - - - i, Je - - - - sus Chri -
40
- - - sus Chri - - - stus. A - - - - - men.
- - - - - - - - stus. A - - - - men.
Chri - - - stus. A - - - - - - men.
- - - - - stus. A - - - - - - - men.

3.

Intemerata Dei mater

25
ju - bi - lan - do me re - - - - - - - mur, me - re -
- - - do me - re - - - - mur, me - re - - -
- do me - - - - re - - mur, me - - re - - mur.
- - do me - - - - re - - - - - - - - -
30
Tu scis, vir - go de - - - - cens,
mur. Tu scis, vir - go de - cens, quan - ti dis - cri - mi -
mur. Tu scis, vir - go de - - cens, quan - ti dis -
Tu scis, vir - go de - cens, quan - ti dis -
mur. Tu scis, vir - - go de - cens, quan - ti dis - - -
35
quan - ti dis - cri - mi - ne a - ga - tur ex - su - - li-bus pas -
ne a - ga - tur ex - su - li - bus pas -
cri - - mi - - ne a - ga - tur ex - su - - li - bus pas -
cri - - - mi - ne a - ga - tur ex - su - - li - bus pas -
cri - - - - mi - ne a - ga - tur ex - su - - li - bus
40
sim - que qui - - bus jac - te - mur a - re - nis.
sim - que qui - - bus jac - te - - mur a - re - nis.
sim - que qui - bus jac - te - - - mur a - re - - - nis.
sim - que qui - bus jac - - te - mur a - re - nis.
pas - sim - que qui - bus jac - te - mur a - - - re - nis.

Nec si - ne te ma - net ul - la qui - - - es
Nec si - ne te ma - net ul - la qui - - es
Nec si - ne te ma - net ul - la qui - es spes nul - la la - bo -
spes nul - la la - - bo -
spes nul - la la - - bo -
nul - - - la sa - lus pa - - - tri - ae,
nul - - la sa - lus pa - - - - tri - ae,
ris, nul - - - - la sa - lus pa - - tri - ae, do - - mus aut po -
ris, ae, do - - mus aut po -
ris, do - - mus aut po -
cu - - i re - gi - na prae - - - es,
cu - - i re - gi - - na prae - es, dis -
ti - un - da pa - - ren - - - tis
ti - un - da pa - ren - - - tis cu - i re - gi - na prae - - es, dis - pen - sans
ti - un - - da pa - ren - tis
dis - pen - sans o - mni - - a. dul -
pen - sans o - mni - - a; lae - to su - sci - - pis o - - re pi - - os, dul - ci
su - - sci - - pis o - - re pi - - os, dul - ci
o - mni - - a; lae - to su - - sci - pis o - re pi - - - os dul -
dul - -

ci quos nec - ta - re po - tas, et fa - cis as - si - - du - - os
quos nec - ta - re po - tas, et fa - cis as - - si - - du - - os e - pu -
quos nec - ta - re po - tas, et fa - - - - cis as - si - du -
ci quos nec - ta - re po - - - tas, et fa - - cis as - - si - du - os
ci quos nec - ta - re po - - tas, et
e - pu - lis ac - - cum - be - re sa - - - - - - - cris, sa cris.
lis ac cum - - - be - - re sa - - - cris.
os e - - pu - lis ac - - cum - - be - - - re sa - - cris, sa - cris.
e - pu - lis ac - - cum - be - - re sa - cris.
fa - cis e - pu - - lis ac - cum - - be - re sa - - - cris, sa - cris.
A - spi - ci - at fa - - ci - to mi - se - ros pi - e - ta - tis
A - spi - ci - at fa - - ci - to mi - se - ros pi - e - ta - tis o -
mi - se - ros pi - e - - ta - tis o - cel -
mi - se - ros pi - e - ta - tis o -
o - cel - - lo Fi - li - us, ip - sa po - - - tes; fes - sos hinc
cel - - - lo Fi - li - us, ip - sa po - - - tes; fes - sos hinc ar - ri -
- - - - - lo Fi - li - us, ip - sa po - - - tes; fes -
cel - - - lo Fi - li - us, ip - sa po - - tes;
Fi - li - us, ip - sa po - - tes; fes - sos hinc

115
ar - ri - - - pe sur - - - sum, di - va vir -
- pe sur - - - sum, di - - - - va vir - go
- - sos hinc ar - - - - ri - pe sur - sum, di - va vir -
fes - sos hinc ar - ri pe sur - - sum, di - va vir - go
ar - - - ri - pe sur - - - - - sum, di - va vir - go
120
125
go ma - nu, tu - tos et in ar - ce lo - ca - - -
ma - nu, tu - tos et in ar - ce
go ma - nu, tu - tos et in ar - -
ma - nu, tu - - - tos et in ar - ce lo -
ma - nu, tu - tos et in ar - ce
130
- - - to, lo - ca - - - -
lo - ca - - to, lo - - - ca - to, lo -
ce lo - - - - ca - - to, lo - ca -
ca - - - - to, lo - - ca - - -
lo - ca - - - - - to, lo - - -
135
- - to. [A - - - - men.]
- - - - ca - to. [A - - - - - men.]
- to. [A - - men, a - - - men.]
- to. [A - - - men, a - - men.]
ca - - - to. [A - - - - - - men, a - men.]

4.

Salve regina [I]

30
35
- ce - - do, et spes no - - - - stra, sal - -
et spes no - - - - -
- do, et spes no - - - stra, sal - -
- - - do, et spes no - stra,
40
- - - - ve, sal - - - - - ve. Ad
- - - - strа, sal - ve, sal - ve. Ad
- - - ve, sal - - - - - ve.
sal - - - - - - - ve.
45
te cla - ma - - - - mus, ex - su - - les fi-
te cla - ma - mus, ex - su - les fi - - li - i
Ad te cla - ma - mus, ex - - su - - les
Ad te cla - ma - - - - - - - mus, ex - su -
50
- li - - i E - - vae, ad te,
E - - vae, ad te, ad te su -
fi - li - - i, fi - li - i E - - - - -
les fi - - - li - i E - - - vae,
55
ad te su - - spi - ra - mus,
spi - - - ra - - - mus,
- - vae, su - spi - ra - mus, ge - men - -
ad te su - spi - - - - - ra - -

60
65
ge - men - - tes et flen - - - tes in hac
ge - men - tes et flen - - - tes in hac
tes et flen - tes in hac
mus, ge - men - - - tes et flen - tes in hac la -
70
la - cri - ma - - rum val - le, va - - - le.
la - cri - - ma - - - rum val - - - - - - le.
la - - cri - - - ma - - - rum val - - - - le.
- - - cri - ma - rum val - - - - - - le, - le.
75
80
no - - -
no - stra,
E - ia, e - - ia er - go, ad - vo - ca - - ta
E - - - ia er - go, ad - - vo - ca - - - ta no - - stra,
85
90
95
stra, il - - - los tu - os mi - se - ri -
il - - - los mi - se - ri - cor - - - des o - - - -
il - los tu - - - - - - os mi - se - ri - cor -
100
105
110
cor - des o - cu - los ad nos con -
- - - - cu - - - los ad nos con - ver - - -
ad nos con - ver - - - -
- - des o - - - - cu - - - los ad

ver - te. Et Je -
te. Et Je - sum, be - ne - di -
te, con - ver -
nos con - ver -
sum, be - ne - di - ctum fru - ctum
ctum, be - ne - di - ctum
te. Et Je - sum, be - ne - di - ctum
te.
ven - tris tu - i, no -
fru - ctum ven - tris tu - i,
fru - ctum ven - tris
fru - ctum ven - tris tu - i, no -
bis post hoc ex - si - li - um o -
no - bis post hoc ex - si - li - um o -
tu - i, no - bis post hoc
bis post hoc ex - si - li - um
sten - de.
sten - de, o - sten - de.
ex - si - li - um o - sten - de, o - sten - de.
o - sten - de, de.

O cle - mens, O cle - mens,
O cle - - - - - mens, O cle - - - - mens,
O cle - - - mens, cle - - - mens,
O cle - - - - - mens,
O pi - - - a, pi - - - - - - - a,
O pi - - - a, pi - - - - - - - a,
O pi - - - - - - a,
O pi - - - - - - - a,
O dul - - - - cis vir - - - - go sem - - - - - - - per, sem - - - - per, sem - per, sem - per Ma - ri - - - - - a.
O dul - cis, dul - cis vir - - go sem - - - - per Ma - - ri - - - - - a, Ma - ri - - - - a.
O dul - cis vir - go sem - - - - - - - per Ma - ri - - - - - - - a, Ma - ri - a, Ma - ri - a.
O dul - - - - cis vir - - - - - - go sem - per Ma - ri - - a, Ma - ri - - - - - - - - - - a.

5.

Ut heremita solus

C (𝆷 = 𝆷)

65
70
75
O (⊨ = ⊨·)
¢ (⊨ = 𝅗𝅥)
80
O (⊨ = 𝅝·)

85
90
95
100
105
110

Ut heremita

140
145
150
155
160
165
O (𝍠 = o.)
6
4

170
175
180
185
190
195

6.
Vivit Dominus

7.

Caeleste beneficium

25
- fi - ci - um, be - ne - fi - ci - um, cae - le - ste be - ne - fi -
- ci - - - - - um, be - ne - fi - ci - um, be -
be - - - - ne - - - fi - - - - -
- ste be - ne - fi - ci - um in - tro - i - vit in or -
ci - um, be - ne - fi - ci - um in - tro - i - vit
30
ci - um in - tro - i - vit, in - tro - i - vit in or - bem, in - tro - i -
ne - fi - ci - um, be - ne - fi - ci - um, in - tro - i - vit in or -
- - - - - ci - - - um
- - bem, in - tro - i - vit in or - bem, in - tro - i - - - -
in or - - - - - bem, in or - bem, in -
35
- vit, in - tro - i - vit in or - bem
- bem, in - tro - i - vit in or - - -
in - tro - i - vit in or - bem
- vit in or - bem, in or - bem
- tro - i - vit in or - bem ver - bum De-
40
ver - bum De - - i, ver-
- - - bem
ver - bum De - i, ver - bum De -
- - - - i, ver - bum De - i,

45
- bum De - - i, ver-bum De - - i, ver - bum De -
ver - bum De - - - - - i, ver - bum De - i,
i, ver - bum De - i, ver -
ver - bum De - - - -
50
- - i, ver - bum De - - - i, ver-bum De - i,
De - i, ver - bum De - i, ver-bum De -
- bum De - - i, ver - bum De - i, De - - i, ver -
- - - i, ver - - - - bum De - i,
55
ver - bum De - i quod ful - - - get, quod ful -
i quod ful - get, ful - get, quod ful - get,
ver - bum De - i
bum De - i, ver - bum De - i quod ful - - -
ver - bum De - i, ver - bum De - i quod ful -
60
get, quod ful - - - - get, quod ful - get, ful - get, quod
quod ful - get, quod ful -
quod ful - - -
get, quod ful - get, quod ful - get, quod ful - get, quod ful - get, ful -
- get no - - bis, quod ful - get, quod ful - - - - -

ful - get, quod ful - get, ful - get no -
- get, quod ful - get, quod ful - get no - - - -
- - - - get
- - get, ful - get no-bis, no - - bis, no -
get no - - - - bis, no - bis,
bis, quod ful - get no - bis, no - bis, no - bis,
bis, quod ful - - get no - bis per Ger - ma -
quod ful - get no - - - -
- - - bis per Ger - ma - ni - am, Ger - ma -
quod ful - get no - - bis per
no - bis per Ger - ma - - ni -
ni - am, Ger-ma - ni - am, per Ger - ma - - - ni - - am, per
- bis per Ger - ma -
ni - am, per Ger - ma - ni - am, per Ger - ma - - ni - am,
Ger - ma - ni - am, Ger-ma - - ni - am, Ger-ma - - ni-am,
am, per Ger-ma - - ni-am, per Ger-ma - - - - ni - am.
Ger-ma - ni - am, per Ger - ma - - - ni - am.
ni - am, per Ger - ma - - - ni - am.
per Ger - ma-ni-am, per Ger-ma - - ni-am.
per Ger-ma - ni - am, per Ger - ma - ni - am.

90
95
Cae - le - - - ste be -
Cae - le - - - - - - - ste, cae - le - ste be - ne -
Cae - le - - - - -
Cae - le - - - ste be -
100
105
- ne - fi - ci - um, cae - le - - - - - ste
fi - ci - um, cae - - le - ste be - ne - fi - ci -
- - - - - - ste, cae - le - - ste, cae -
- ne - fi - ci - um, cae - le - - ste
110
115
be - ne - fi - ci - um, be - ne - fi - ci - um,
um, cae - - - - - le - ste be - ne - fi -
Cae - - - - le -
le - - ste be - ne - fi - ci um, cae -
be - ni - fi - - - - ci - um, cae - le - ste be -
120
125
cae - le - ste be - ne - fi - ci - um, cae - le -
- ci - um, be - ne - fi - - ci - - um, cae -
- - - - - - - ste
le - ste be - ne - fi - ci - um, cae - le - ste be -
ne - fi - ci - um, cae - le - ste, cae -

130
135
- - ste be - ne - fi - - ci - um,
- - le - - ste, cae - le - - - ste be - ne - fi - - ci -
ne - - fi - - ci - um, be - - ne - - fi ci - - um, be - ne - fi - -
le - - ste be - - ne - - fi - - ci - um, cae - le - ste
140
um, be - - fi - - - ci - - um,
um, be - ne - fi - ci - um, be - ne - fi - - ci - um, cae -
- ci - um, cae - le - - - - ste be - ne - fi -
be - - ne - - fi - - ci - - um, be - - ne - fi - - -
145
150
cae - le - ste be - - ne - - fi - ci - - um, be - - - ne - fi -
le - ste be - - - ne - fi - - ci - - um, be - ne - fi - - ci - - um,
be - - - -
- ci - um, cae - le - ste be - - ne - fi - ci - um, be - ne - fi - ci -
ci - um, cae - le - ste be - ne - fi - - ci - um
155
- ci - um, cae - - le - ste be - ne - fi - - - ci - um ac - - ci - pe,
cae - - le - ste be - ne - - fi - ci - um ac - ci - pe, ac - ci -
ne - - - - - - fi - - - - - -
um, cae - - le - ste be - ne - fi - - ci - um ac - - ci - pe, ac -
ac - ci - pe, ac - - ci - pe, ac - ci - pe, ac - ci - pe,

160
165
ac - ci - pe Ger - ma - ni - a, Ger - ma - ni - a
pe, ac - ci - pe, ac - ci - pe Ger - ma - ni - a
ci - um
ci - pe, ac - ci - pe Ger - ma - ni - a gra - ta,
ac - ci - pe Ger - ma - ni - a
170
175
gra - ta, ac - ci - pe Ger - ma - ni - a gra - ta, gra - ta,
gra - ta, gra -
ac - ci - pe
ac - ci - pe Ger - ma - ni - a, Ger - ma - ni - a gra - ta, gra -
gra - ta, gra -
180
gra - ta, *gra - ta,* gra - ta, gra - ta,
ta, gra - ta, gra - ta, gra - ta, gra - ta, qui - a ti - bi, qui -
Ger - ma - ni - a gra - ta,
ta, gra - ta, gra - ta, qui - a ti - bi, ti - bi,
ta, gra - ta, gra - ta, gra - ta, qui - a ti - bi,
185
190
qui - a ti - bi, ti - bi,
a ti - bi, qui - a ti - bi, qui - a ti - bi,
qui -
qui - a ti - bi, ti - bi, qui - a ti bi,
qui - a ti - bi, ti - bi re -

195
200
qui - a ti - bi re - so - nu - it, re - so -
ti - bi re - so - nu - it, ti - bi re - so - nu - it, re - so - nu -
- - - - - - a ti - bi re - so -
ti - bi re - so - nu - it, re - so - nu - it
- so - nu - it, ti - bi re - so - nu - it, ti - bi
205
- nu - it vox, vox tan - -
it, re - so - nu - it vox, vox tan - dem, vox
- nu - it vox
vox tan - dem, tan - dem, vox tan -
re - so - nu - it vox tan - dem,
210
215
dem, vox tan - dem, vox tan - dem ae - ter -
tan - dem ae - ter - ni nu - -
tan - dem ae -
- dem, tan - dem ae - ter - ni nu - mi - nis,
vox tan - dem, vox tan - - - - -
220
225
ni nu - mi - nis, ae - ter - ni nu - mi - nis sa - lu - tem
mi - nis, ae - ter - ni nu - mi - nis, nu - mi - nis
ter - - ni nu - mi - nis
ae - ter - ni nu - mi - nis, ae - ter - ni nu - mi - nis
dem ae - ter - ni nu - mi - nis, ae - ter -

ad - es - - se nun - ci - ans, sa - - lu - tem ad - es - se
sa - lu - tem ad - es - se nun - ci - ans, sa - lu - tem ad - es - se nun -
sa - lu - tem ad - es - - - - - se nun - ci - ans, sa -
ni nu - mi - nis, nu - mi - nis sa - lu - tem
nun - ci - ans, sa - lu - tem ad - es - se nun - ci - ans,
- ci - ans, nun - ci - ans, sa - lu - tem ad - es - se,
sa - lu -
lu - tem ad - es - se nun - ci - ans, ad - es - se
ad - es - se nun - ci - ans, sa - lu - tem ad - es -
ad - es - se nun - ci - ans. Am - bu - la - -
ad - es - se nun - ci - ans. Am - bu - la -
tem ad - es - se nun - ci - ans. Am - bu - la -
nun - ci - ans, nun - ci - ans. Am - bu - la - te
se nun - ci - ans. Am - bu - la - - - - - -
te dum lu - cem, dum lu - cem ha - be - tis.
- - te dum lu - cem, lu - cem ha - be - tis.
- - te dum lu - cem ha - be - tis.
dum lu - cem, lu - cem ha - be - tis, ha - be - tis, tis.
- - te dum lu - cem, dum lu - cem ha - be - tis.

8.

Deo gratia

(Canon XXXVI vocum)

10
S.1
gra - ti - a.
S.2
De - o gra - ti - a.
S.3
De - o gra - ti - a, De - o gra - ti - a.
S.4
gra - ti - a, De - o gra - ti - a, De - o gra - ti -
S.5
- a, De - o gra - ti - a, De - o gra - ti - a, De - o
S.6
- o gra - ti - - a, De - o gra - ti - a, De - o gra - ti - a,
S.7
De - - o gra - ti - - a, De - o gra - ti - a,
S.8
gra - ti - a, De - - o gra - ti - - a, De - o
S.9
De - o gra - ti - a, De - - o gra - ti -
A.1
De - - o gra - ti - a, De - o gra -
A.2
De - - o gra - ti - a, De -
A.3
De - - o gra - ti - a,
A.4
De - -
A.5-9
T.1-9
B.1-9

15
S.1-3
S.4
- a.
S.5
gra - ti - a.
S.6
De - o gra - ti - a.
S.7
De - o gra - ti - a, De - o gra - ti - a.
S.8
gra - ti - a, De - o gra - ti - a, De - o gra - ti -
S.9
- a, De - o gra - ti - a, De - o gra - ti - a, De - o
A.1
- ti - a, De - o gra - - ti - a, De - o gra - ti - a,
A.2
- o gra - - ti - a, De - o gra - ti - a, De - -
A.3
De - o gra - ti a, De - o gra - -
A.4
- o gra - ti - a, De - o gra - - ti - a, De -
A.5
De - - o gra - ti - a, De - o gra -
A.6
De - - o gra - ti - a, De -
A.7
De - - o gra - ti - a,
A.8
De - -
A.9
T.1-9
B.1-9

20
S.1-7
S.8
- a.
S.9
gra - ti - a.
A.1
De - o gra - ti - a.
A.2
- o gra - ti - a, De - o gra - ti - a.
A.3
- ti - a, De - o gra - ti - a, De - o gra - ti - a.
A.4
- o gra - ti - a, De - o gra - ti - a, De - o gra - ti-
A.5
- ti - a, De - o gra - ti - a, De - o gra - ti - a,
A.6
- o gra - ti - a, De - o gra - ti - a, De -
A.7
De - o gra - ti - a, De - o gra -
A.8
- o gra - ti - a, De - o gra - ti - a, De-
A.9
De - o gra - ti a, De- o gra -
T.1
De - o gra - ti - a,
T.2
De - o gra -
T.3
De - o
T.4
De -
T.5-9
B.1-9

S.1-9
A.1-3
A.4
- a.
A.5
De - o gra - ti - a.
A.6
- o gra - ti - a, De - o gra - ti - a.
A.7
- ti - a, De - o gra - ti - a, De - o gra - ti - a.
A.8
- o gra - ti - a, De - o gra - ti - a, De - o gra - ti -
A.9
- ti - a, De - o gra - ti - a, De - o gra - ti - a,
T.1
De - o gra - ti - a, De - o gra - ti - a,
T.2
ti - a, De - o gra - ti - a, De - o gra -
T.3
gra - ti - a, De - o gra - ti - a,
T.4
- o gra - ti - a, De -
T.5
De - o gra - ti - a,
T.6
De - o gra -
T.7
De - o
T.8
De -
T.9
B.1-9

25
S.1-9
A.1-7
A.8
- a.
A.9
De - o gra - ti - a,
T.1
De - o gra - ti - a, De - - o gra - ti-
T.2
- ti - a, De - o gra - ti - a, De - -
T.3
De - o gra - - ti - a, De - o gra - ti - a,
T.4
- o gra - ti - a, De - o gra - - ti - a, De - o
T.5
De - o gra - ti - a, De - o gra - - ti - a,
T.6
ti - a, De - o gra - ti - a, De - o gra -
T.7
gra - - ti - a, De - o gra - ti - a,
T.8
- o gra - - ti - a, De -
T.9
De - o gra - - ti - a,
B.1
De - o gra - ti - a, De - - o gra - ti-
B.2
De - o gra - ti - a, De-
B.3
De - o gra - ti - a,
B.4
De - o gra - ti-
B.5-9

30
S.1-9
A.1-9
T.1
- a, De - o gra - ti - a, De - o gra - ti -
T.2
- o gra - ti - a, De - o gra - ti - a,
T.3
De - - o gra - ti - a, De - o gra - ti -
T.4
gra - ti - a, De - - o gra - ti - a,
T.5
De - o gra - ti - a, De - - o gra - ti -
T.6
- ti - a, De - o gra - ti - a, De - -
T.7
De - o gra - - ti - a, De - o gra - ti - a,
T.8
- o gra - ti - a, De - o gra - - ti - a, De - o
T.9
De - o gra - ti - a, De - o gra - - ti - a,
B.1
- a, De - - o gra - ti - a, De -
B.2
- o gra - ti - a, De - - o gra - ti - a,
B.3
De - - o gra - ti - a, De - - o
B.4
- a, De - - o gra - ti - a,
B.5
De - o gra - ti - a, De - - o gra - ti -
B.6
De - o gra - ti - a, De -
B.7
De - o gra - ti - a,
B.8
De - o gra - ti -
B.9

S.1-9
A.1-9
T.1
T.2
T.3
T.4
T.5
T.6
T.7
T.8
T.9
B.1
B.2
B.3
B.4
B.5
B.6
B.7
B.8
B.9
35
-a, De-o gra-ti-a, De-o gra-ti-a.
De-o gra-ti-a, De-o gra-ti-a, De-o gra-ti-a.
-a, De-o gra-ti-a, De-o gra-ti-a.
De-o gra-ti-a, De-o gra-ti-a, De-o.
-a, De-o gra-ti-a, De-o gra-ti-a.
-o gra-ti-a, De-o gra-ti-a.
De-o gra-ti-a, De-o gra-ti-a.
gra-ti-a, De-o gra-ti-a.
De-o gra-ti-a, De-o gra-ti-a.
-o gra-ti-a, De-o gra-ti-a.
De-o gra-ti-a, De-o.
gra-ti-a, De-o gra-ti-a.
De-o gra-ti-a, De-o.
-a, De-o gra-ti-a, De-o.
-o gra ti a, De-o gra-ti-a.
De-o gra-ti-a, De-o.
-a, De-o gra-ti-a.
De-o gra-ti-a, De-o gra-ti-a.

9.

Gaude Maria

20
- - - - - - - go, vir - - - - - go, vir - -
vir - - - - go, vir - - - - - go, vir -
25
- - go, vir - - go, cun - ctas hae - re - ses
- - go, vir - - go, cun - ctas hae - re -
30
in - ter - e - mi - sti, in - ter - - e - mi -
in - ter - e - mi - - - - - -
so - - - la quae
ses so - la in - ter - e - mi - -
35
- sti, quae Ga - bri - e - - - - -
sti, quae Ga - - bri - e - lis, Ga -
Ga - - - bri - e - - - lis arch -
sti, quae Ga - - - - bri - e lis arch - an - - -

40
lis, quae Ga - - bri - e - lis arch - an - ge -
bri - e - - lis arch - an - - ge - li,
an - - - ge - li, arch - an - - - ge -
ge - li, quae, quae Ga-
45
li, arch - an - - ge - li, quae Ga - bri - e - lis arch - an - ge -
Ga - bri - e - - lis arch - an - - - ge - li, Ga-
Gau - de Ma - ri -
li, Ga - bri - e - - lis arch - - an - ge - li
bri - e - lis arch - an - - ge - li, arch - an -
50
li, arch - an - - - -
bri - e - - lis arch - an - - ge -
a, vir -
di - ctis, di -
ge - li di - ctis, di - ctis cre -
55
ge - li di - - ctis, di -
li di - ctis, di - ctis cre -
ctis cre - di - di - sti, cre - di - di - sti,
di - di - sti, cre - di - di - sti, di -

60
ctis, di - - ctis cre - - - - - - - di -
- di - - - di - sti, cre - di - di - sti, cre - di -
- - - - - - - go, cun - ctas hae - re - - -
cre - di - di - - sti, cre - di - di - sti, cre -
ctis cre - di - di - sti, cre - di - di - sti,
65
- di - sti, cre - di - di - sti: Dum vir - go De -
- di - sti, cre - di - - - di - - sti:
- ses so - la in - ter - e - mi - sti,
- di - di - sti: Dum vir - go, dum vir - - go, dum
cre - di - di - sti:
70
- - um, dum vir - go De - um et ho - - - - -
vir - go De - um, De - um et ho - - - mi -
et post,
75
- - - mi - nem ge - - nu - - i - sti, et
et ho - - mi - nem ge - -
nem, et ho - - mi - nem ge - nu -
post par - - - - tum, et

80
post ___ par - - tum, post par - tum vir - go,
- - nu - i - - - - - - sti et ___ post ___
Dum vir - - - go De - um
i - - - sti, et ___ post ___ par - - - -
post ___ par - tum vir - go, et ___ post ___
85
et post par - tum, post ___ par - tum vir - go,
par - - - - tum, post ___ par - - - tum vir -
___ et ho - mi - nem et post
- - - - - tum, par - - - - -
par - tum vir - - - - - - go, vir - - -
90
vir - - - go, ___ vir - - - - - - -
- - - - - - - - - - -
par - - - - - - - - -
- - tum, ___ post ___ par - tum ___ vir - go,
- - - go, in-,
95
- go, ___ in - vi - o - la -
go, in - vi - o - la - - ta, ___ in - vi - - o - - la -
tum, in - vi - o - la - - -
vir - - - - - go, ___
in - vi - o - la - - - - - - ta, in -

ta per - - - man - si - - - - - -
ta, in - vi - o - la - ta per - man - - - si - - - sti,
ta per - - - man - - si - -
in - vi - o - la - ta, in - vi - o - la - ta
vi - o - la - - - - ta per - - - man - si - sti,
100
sti, per - man - si - sti - sti.
per - man - si - - sti.
sti - sti.
per - man - si - sti, per - man - si - sti.
per - man - si - sti, per - man - si - sti.
105 110 115
Ga - bri - e - - - lem
Ga - bri - e -
Ga - bri - e - - - - - - - lem
Ga - bri - e - lem
120 125
arch - an - ge - lum, arch -
arch - an - ge - lum
- lem arch -
arch - an - ge - - - lum, arch - an -
arch - an - ge - - lum, arch - an -

an - ge - lum, arch - an - ge - lum
cre - di - mus
an - ge - lum
- ge - lum, arch - an - ge - lum cre - di - mus, cre -
ge - lum, arch - an - ge - lum cre -
te es - se af - fa -
te es - se af -
di - vi - ni - tus
- di - mus di - vi - ni - tus
di - mus di - vi -
- tum -tum:
- fa - tum:
-tum:
te es - se af - fa - tum: U - te - rum
- ni - tus te es - se af - fa - tum: U - te - rum
U - te - rum, u - te - rum, u -
U - te - rum tu - um,
U - te -
tu - um, u - te - rum tu - um, u -
tu - um, tu - um, u -

- - te- rum tu- - - - - - um de
tu- - - - - - - - - - - - - um de Spi- - -
rum tu- - - - - - um
te- rum tu - um de Spi- - - ri - tu,
- te-rum tu- - - - - - um de Spi- - - ri - tu
Spi- - - ri - tu, de Spi- ri - tu San cto
- - - ri - tu San- - cto, San- cto cre-di- - mus im-
de Spi- - ri - tu San - cto cre- - - - di- - - -
Spi- ri- tu San- cto cre- - di- - - mus im- - - -
San- - cto cre- - di- - - - - mus im- - - - - pre-
cre- - di- - - - mus im- - pre- - gna- - tum:
pre- - gna- - tum, im-pre-gna- - tum, im- - pre - gna- - - tum:
mus im- - pre - gna- - - - - - - tum:
- - - - - pre- - - - - gna- - - tum, im- - pre-gna- tum:
- - - - - gna - tum -tum:
Ju - dae- - - us in-
E- - ru - be - - scat Ju - dae - us in-
Ju - dae- - - - us in -
E- - ru - be - - - - scat,

210
fe - lix, qui di - cit Chri - stum
fe - lix, qui di - cit, qui di - cit Chri - stum de
qui di - cit Chri - stum de
fe - lix, qui di - cit, qui di - cit Chri - stum de Jo -
qui, qui di - cit Chri - stum de Jo - seph, de
215
de Jo - seph se - mi - ne
Jo - seph, de Jo - seph se - mi - ne es -
Jo - seph se - ne es - se
seph se - mi - ne es -
Jo - seph se - mi - ne es - se na -
220
es - se na - tum. Dum vir - go De - um et
se na - tum, na - tum. Dum vir - go De -
na - tum. Dum vir - go De - um et ho -
se na - tum. Dum vir - go De -
tum, na - tum. Dum vir -
225
ho - mi - nem ge - nu -
um et ho - mi - nem, ho - mi - nem ge - nu - i - sti,
mi - nem ge - nu - i - sti,
um et ho - mi - nem ge - nu -
go De - um et ho - mi - nem ge - nu - i - sti, ge - nu - i -

- - - i - sti, et post par - - - tum, et post
et post par - tum vir - - go, et post par - tum,
et post par - -
i - - sti, et
- sti et post par - tum vir - - - go, vir - - -
par - - tum, in -
et post par tum, in - vi - o - la - ta per man - - si-
- - - - tum, in - vi - o - la -
post par - tum, post par - - tum,
go, in - vi - o - la - - - - - ta,
vi - o - la - ta per - - - man - si - - -
- - - - sti, per - man - si - sti, in - vi - o - la -
- - - - ta per - - - - man -
in - vi - o - la - ta, in vi - o-
in - vi - o - la - - - - ta per - - - man - si -
- - - sti.
- ta per - man - - si - - sti.
- si - - sti.
la - ta per - man - - si - sti.
- sti, per - man - - si - sti.

10.

Salve regina [II]

30
mus, ge - men - tes et flen - tes in hac la - cri -
spi - ra - mus, ge - men - tes et flen - tes in
stra in hac la - cri - ma - rum
et flen - tes in hac
35
ma - rum val - le, val - le.
hac la - cri - ma - rum val - le, va - le.
val - le.
la - cri - ma - rum val - le, val - le.
40
45
50
E - ia er - go, ad - vo - ca - ta no -
E - ia er - go,
E - ia er - go, ad - vo - ca - ta no -
55
60
stra, o -
il - los tu - os mi - se - ri - cor - des
stra,
il - los tu - os mi - se - ri - cor - des
65
70
cu - los ad nos con - ver - te. Et Je -
o - cu - los ad nos con - ver - te. Et Je -
Et
Et Je -

sum, be - ne - di - ctum fru - ctum ven - tris tu -
sum, be - ne - di - ctum, be - ne - di -
Je - sum, be - ne - di - ctum fru -
sum, be - ne - di - ctum fru -
i, no - bis post hoc ex - si - li -
ctum no - bis post hoc ex - si - li - um
ctum ven - tris tu - i no -
ctum ven - tris
um o - sten - de. O cle - mens,
o - sten - de. O cle - mens, O
bis o - sten - de. O
tu - i o -
O pi - a, O
pi - a, O
cle - mens, O pi -
sten - de. O cle - mens, O pi -
dul - cis Ma - ri - a.
dul - cis, dul - cis, dul - cis Ma - ri - a.
a, O dul - cis Ma - ri - a.
a, O dul - cis Ma - ri - a, (ri) - a.

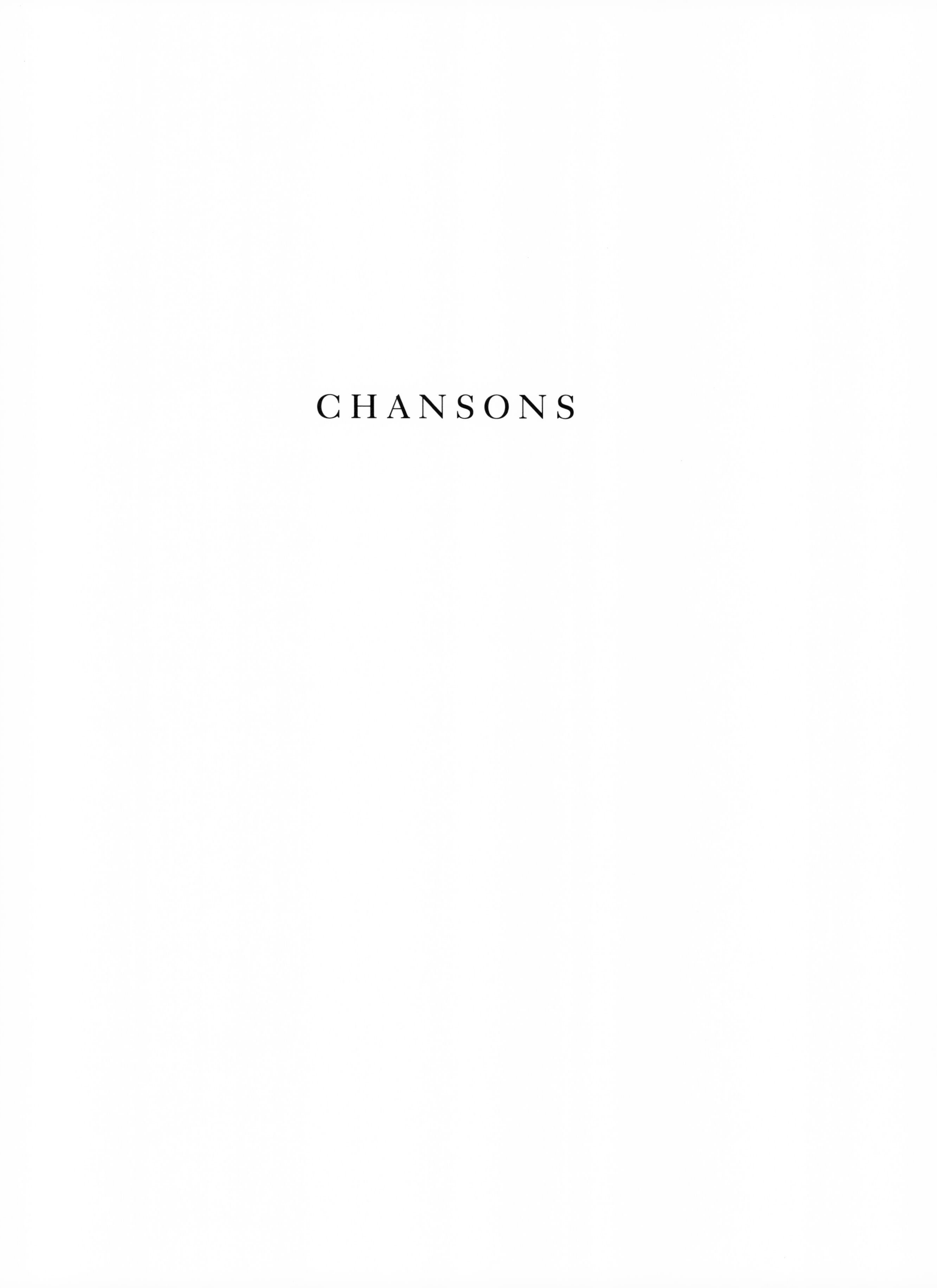

CHANSONS

1.

Aultre Venus

2. Celuy qui les amours detaille
Peult de vous dire par droicture:
Aultre Venus . . .

4. Qui contredit, j'offre bataille
A oultrance et a desmesure,
Maintenant qu'il vous fait injure,
Se le tiltre tel ne vous baille.
Aultre Venus . . .

2.

Baisiés moy

*The sharp is valid for the conclusions of the short strophe and the short refrain only; for both full refrains and the full strophe, the natural is needed.

3.

D'un autre amer

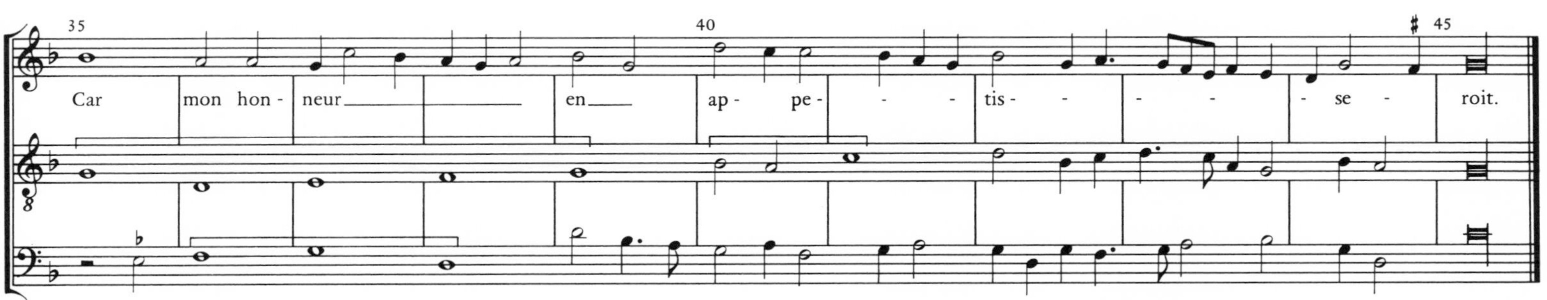

2. Je l'aime tant que jamais ne seroit
Possible a moi de consentir l'eschange
D'un autre amer . . .

4. La mort, par Dieu, avant me desferoit
Qu'en mon vivant j'acointasse ung estrange.
Ne cuide nul qu'a cela je me range;
Ma leauté trop fort se mesferoit.
D'un autre amer . . .

4.

Fors seulement l'actente

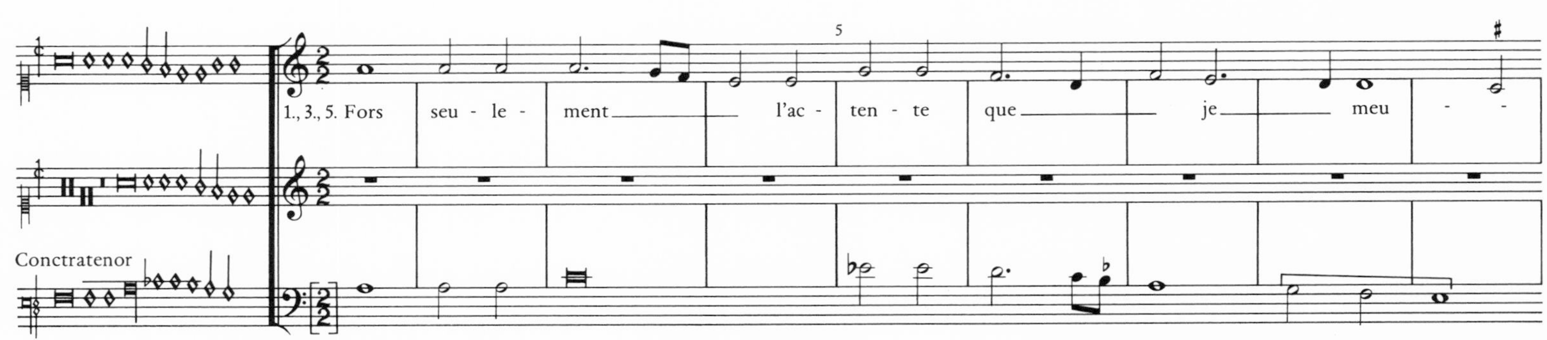
1., 3., 5. Fors seu - le - ment l'ac - ten - te que je meu - -
Conctratenor

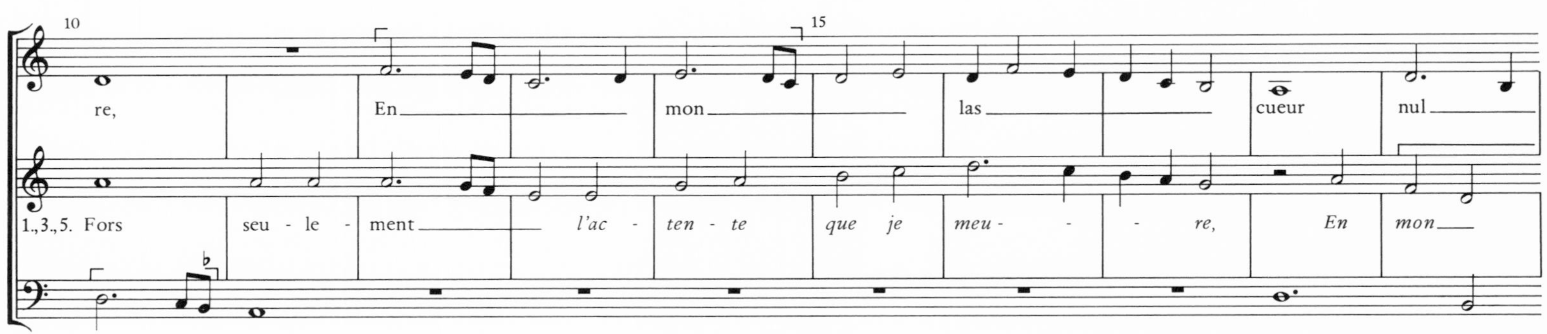
re, En mon las cueur nul
1.,3.,5. Fors seu - le - ment l'ac - ten - te que je meu - - - re, En mon

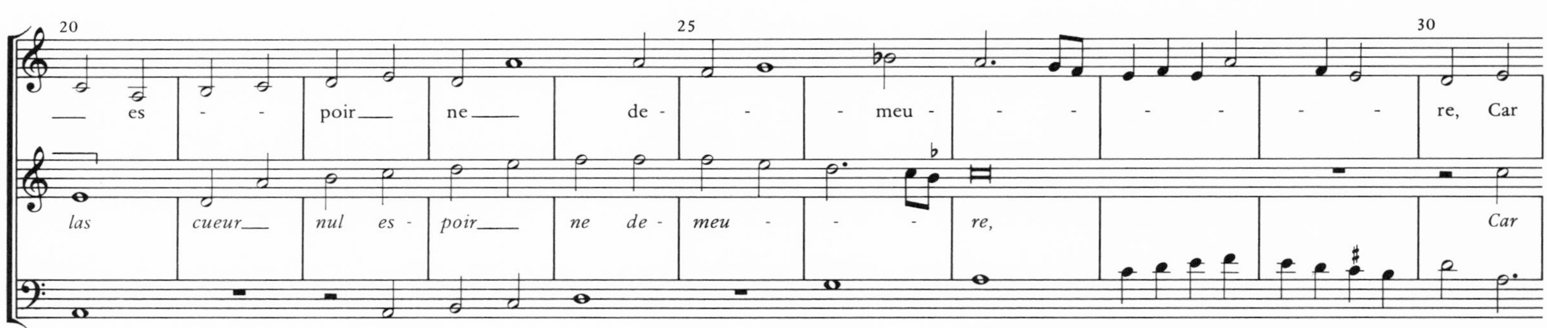
es - - poir ne de - - - meu - - - - - - - re, Car
las cueur nul es - poir ne de - meu - - - re, Car

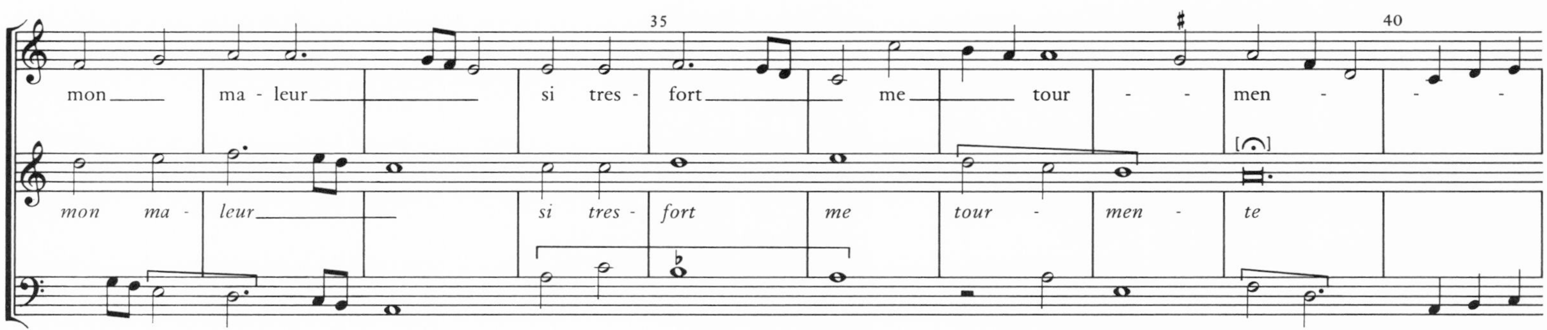
mon ma - leur si tres - fort me tour - - men - - -
mon ma - leur si tres - fort me tour - men - te

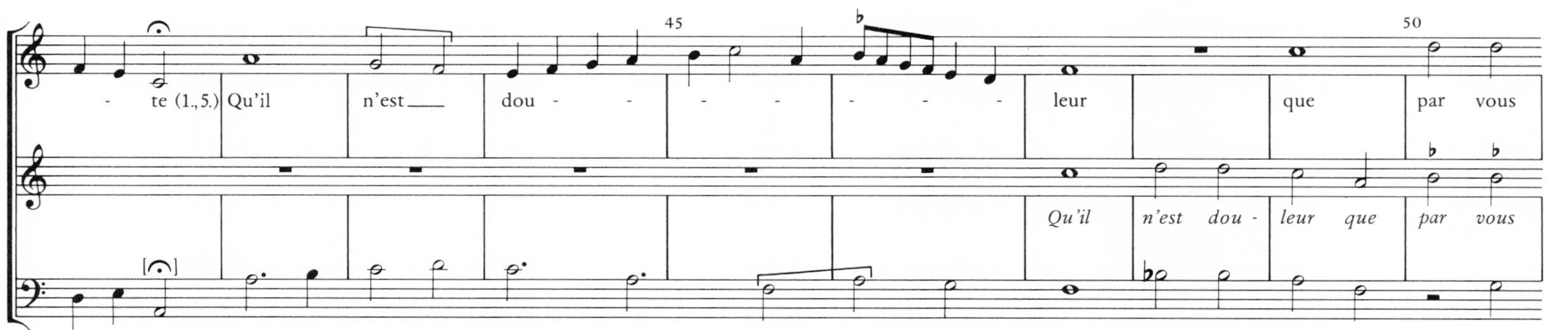

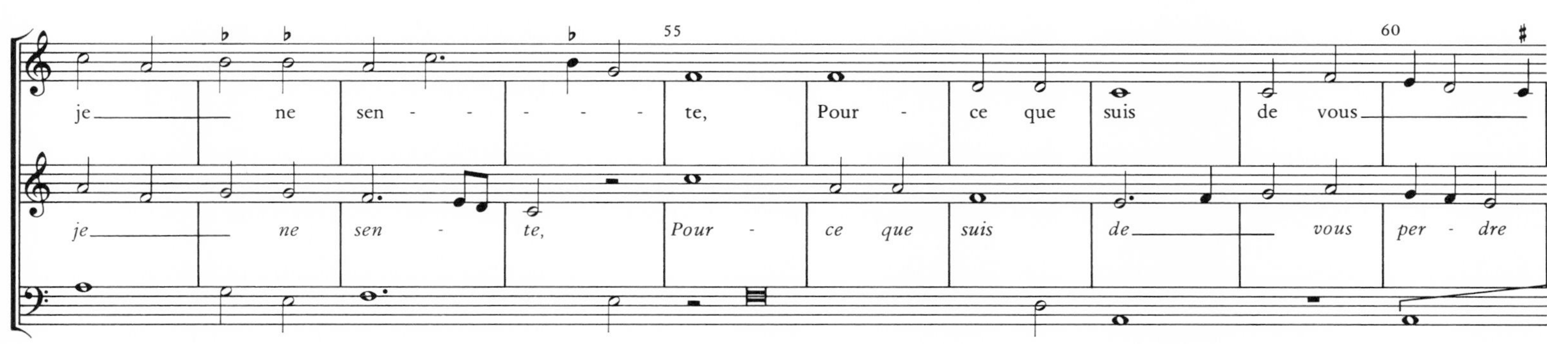

2. Vostre rigueur tellement m'y queurt seure
Qu'en ce parti il fault que je m'asseure,
Dont je n'ay bien qui en riens me contente
Fors seulement l'actente . . .

4. Mon desconfort toute seule je pleure,
En maudisant sur ma foy a toute heure
Ma leauté qui tant m'a fait dolente.
Las, que je suis de vivre mal contente
Quant de par vous n'ay riens qui me demeure
Fors seulement l'actente . . .

5.

Fors seullement contre

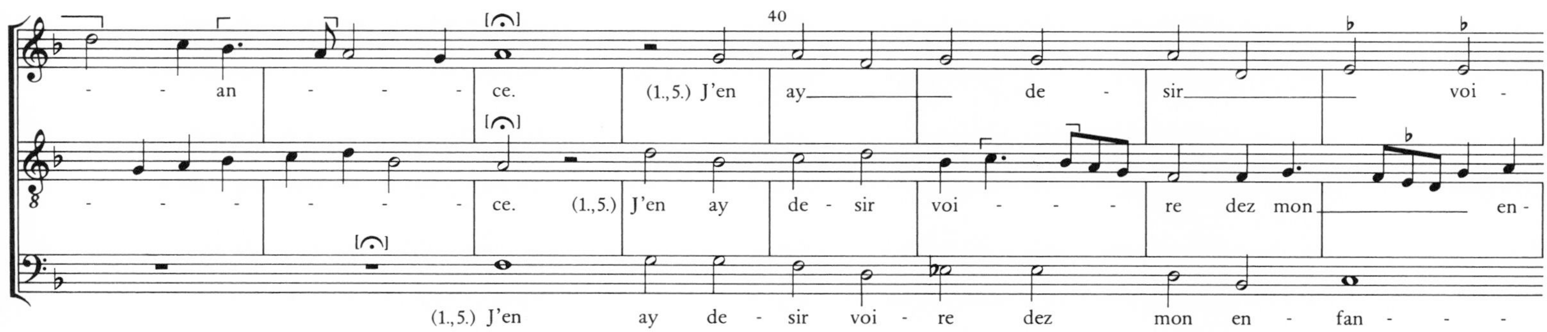

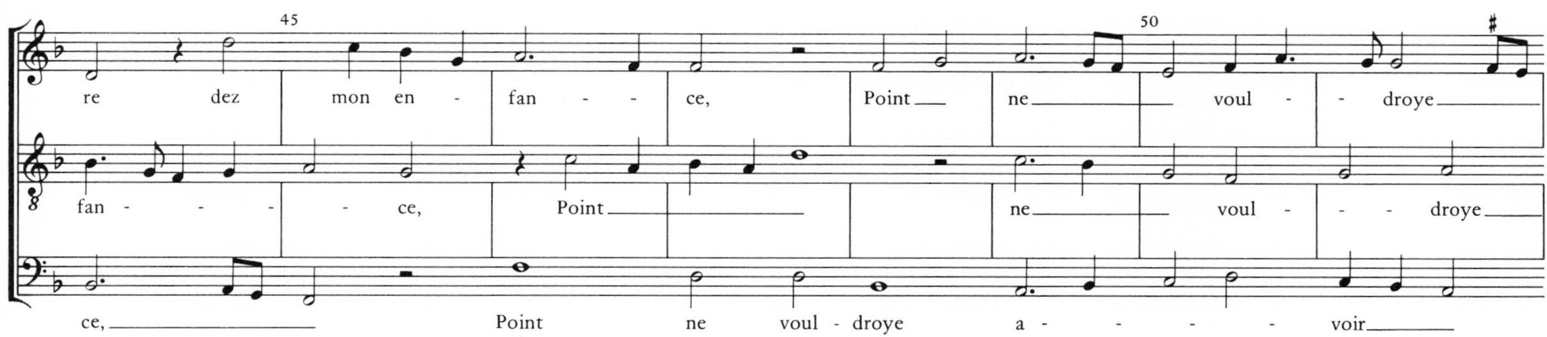

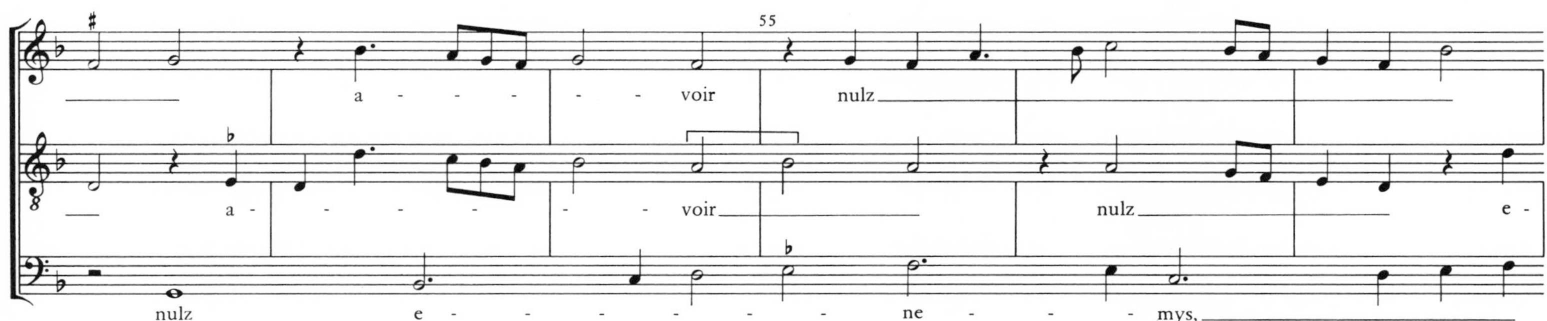

2. Mon vouloir j'ay tout en cela soubmis
Et hors de la ja ne serai transmis;
Garder ny veul ordre, sens ne prudence.
Fors seullement . . .

4. Je cuide avoir en terre des amys
Et que en eulx ay ma fiance remys;
On doibt sçavoir que n'ay nulle doubtance,
Ou aultrement querroye ma desfiance,
Car je sçeray de tout honneur desmys.
Fors seullement . . .

6.

Il ne m'en chault

2. Qu'on m'en loue ne qu'on m'en blame,
   Quoy qu'on en disoit, homme ou femme,
   Ilz en ont tous beau grumeller.
      Il ne m'en chault . . .

4. Car pour tout m'en vous tiens et clame
   Que tant je vueil et que tant j'ame
   Plus que nul sans riens excepter,
   S'ilz en devoyent tous crever
   Et deusse perdre du corps l'ame.
      Il ne m'en chault . . .

7.

J'en ay dueil

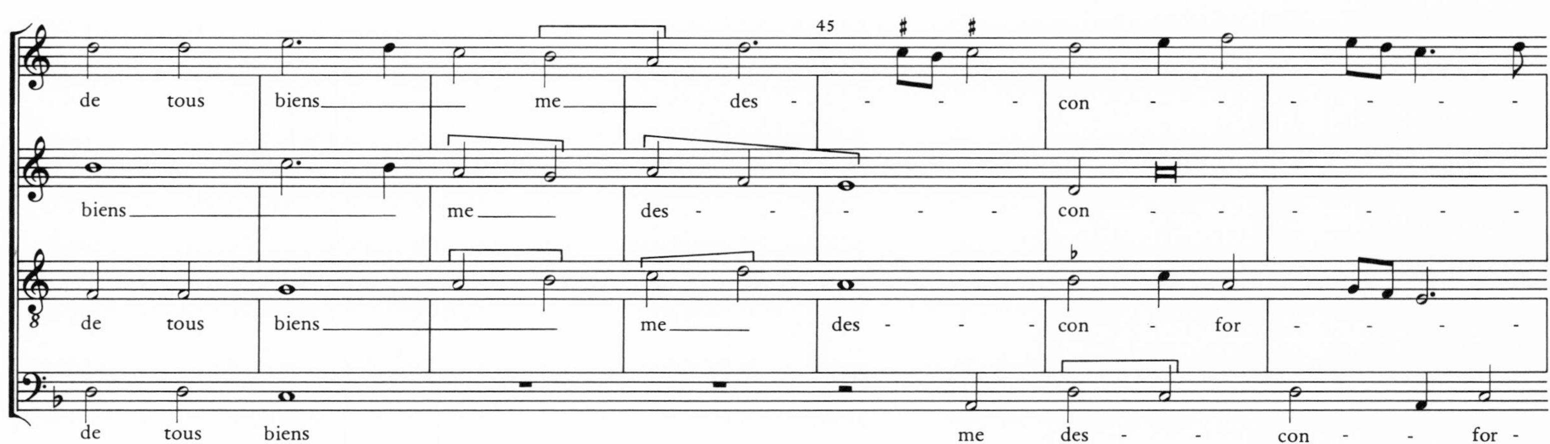

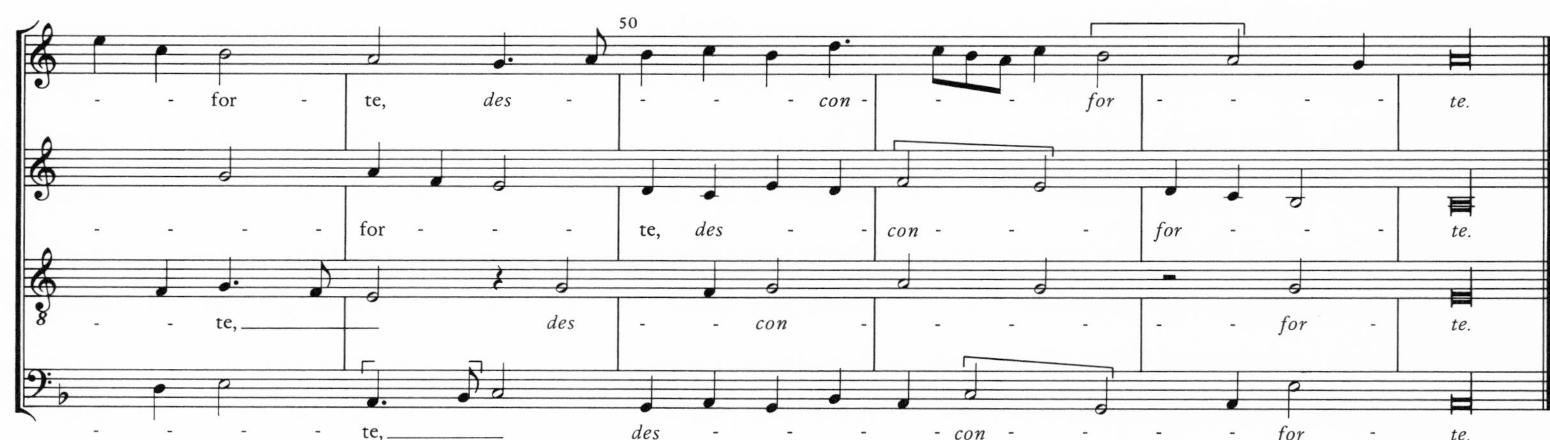

2. Ma douleur est plus que trop forte,
   Car sans avoir aucun plaisir,
      J'en ay dueil . . .

4. Je n'ay plus riens qui me conforte;
   D'oeil ne voy plus que desplaisir.
   Mort est le plus de mon desir,
   Car quelque chose qu'on m'aporte,
      J'en ay dueil . . .

7a.
Je n'ay deul

8.

La despourveue

Tenor
Conctra
1.,3.,5. La des - pour - veue et la ban - ny - - - - e De cil qui m'a don - né ma vi - - - - - e, Seu - le - ment par ung faulx rap - - - port.
La despourveue
La despourveue
(1.,5.)Ha, For - tu - ne, n'as tu pas tort D'a - voir sans cause ain - si pu - - - - - - - - - - - gni - - - - e!

2. Le povre cueur ne pensoit mye
D'estre de luy si fort haye;
Puis qu'il luy plaist, elle est d'acord,
La despourveue . . .

4. Elle ne veult plus de compaignie,
Fortune l'a trop esbaye
D'avoir esté tout son confort.
Plus ne desire que la mort,
Puis qu'ainsi suis par sa faulce envie.
La despourveue . . .

9.

L'autre d'antan

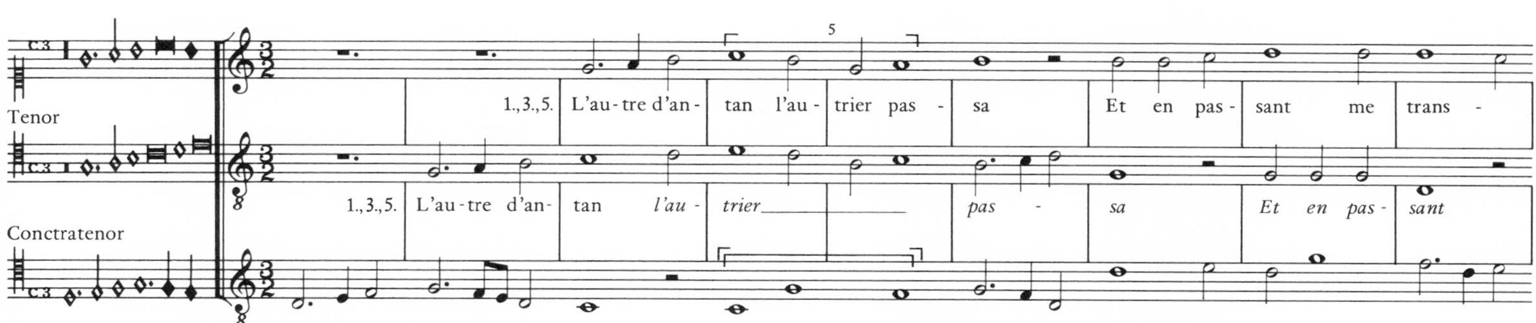

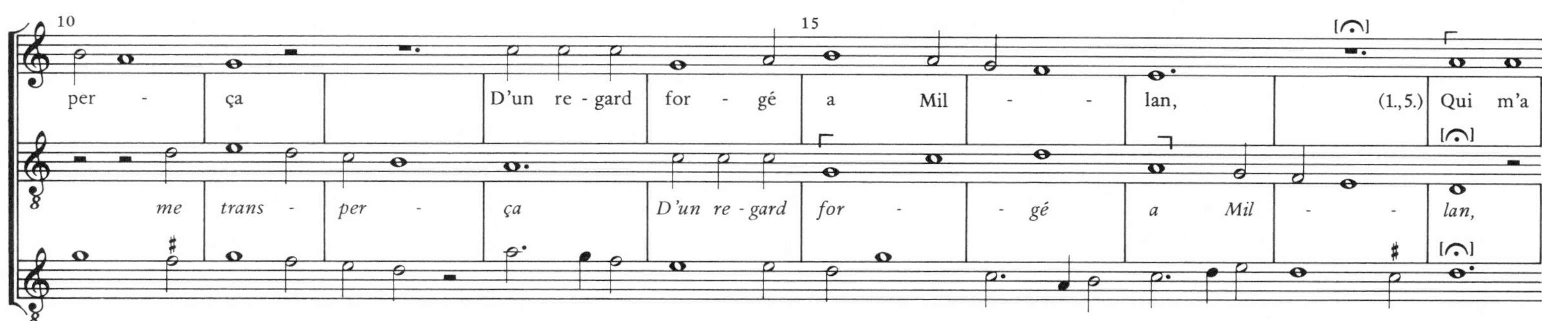

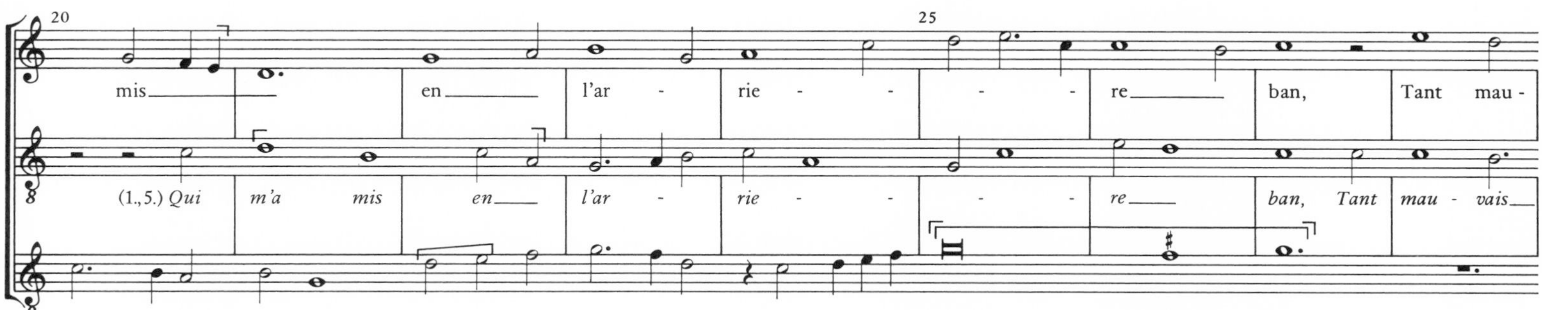

2. Par tel façon me fricassa
Que de ses gaiges me cassa,
Mais, par Dieu, elle fist son dan!
L'autre d'antan . . .

4. Puis apres nostre amour cessa,
Car oncques puis qu'elle dansa,
L'autre d'antan, l'autre d'antan,
Je n'eus ne bon jour ne bon an,
Tant de mal en moy amassa.
L'autre d'antan . . .

10.
Les desléaulx

Tenor
Concratenor
1.,3.,5. Les des - lé - aulx ont la sai - - - - son Et des bons nes - sun ne tient - - - - - - - comp - - - - te,
Mais Bon Droit de trop se mes - - - - con - - te De souf - - frir si grant des - - - rai - - - - - - son, des - - - - - - rai - - - - - son.
Les desleaulx
Les desleaulx

2. Je ne sçais par quel achoison
   Fortune ainsi hault les seurmonte;
   Les desleaulx . . .

4. Nul ne doit parler sans moison
   De paour d'avoir reprouche ou honte;
   Pour ce me tais, mais fin de compte
   Tout va sans rime et sans raison.
   Les desleaulx . . .

11.

Ma bouche rit

Tenor
Contra
1.,5. Ma bou - che rit et ma pen - sé - e pleu - - - - - - re, Mon oeil s'es - joye et mon cueur maul - dit l'eu - - - re
Ma bouche rit
Ma bouche rit
Qu'il eut le bien qui sa san - té des - -
chas - se Et le plai - - sir que la
mort me pour- chas - - - se Sans res - con -

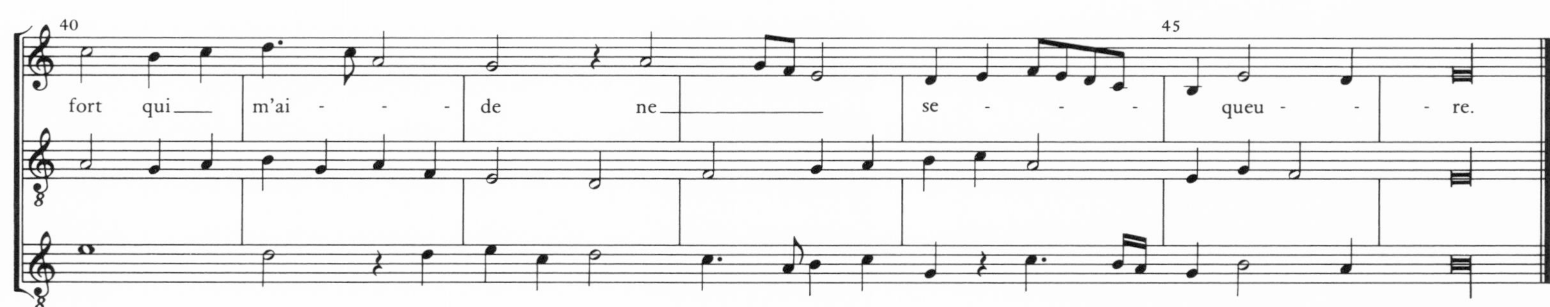
40
45
fort qui m'ai - - - de ne se - - - - queu - - re.

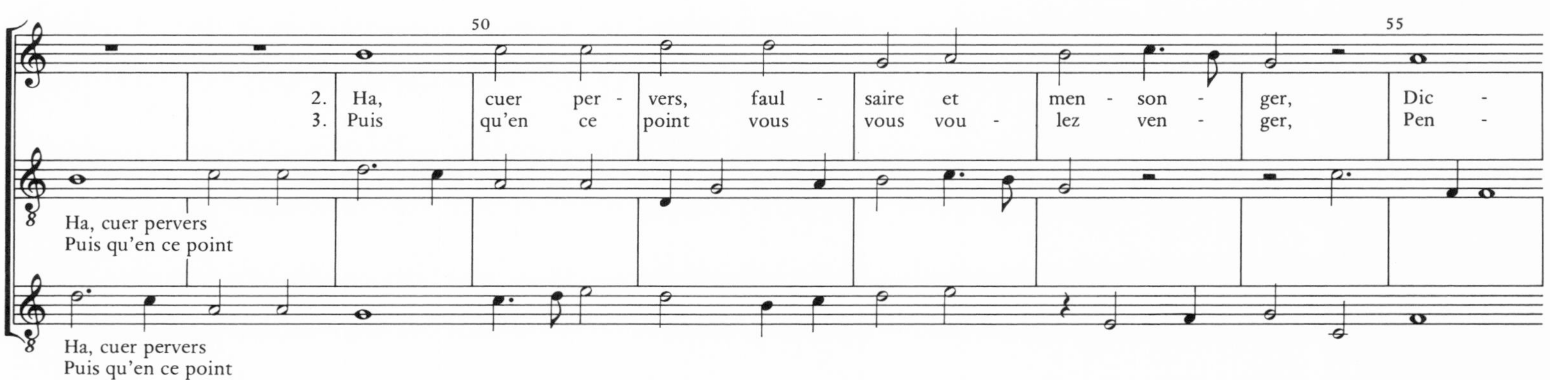
50
55
2. Ha, cuer per - vers, faul - saire et men - son - ger, Dic -
3. Puis qu'en ce point vous vous vou - lez ven - ger, Pen -
Ha, cuer pervers
Puis qu'en ce point
Ha, cuer pervers
Puis qu'en ce point

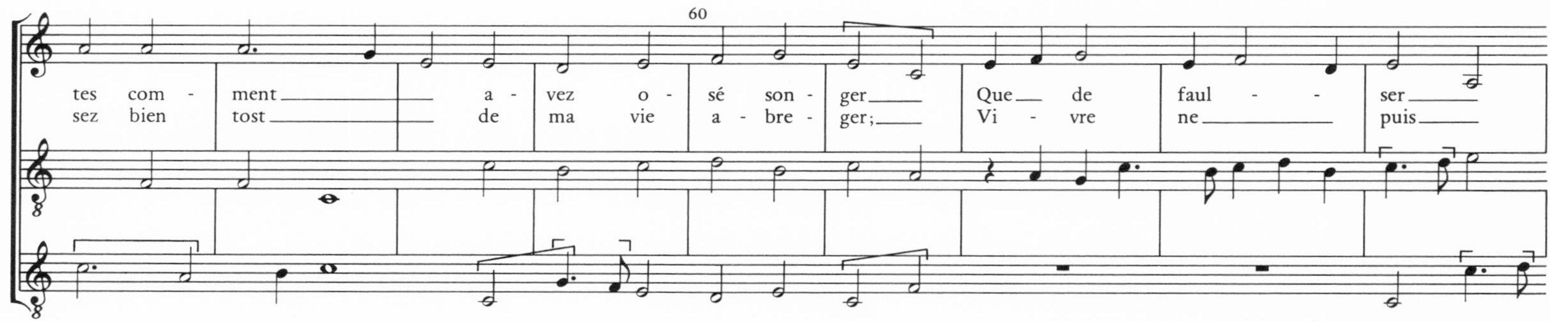
60
tes com - ment a - vez o - sé son - ger Que de faul - ser
sez bien tost de ma vie a - bre - ger; Vi - vre ne puis

65
70
1.
2.
ce que m'a - vez pro - mis.
au point ou m'a - - - - - vez mis.

4. Vostre rigueur veult doncques que je meure,
Mais Pitié veult que vivant je demeure;
Ainsi meurs vif et en vivant trespasse,
Mais pour celer le mal qui ne se passe
Et pour couvrir le dueil ou je labeure,
Ma bouche rit . . .

12.
Ma maistresse

Tenor
Contra
1.,5. Ma mais - tres - se et ma plus grant a - my - e, De mon de - sir la mor-telle en - ne-my - e,
Ma maistresse
Ma maistresse
Par - faicte en biens s'on - ques maiz le fut fem - me,
Cel - le seul - le de qui court bruit et fa - me D'es - tre sans

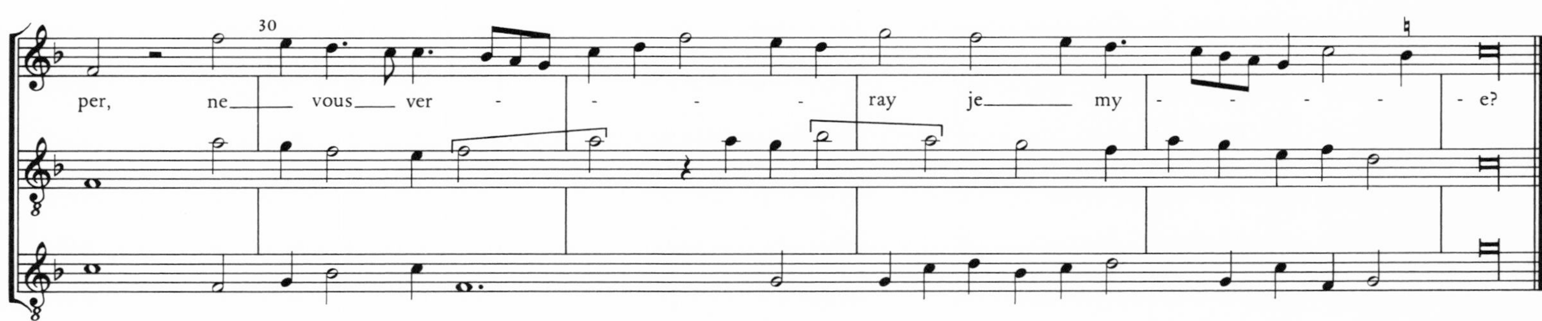
per, ne vous ver - - - - ray je my - - - - - e?

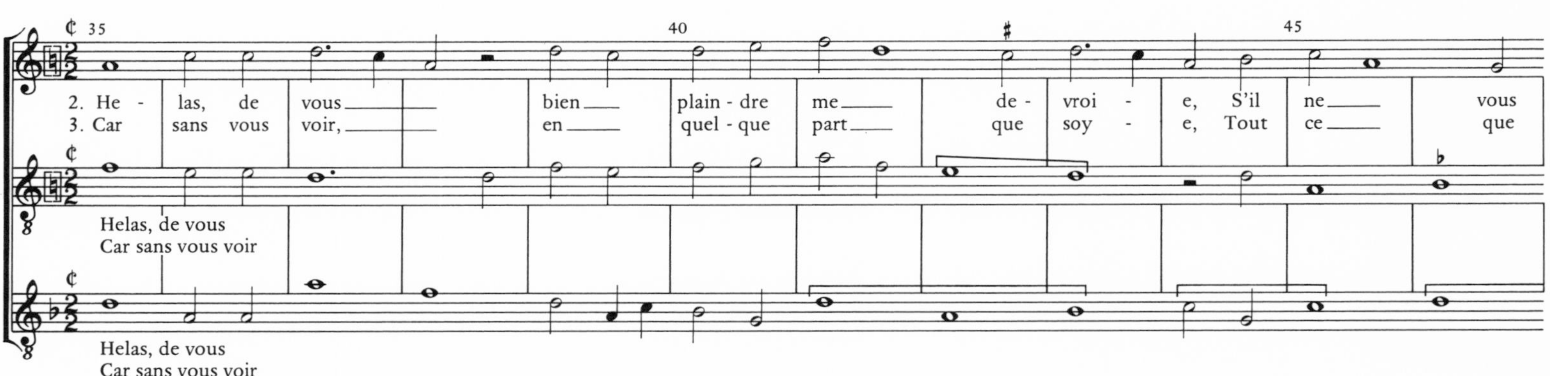
2. He - las, de vous bien plain - dre me de - vroi - e, S'il ne vous
3. Car sans vous voir, en quel - que part que soy - e, Tout ce que
Helas, de vous
Car sans vous voir
Helas, de vous
Car sans vous voir

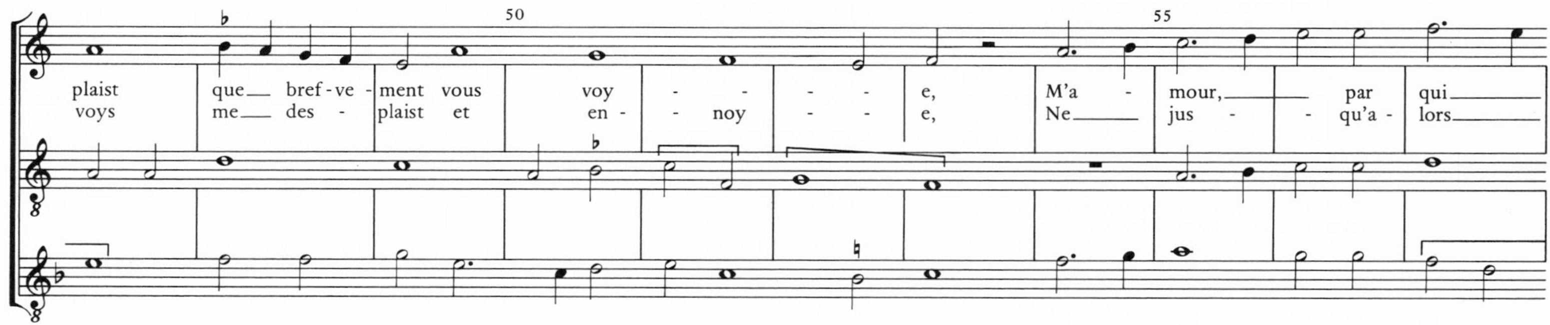
plaist que bref - ve - ment vous voy - - - e, M'a - mour, par qui
voys me des - plaist et en - - noy - - e, Ne jus - - qu'a - lors

d'aultre - - ay - mer n'ay puis - - - san - - ce.
je n'au - ray souf - - fi - - san - - ce.

4. Incessamment mon dolent cueur larmye
Doubtant qu'en vous pitié soit endormye.
Que ja ne soit, ma tant amée dame;
Maiz s'ainsy est, si malheureux me clame,
Que plus ne quiers vivre heure ne demye.
Ma maistresse . . .

13.

Mort tu as navré

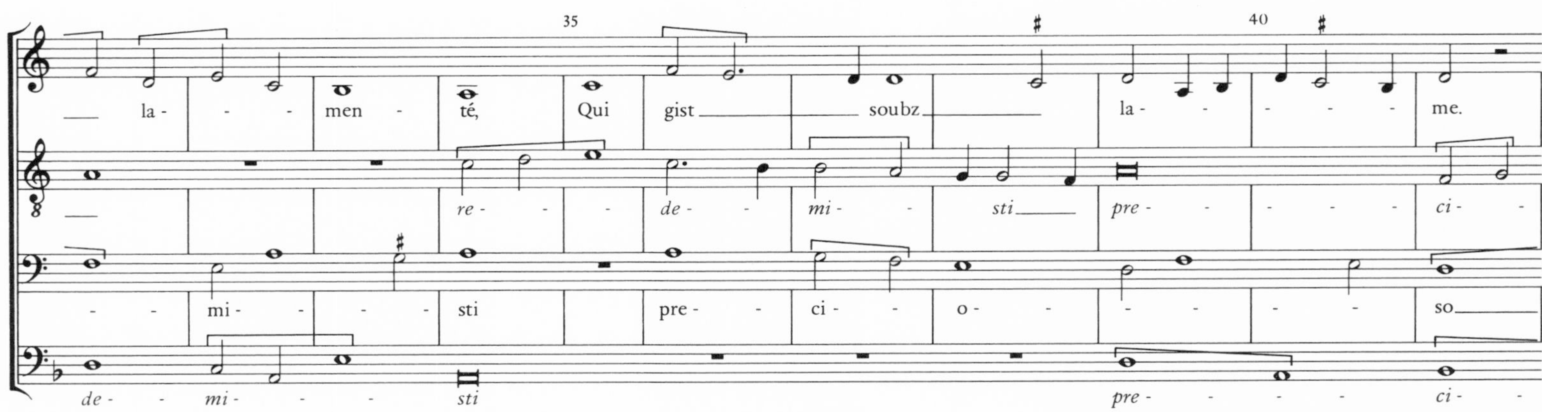

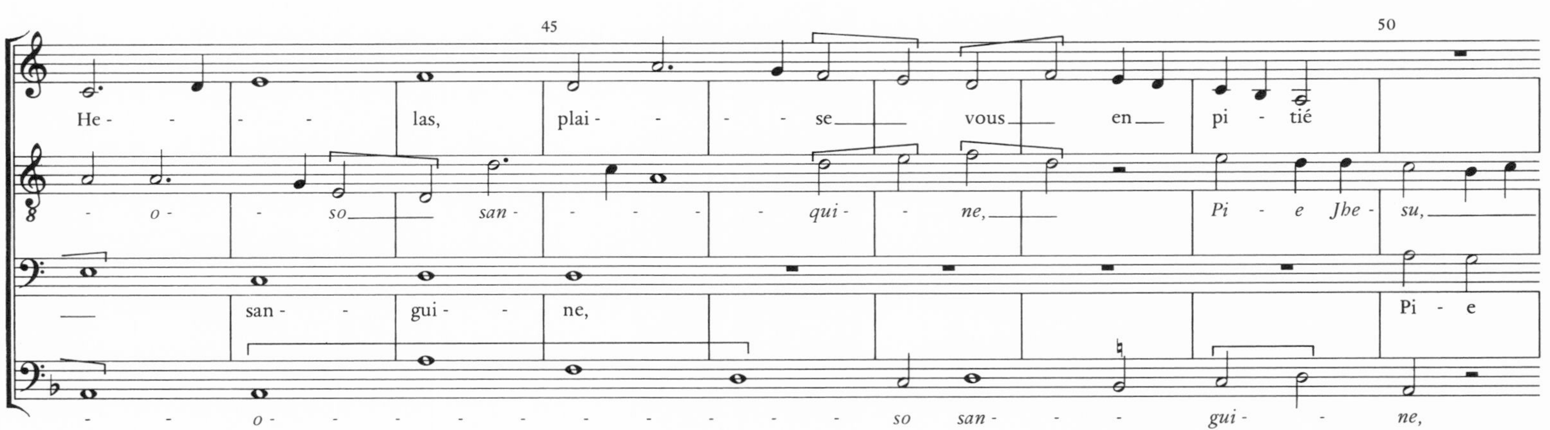

2. En sa jonesse fut soudart
De honnorable mondanité,
Puis a esleu la milleur part
Servant Dieu en humilité,
Tant luy soit en crestienté
Son nom est fame.
Qui detient de grant voulenté,
Priez pour l'ame.

3. Retoricque, se Dieu me gard,
Son serviteur a regretée,
Musicque, par piteux regard,
Fait deul et noir a portée.
Pleurez, hommes de feaulté,
. . . .
Vueillez vostre université
[Prier pour l'ame.]

14.

O rosa bella

15.

Prenez sur moi

(Fuga trium vocum)

2. Servant Amours, me suis trouvé eureux
L'une des foiz, et l'autre malleureux;
Ung jour sentant confort, l'autre destresse.
Prenez sur moi . . .

4. Pour ung plaisir cent pansers ennuieux,
Pour ung solas cent dangiers perilleux,
Pour ung accueil cent regars par rudesse;
S'Amours sert doncques de telz mets a largesse,
Et les loiaux fait les plus doloureux.
Prenez sur moi . . .

16. Presque transi

Conctratenor
Tenor
1.,5. Pres - que tran - si ung peu mains qu'es - tre mort, Vi -
Presque transi
vant en dueil sans a - voir nul con - - - - fort,
Ve - oir l'en me peut es lienx de For - tu - - - ne
Qui sans ces - ser pis qu'au - - - - - tre me for - tu - -
- ne Et me com - bat de plus fort en plus fort.

35
2. He - las, je suis con - tre mon vueil en vi - e, Et si n'est riens dont
3. Mo - rir ne puis et tous - jours m'y con - vi - e, Et m'est bien tart que
Helas, je suis
Morir ne puis
Helas, je suis
Morir ne puis

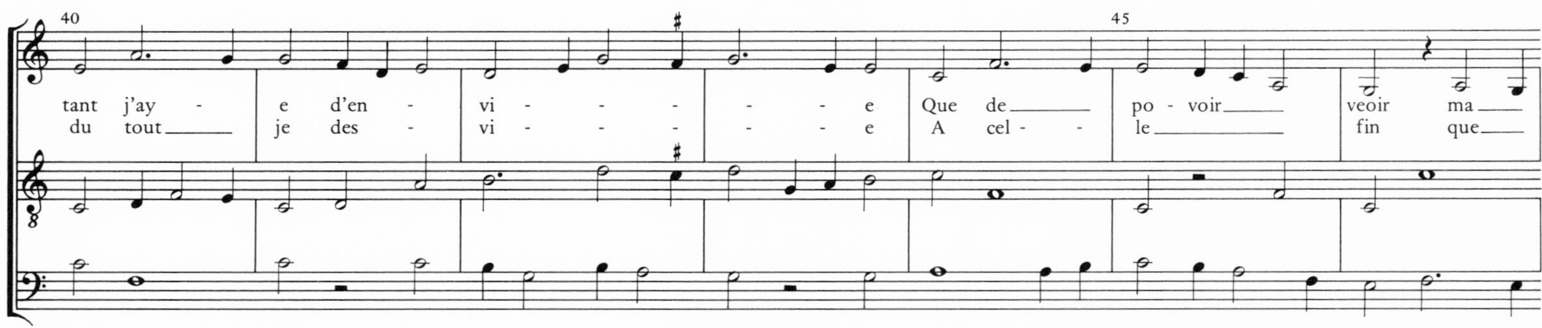
40
45
tant j'ay - e d'en - vi - - - - - - e Que de po - voir veoir ma
du tout je des - vi - - - - - - e A cel - le fin que

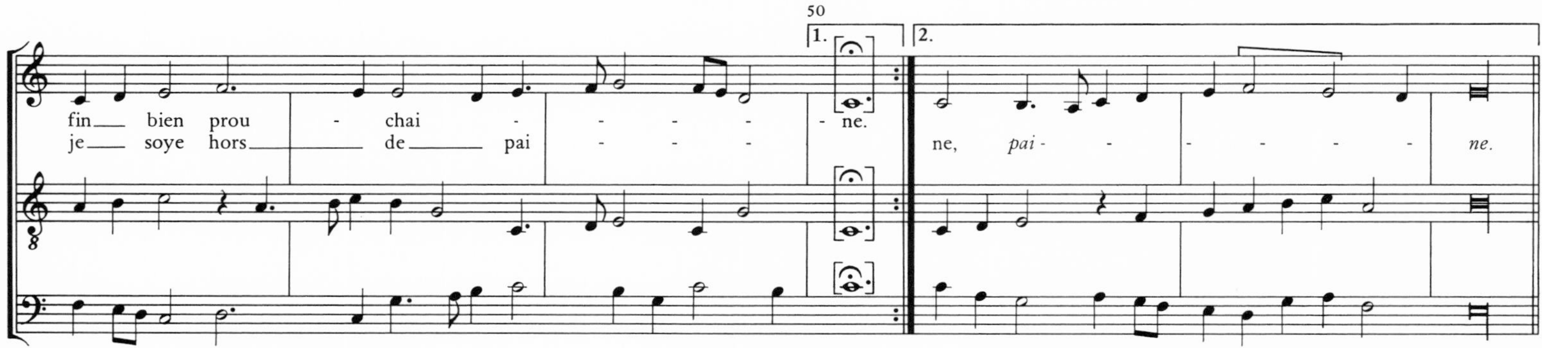
50
1.
2.
fin bien prou - chai - - - - - ne. ne, pai - - - - - - ne.
je soye hors de pai

4. Il m'est advis que la Mort me tient tort
Quant autrement elle ne fait son effort
De moy vengier de ma vie importune;
Car je languis sans avoir joye aucune
Par mon maleur qui me devoure et mort.
Presque transi . . .

17.
Quant de vous seul

2. Pour estre vostre devenue
Plus que nul qui soit soubz la nue,
Toute ma joie me default
Quant de vous seul . . .

4. Dont je voi bien que je suis nue
De tous biens comme beste mue,
A qui de plus riens il ne chault;
Car je sçais bien qu'estre me fault
Seulle de tous biens despourveue,
Quant de vous seul . . .

18.

Qu'es mi vida

4. ¿Para que me preguntays
La pena que he de passar,
Pues amar e lamentar
Es la vida che me days?

18a.
Qu'es mi vida

(Johannes Cornago)

4. ¿Para que me preguntays
La pena que he de passar,
Pues amar e lamentar
Es la vida che me days?

19.

S'elle m'amera – Petite camusete

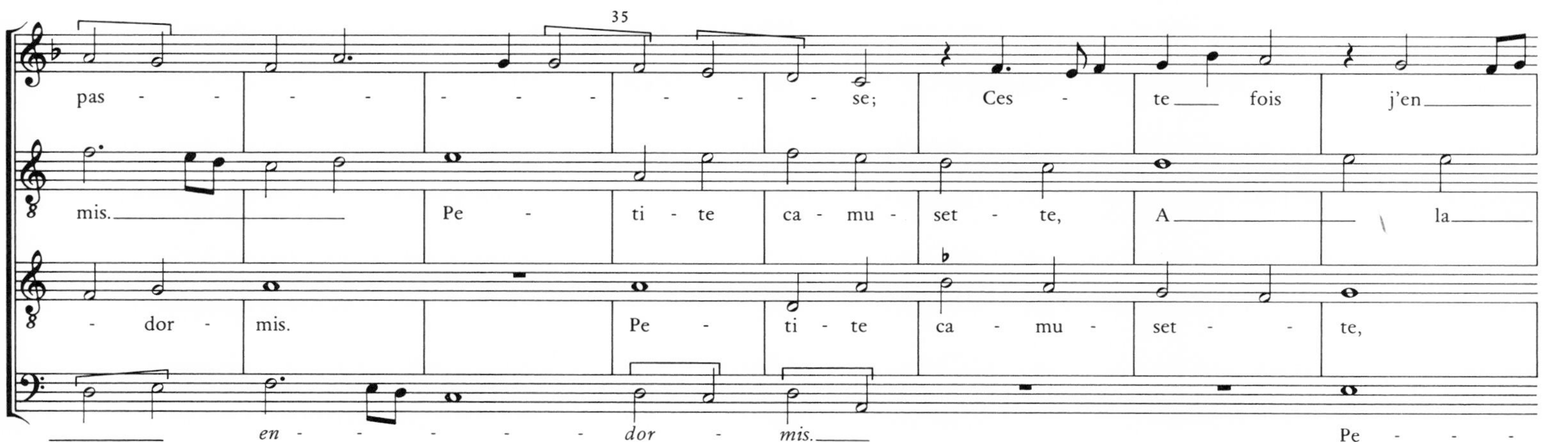

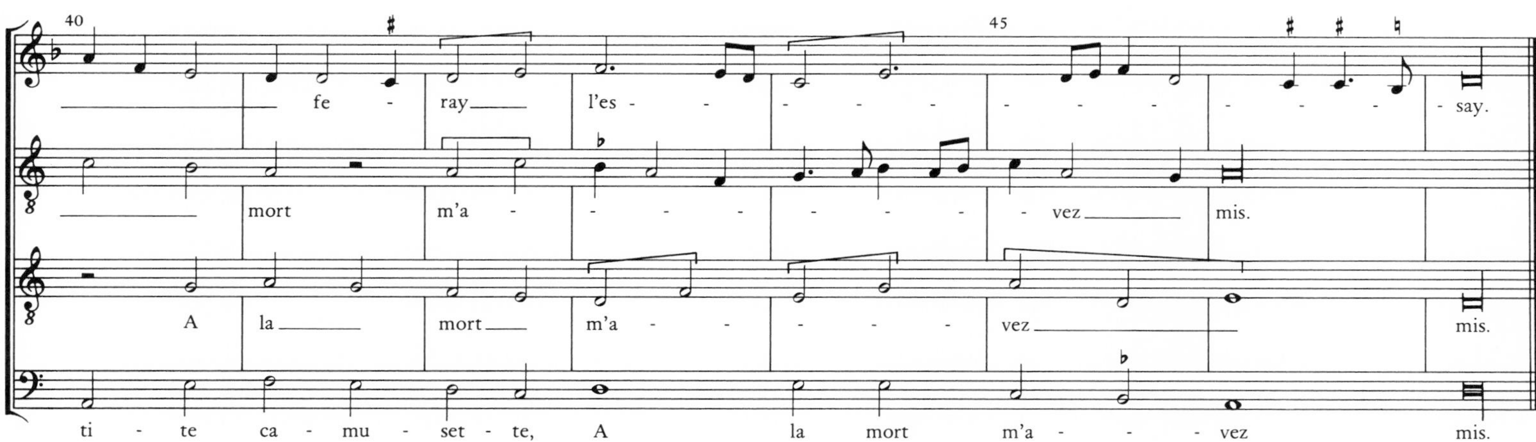

2. L'aultre jour tant je m'avençay
Que presque tout mon cuer lassay
Aler sans que luy demandasse
S'elle m'amera . . .

4. Puis apres le coup me pençay
Que long temps a que ne cessay,
Ne ne fut que je ne l'aimasse;
Mais c'est ung jeu de passe passe,
J'en suis comme je commençay.
S'elle m'amera . . .

20.

Se vostre cuer

21.
Tant fuz gentement

4. Mon leal cuer de dueil nercy,
Taint en de[se]speré soucy
Aloing de toute joye escoux,
M'avez comme a force rescoux
De Mort dont sans nulle mercy
Attendoye les dangereux coupx.
Tant fuz gentement . . .

22.
Ung aultre l'a

2. Je ne vueil pas estre forcluz
D'acorder ou faire reffuz
Mais ce que voulez orendroit
Ung aultre l'a . . .

4. Jamais en ce propos ne fuz
Que mon vouloir fust si confuz
D'entendre a tout ce qu'il voudroit;
De ce faire on me reprendroit
Congnoissant que seroit abuz.
Ung aultre l'a . . .

23.

Au travail suis

Tenor
Contra
1.,3.,5. Au tra - vail suis que peu de gens croi - roi - ent; On le peut bien qui veult a - - - - par - - - ce - - voir, (1.,5.) Maiz c'est pour ce que je ne puis ve - - - oir Ma mais - tres - se ain - si qu'aul - - - - - tres fe - - - - - - - roi - ent.
Au travail suis
Au travail

2. Bien envieux certes aucuns seroient
Se de sa grace du bien povoie avoir.
   Au travail suis . . .

4. S'il m'avenoit grant douleur porteroient,
Car voir mon bien leur feroit recevoir
Mal si tresgrant que s'il duroit pour voir
Je suis tout seur que de dueil creveroient.
   Au travail suis . . .

24.

Departés vous

25.
Malheur me bat

26.
Permanent vierge

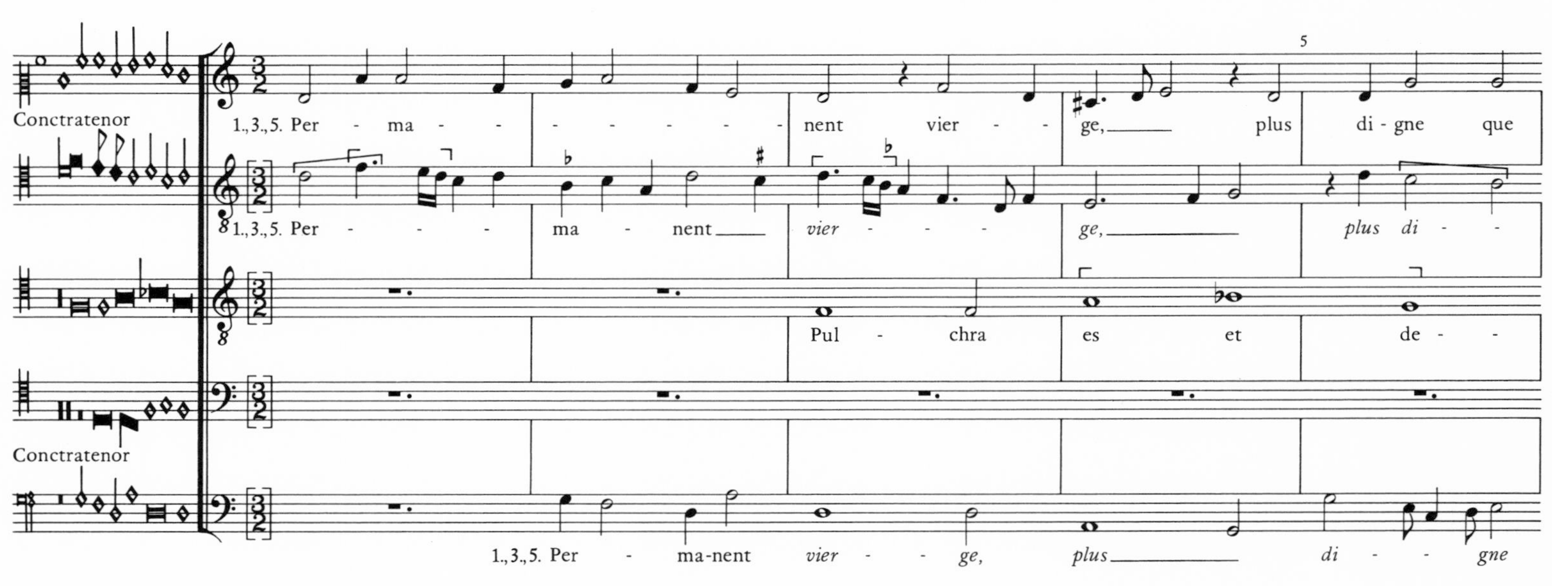

2. Esmerveillant nature et loy commune,
   Tu enfantas par supernel office,
      Permanent vierge . . .

4. Preordonnée sans differance aucune,
   Du Redempteur fille, mere et nourrice,
   Soiez pour nous advocate propice,
   Toy supplions, tres belle, clere, brune,
      Permanent vierge . . .

SUPPLEMENT

Ergone conticuit

("In Ioannem Okegi Musicorum principem, Naenia")

(Johannes Lupi?)

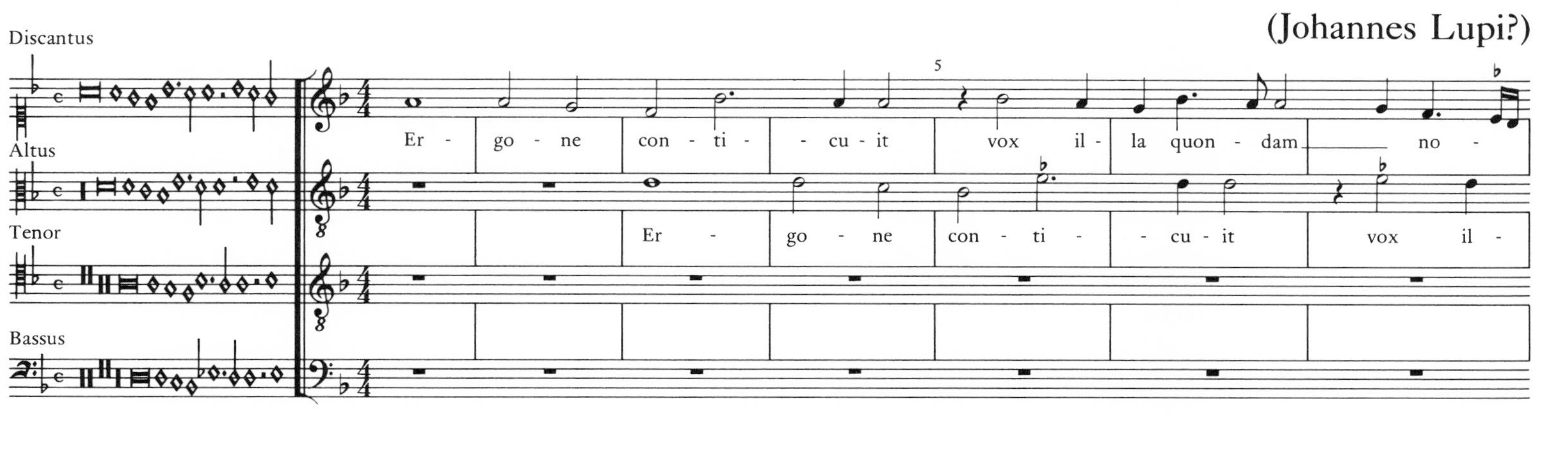

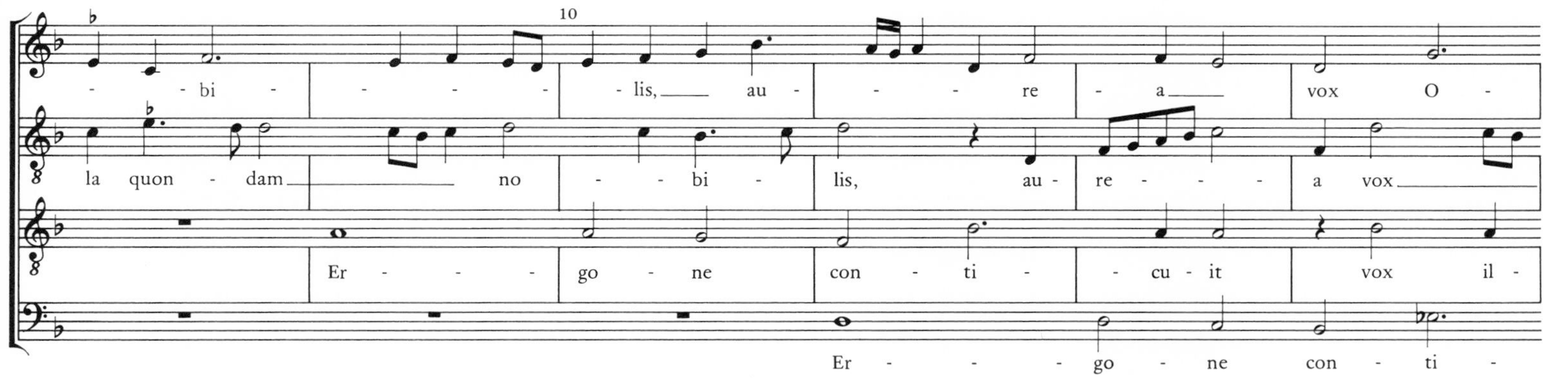

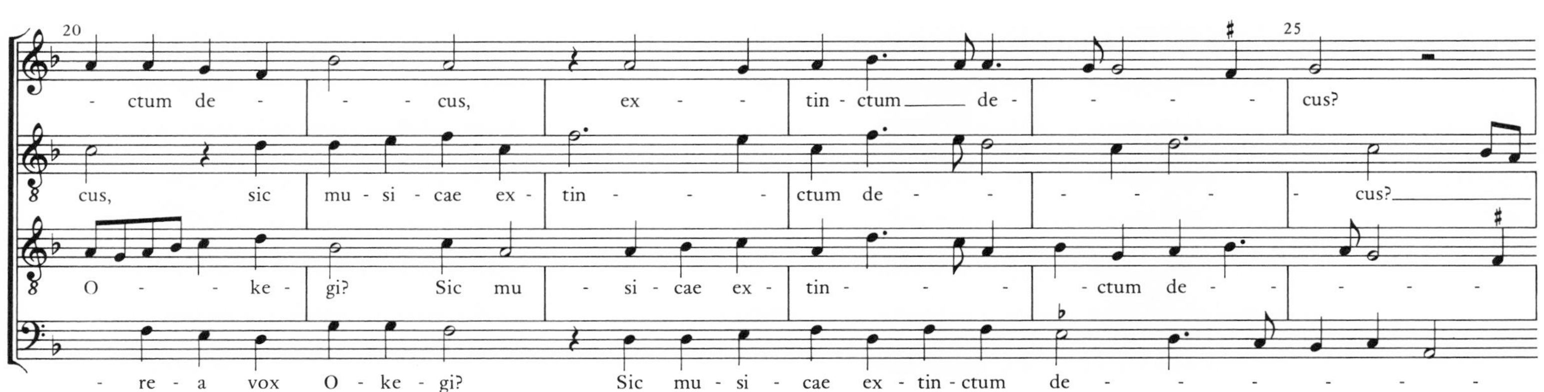

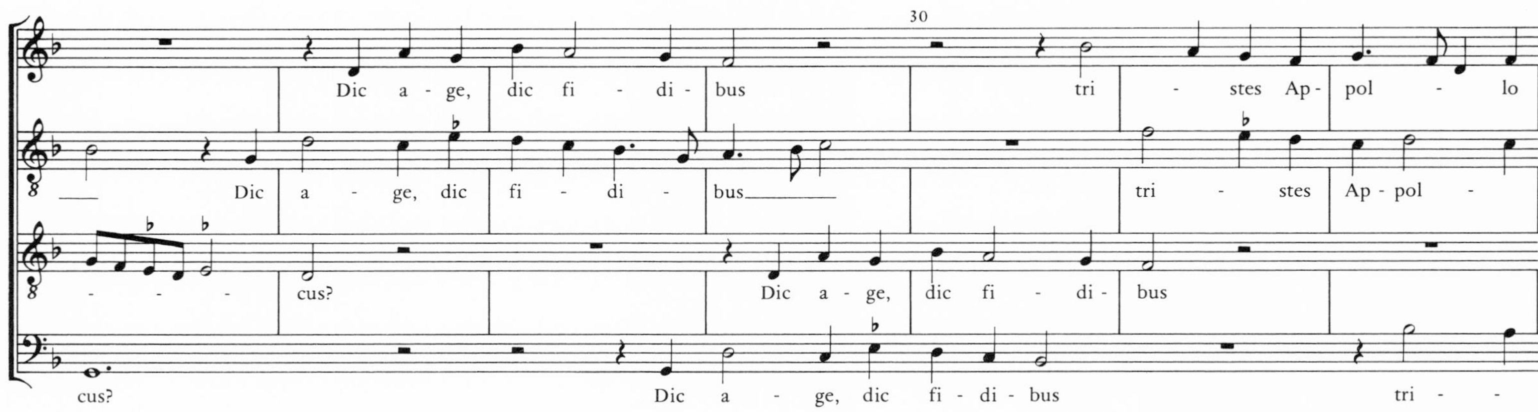
30
Dic a - ge, dic fi - di - bus tri - stes Ap - pol - lo
Dic a - ge, dic fi - di - bus tri - stes Ap - pol -
- - - - cus? Dic a - ge, dic fi - di - bus
cus? Dic a - ge, dic fi - di - bus tri -

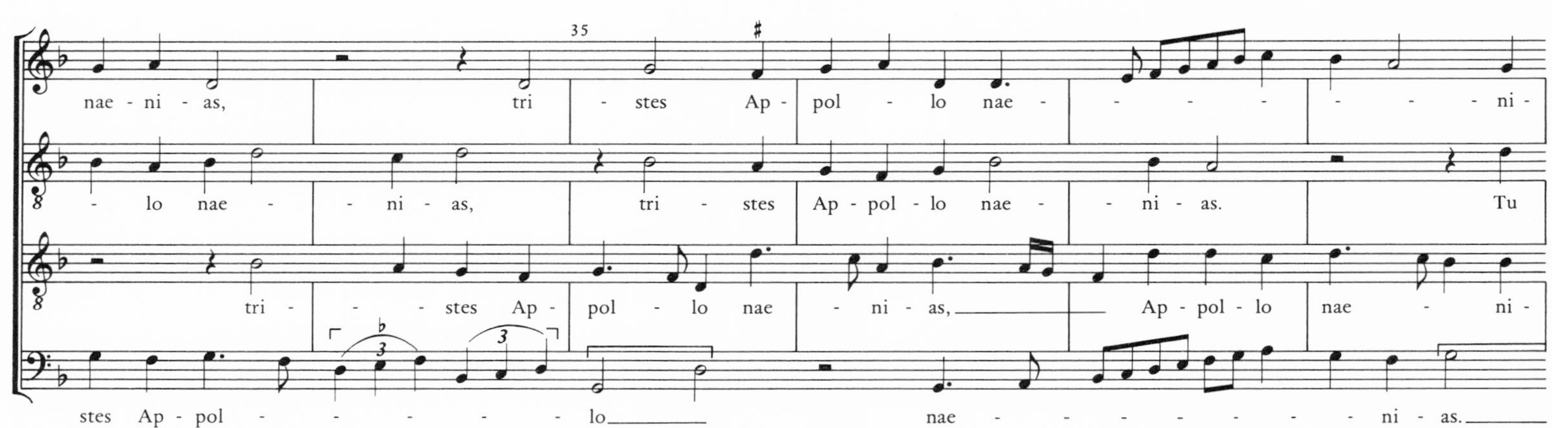
35
nae - ni - as, tri - stes Ap - pol - lo nae - - - - - - - ni -
- lo nae - - ni - as, tri - stes Ap - pol - lo nae - - ni - as. Tu
tri - - stes Ap - pol - lo nae - ni - as, Ap - pol - lo nae - ni -
stes Ap - pol - - - - - - lo nae - - - - - - - - ni - as.

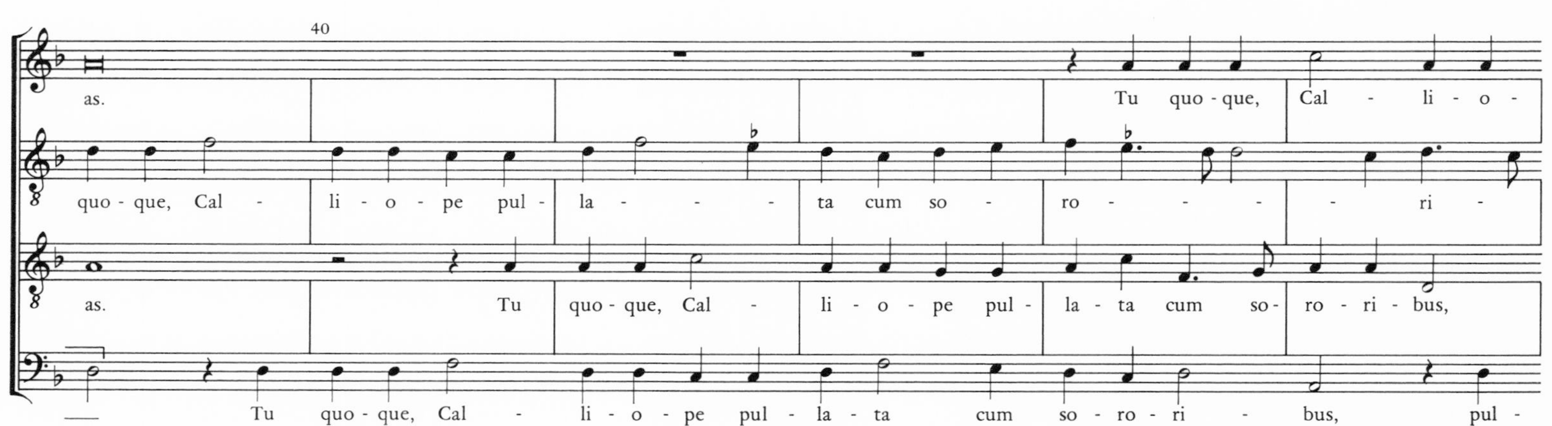
40
as. Tu quo - que, Cal - li - o -
quo - que, Cal - li - o - pe pul - la - - - ta cum so - ro - - - - ri -
as. Tu quo - que, Cal - li - o - pe pul - la - ta cum so - ro - ri - bus,
Tu quo - que, Cal - li - o - pe pul - la - ta cum so - ro - ri - bus, pul -

45
50
pe pul - la - ta cum so - ro - - ri - bus, fun - de pi - as la -
- - bus, fun - de pi - as la - chry - - - mas,
pul - la - ta cum so - ro - ri - bus, fun - de
la - ta cum so - ro - ri - bus, fun - de pi - as la - chry - mas,

55
chry - mas, la - - - chry - mas, fun - de pi - as la - chry -
la - - - - chry - mas, fun - de pi - as la - - - chry -
pi - as, fun - de pi - as la - - chry - mas;
fun - de pi - as la - chry - mas;

60
65
mas; Lu - ge - te, dul - ce
mas; Lu - ge - te, quot - quot mu - si - cae dul - ce ra - - pit stu - di -
Lu - ge - te, quot - quot mu - si - cae dul - ce ra - - pit stu - di - um, dul - - - ce ra - pit
Lu - ge - te, quot - quot mu - si - cae dul - ce ra - pit stu - di - um, ra -

70
ra - pit stu - di - um vi - rum - que fer - te lau - - - - - - -
um vi - rum - que fer - te lau - - - - - - di -
stu - - - - - - di - - um vi - - rum - que
- - pit stu - - di - - um

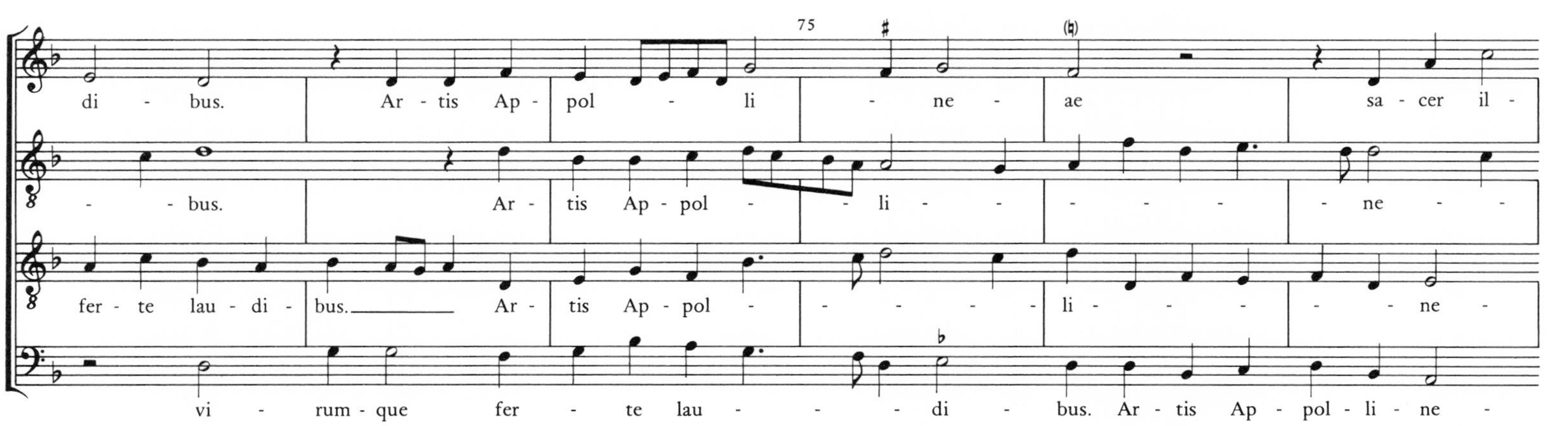
75
di - bus. Ar - tis Ap - pol - li - ne - ae sa - cer il -
- bus. Ar - tis Ap - pol - - li - - - - - ne - -
fer - te lau - di - bus. Ar - tis Ap - pol - - - - - li - - - - - ne -
vi - rum - que fer - te lau - - - di - bus. Ar - tis Ap - pol - li - ne -

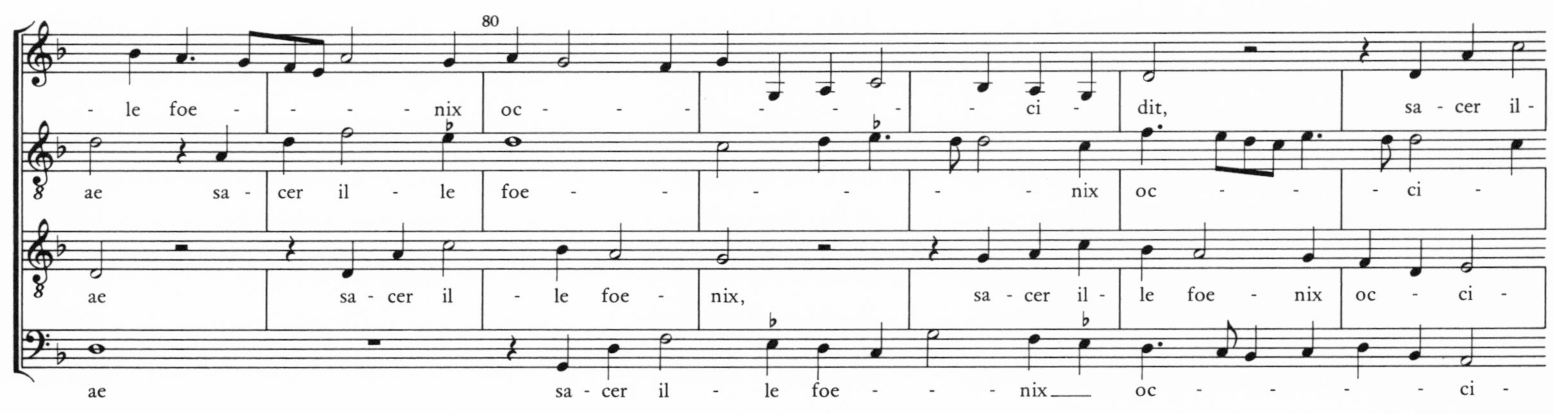

Secunda Pars.

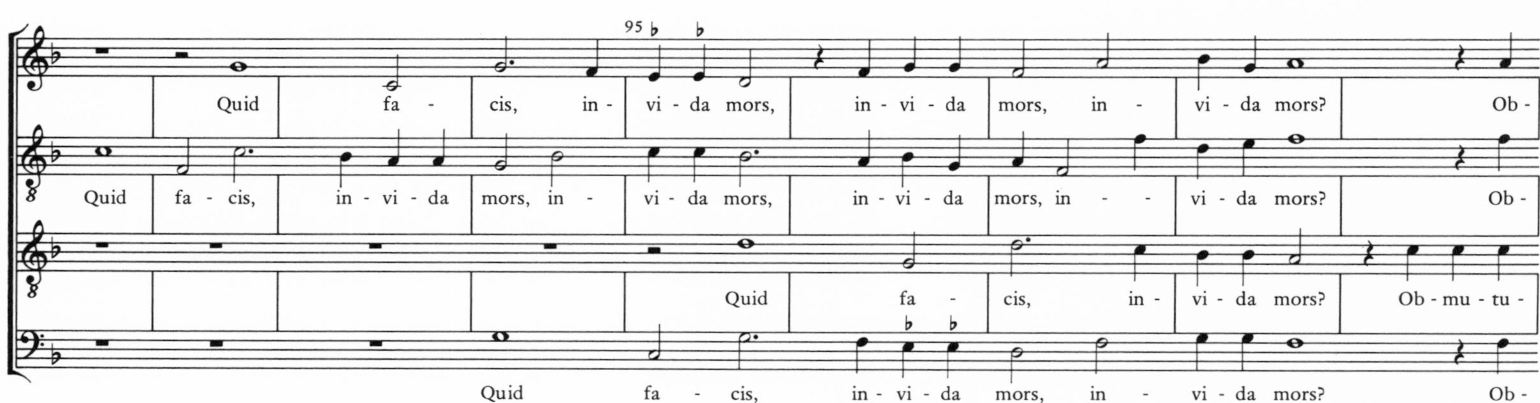

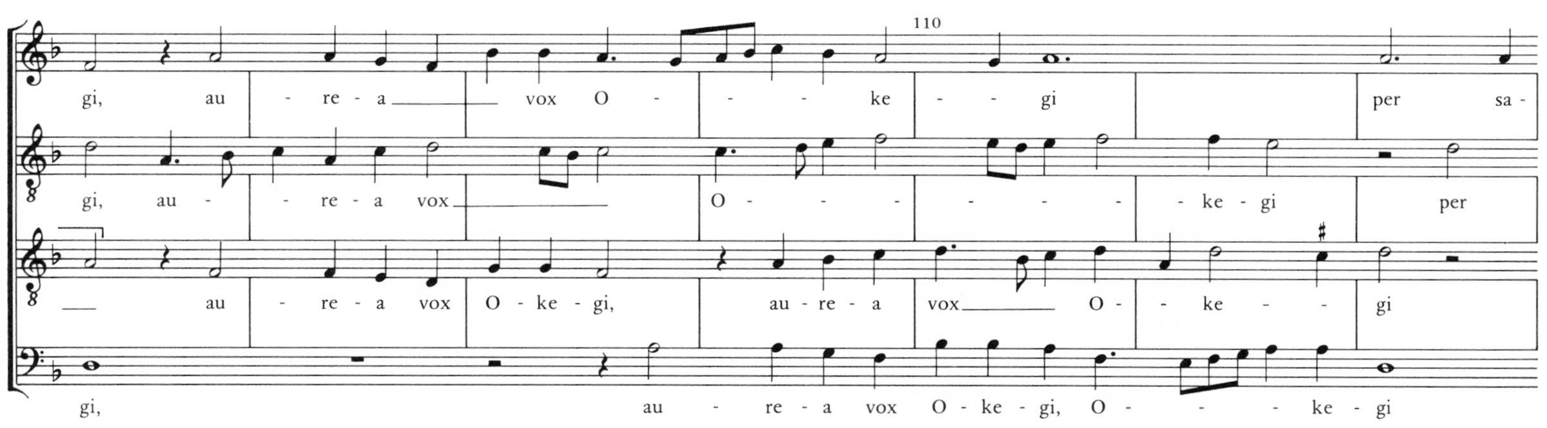
110
gi, au - re - a vox O - - - ke - - gi per sa -
gi, au - - re - a vox O - - - - - - - ke - gi per
au - re - a vox O - ke - gi, au - re - a vox O - ke - - gi
gi, au - re - a vox O - ke - gi, O - - - ke - gi

115
cra te - cta so - - - - - - nans,
sa - cra te - cta so - - - - - - nans,
per sa - cra te - cta so - - - - -
per sa - cra te - cta so - - - - -

120
125
per sa - cra te - cta so - - - nans. De - mul - sit
per sa - cra te - cta so - - nans. De - mul - sit au - res cae - li - tum, de -
- nans. De - mul - sit au - res cae - li - tum, de - mul - sit au - - res,
- nans. De - mul - sit au - - res cae - li - - tum

130
au - - res cae - - - - li - - tum
- - - mul - sit au - res cae - li - - tum ter -
de - mul - sit au - - res cae - li - tum ter - ri - ge - num - que
Ter - ri - ge - num - que si -

135
ter - ri - ge - num - que si - mul pe - ni - tus - que mo - vit
ri - ge - num - que si - mul pe - ni - tus - que mo - - - - - vit
si - mul pe - ni - tus - que mo - - vit pe - - - - -
mul pe - ni - tus - que mo - vit pe - cto - ra,

140
pe - cto - ra, pe - ni - tus - que mo - vit pe - cto - ra, mo -
pe - cto - ra, pe - - - ni - - tus - que mo - - vit pe - cto - ra, pe -
- cto - ra, pe - ni - tus - que mo - - - - - vit, pe - ni - tus - que
pe - ni - tus - que mo - vit pe - cto - ra, pe - ni - tus - que mo - vit

145
150
- vit pe - - - cto - - - - ra. Quid fa - cis, in -
ni - tus - que mo - vit pe - cto - ra. Quid fa - cis, in - vi - da mors, in -
mo - vit pe - - cto - ra.
pe - cto - ra, mo - vit pe - cto - ra. Quid fa - cis, quid

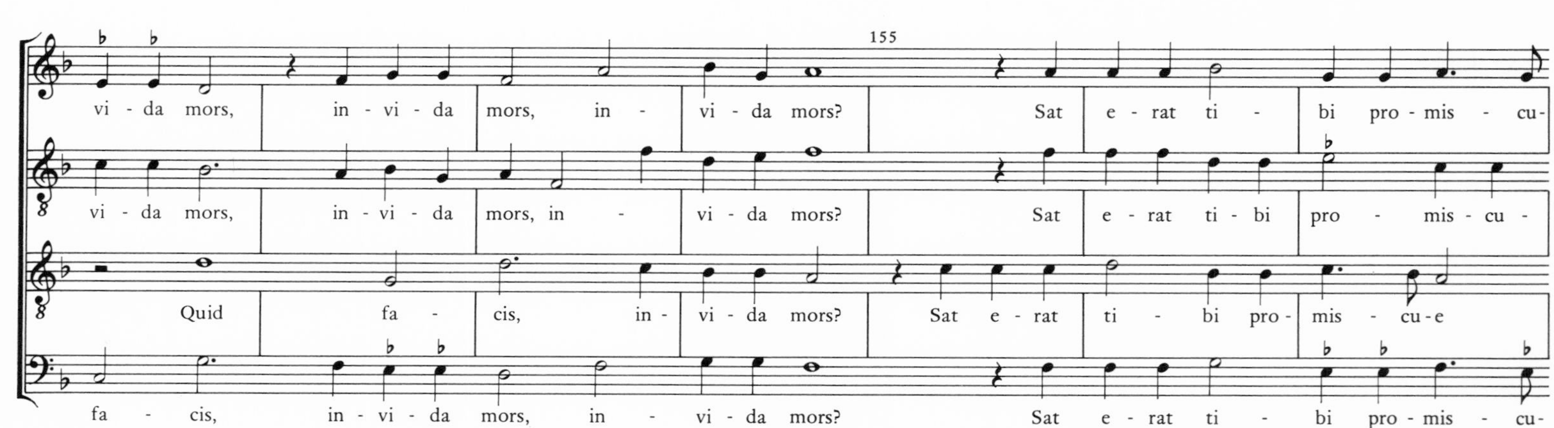
155
vi - da mors, in - vi - da mors, in - vi - da mors? Sat e - rat ti - bi pro - mis - cu-
vi - da mors, in - vi - da mors, in - vi - da mors? Sat e - rat ti - bi pro - mis - cu -
Quid fa - cis, in - vi - da mors? Sat e - rat ti - bi pro - mis - cu - e
fa - cis, in - vi - da mors, in - vi - da mors? Sat e - rat ti - bi pro - mis - cu-

160
e tol - le - re res ho - mi - num; Di - vi - - na res est
e tol - le - re res ho - mi - num; Di - vi - na res est mu - si - ca,
tol - le - re res ho - mi - num, tol - le - re res ho - mi - num; Di - vi - na res est
e tol - le - re res ho - mi - num, res ho - mi - num; Di - vi - na res

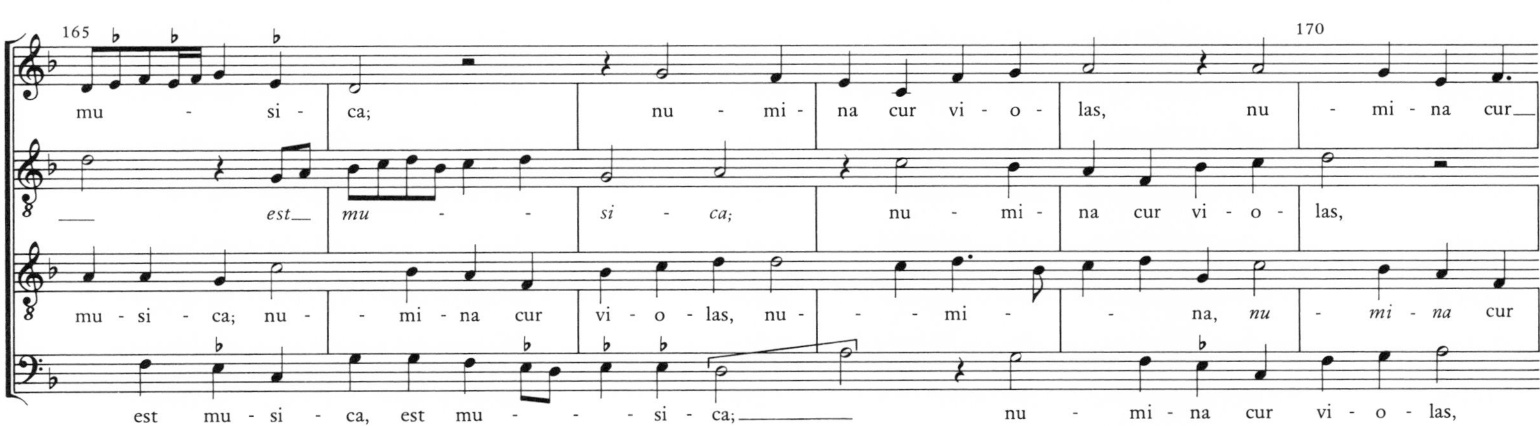
165
170
mu - si - ca; nu - mi - na cur vi - o - las, nu - mi - na cur
est mu - si - ca; nu - mi - na cur vi - o - las,
mu - si - ca; nu - mi - na cur vi - o - las, nu - mi - na, nu - mi - na cur
est mu - si - ca, est mu - si - ca; nu - mi - na cur vi - o - las,

175
vi - o - las, nu - mi -
nu - mi - na cur vi - o - las,
vi - o - las, nu - mi - na cur vi - o - las, nu -
nu - mi - na cur vi - o - las, nu - mi - na cur vi - o - las,

180
6/4
na cur vi - o - las, nu - mi - na cur vi - o - las?
nu - mi - na cur vi - o - las, nu - mi - na cur vi - o - las?
mi - na, nu - mi - na cur vi - o - las?
nu - mi - na cur vi - o - las, cur vi - o - las?